COLLECTIONS IN CONTEXT

COLLECTIONS IN CONTEXT

The Museum of the Royal Society of Edinburgh
and the inception of a National Museum for Scotland

Charles D Waterston

NATIONAL MUSEUMS OF SCOTLAND

Published by NMS Publishing, Chambers Street, Edinburgh EH1 1JF in association with
The Royal Society of Edinburgh

British Library Cataloguing in Publication Data

A catalogue record of this book is available from the British Library

ISBN 0 948636 87 4

Designed by NMS Publishing

Printed in the Republic of Ireland by ColourBooks Ltd

CONTENTS

ACKNOWLEDGEMENTS

During its history the museum of the Royal Society of Edinburgh has contained minerals, rocks and fossils; zoological and botanical specimens; objects of ethnological, oriental and antiquarian interest; items relating to technological advance and scientific instruments. All required attention in the present work. In attempting the project, of which the results are presented here, it has been a pleasure for me, a geologist, to widen my horizons through the study of the relevant literature and particularly through the generous help of those in other disciplines. I hope they will forgive me for taxing their patience and deal kindly with any errors in their own fields which they may detect in these pages and for which I alone must be responsible.

I have drawn on a considerable body of literature – the work of institutional, science and social historians – which has been published on the Royal Society of Edinburgh and on the Enlightenment from which it sprang. Sources are acknowledged as appropriate but reference must be made here to the Society's own historians whose influence has been so pervasive that it may not always have been explicit. These include Forbes (1866), Brewster (1866), Christison (1869), Moncreiff (1884), Turner (1909), Thompson (1935) and, in particular, Campbell and Smellie (1983). Another influential work of the pervasive sort, which must be specially acknowledged, is Shapin's history of the founding of the Society (Edinburgh University PhD thesis and Shapin 1974).

Among friends and colleagues who have given me their expert advice I am happy to acknowledge Dr Robert Anderson, Dr Mahala Andrews, Dr Iain Brown, Dr Patrick Cadell, Dr Andrew Doig, Dr Leonard Forman, Dr Andrew Fraser, Professor J R Harris, Professor Douglas Henderson, Mr James Holloway, Dr Gaynor Kavanagh, Dr Ian Rolfe, Professor Graham Smith and Mr Geoffrey N Swinney. Special thanks are due to Mrs Jean Jones for reading the manuscript and allowing me to use her unpublished notes.

I am indebted to museum colleagues for using their specialist knowledge to search for, and where possible identify, specimens in their collections which I believed were formerly in the museum of the Royal Society of Edinburgh. In the National Museums of Scotland I thank Miss Dale Idiens (Ethnography), Miss Jennifer Scarce (Oriental), Mr Nicholas Holmes (Coins), Dr Alec Livingstone (Minerals and Rocks), Dr Bobbie Paton (Fossil Fishes), Mr William Baird (Fossil plants), Mr David Heppell (Shells), Mr

Geoffrey Swinney (Reptiles), Dr Andrew Kitchener (Mammals), Mr David Bryden (Technology), Dr Allen Simpson and Miss Alison Morrison-Low (Scientific Instruments); in the Royal Botanic Garden Mr Ian Hedge and Mr David Long; in the Hunterian Museum Dr Graham Durant, Dr Neil Clark, Mr Michael Jewkes and Mr John Faithful; in the Museum of the Department of Geology, University of Edinburgh Mr Peder Aspen; in the Muséum National d'Histoire Naturelle, Paris, Professor Daniél Robineau.

I am grateful for the help and patience of curators of manuscripts at the Department of Education Library, the City of Edinburgh, the City of Glasgow, Hopetoun House, the National Library of Scotland, the Oriental and India Office Collections of British Library, the Royal Botanic Garden, Edinburgh, the Royal High School of Edinburgh, the Royal Highland and Agricultural Society, the Royal Society of Edinburgh, the Scottish Office Library, the Society of Antiquaries of Scotland, the Scottish Record Office, the University of Edinburgh and the University of Glasgow. I am indebted to these institutions for permission to quote from manuscripts in their collections.

For permission to quote from published works I thank the following: Professor Ronald M Birse, The Regents of the University of California, Constable Publishers, Edinburgh Botanic Garden Sibbald Trust, Mrs Melita Mew for the estate of Sir Karl Popper, MIT Press, The Museums Association, Oxford University Press, The Royal Society of Edinburgh, The National Museums of Scotland, The Society of Antiquaries of Scotland, The Society for the History of Natural Science, Taylor & Francis.

For permission to reproduce portraits or photographs of material in their care I am grateful to the trustees of The British Museum, The Courtauld Institute of Art, The City of Edinburgh Museums and Galleries, The Hunterian Museum of the University of Glasgow, The Royal Botanic Garden, Edinburgh, The Royal Observatory, Edinburgh, The Scottish National Portrait Gallery, and The University of Edinburgh. I am indebted to the curators of these institutions for their assistance in picture research. My thanks are due especially to owners of portraits in private hands for permission to reproduce them.

Jenni Calder (NMS), Helen Kemp (NMS), Elizabeth Robertson (NMS) and Tracey Dart (RSE) have generously helped in preparing the publication. I am indebted to the Royal Society of Edinburgh for allowing me to make free use of the Society's archives over a number of years and for financial assistance towards the publication of this work. I am especially grateful to the Director of the National Museums of Scotland for facilitating publication. The work was assisted by a grant from the National Museums of Scotland Charitable Trust and I thank the Trustees for their generosity.

CHAPTER ONE

CONSTANT OBJECTIVES AND CHANGING MEANS

... per Nomen et Titulum REGALIS SOCIETATIS EDINBURGI, ad promovendas Literas et Scientiam utilem ..., ad Statum illius partis Imperii nostri quae Scotia vocatur accomodata.[1]

Charter of George III, 1783

OBJECTIVES OF THE ROYAL SOCIETY OF EDINBURGH

The Royal Charter of 1783, which established the Royal Society of Edinburgh, defined the Society's objectives as the advancement of learning and useful knowledge in Scotland. The significance of these words would have been understood by contemporary Scots intellectuals but times have changed and today we may wonder if they have any meaning beyond a general commendation of learning. An understanding of the Enlightenment context in which the Charter was written, however, rekindles the challenge which the Society's objectives undoubtedly have for our own day.

The encouragement of learning has been interpreted by the Society as the encouragement of the process of learning, or education, as well as the substance of what is learned, or scholarship. These matters have formed part of the bedrock of Scottish social life and values since at least Knox's *First Book of Discipline* of 1560. Knox's prescriptions have been dubbed 'devout imaginations' because they sprang from reformation theology and were only partially fulfilled. Nevertheless they were fundamental to ideas on education and learning in Scotland. The metaphysical basis of education was still a key feature of Scots thinking when the Society was founded. As Shapin (1993, 276) has noted, the educated man was then expected 'to reflect on the basis of knowledge' and to agree with others on its foundations. In the same way science was seen, not as a set of techniques, but as 'an intellectual pursuit... the social implications of which one discussed as an integral part of the exercise' (Shapin, 1993, 275-6). The nature of Enlightenment scholarship thus required one branch of learning to be informed and counterbalanced by another.

Expression was given to this concept in the comprehensive nature of the Society's Fellowship, drawn from people of 'research and intelligence' in arts and science, commerce and law, philosophy and the church, medicine and the armed forces. As Principal Forbes put it, 'the co-operation of men of all ranks, of the most varied occupations and acquirements' is the very corner-stone of

I

the Society (Forbes, 1866, 6). This catholicity distinguishes it from its sister institutions in London where the Royal Society remains science based and the British Academy arts based. The Edinburgh Society shares its comprehensive interests with many European academies and, nearer home, with the Royal Irish Academy. The latter was founded a year after the Edinburgh Society and, like it, was inspired by Enlightenment ideas.

The social implications of learning, referred to by Shapin, encompassed the second of the Society's chartered objectives, the advancement of 'useful knowledge'. Many 'useful' discoveries and inventions have been made by Fellows of the Society. Among such practical applications was Brewster's elaboration of the dioptric lens to lighthouse illumination and Kelvin's development of stranded cables and sensitive receivers to transatlantic telegraphy. John Scott Russell's discovery of the wave of transition allowed the development of the wave-line system of ship construction. Such techniques, however, do not fully exemplify the Enlightenment concept of 'useful knowledge' which, it can be argued, grew from Knox's exhortation of 1560 that scholarship should proceed 'to the profit of the Church and Commonwealth' or, in Francis Bacon's words, to 'the relief of man's estate'. Daiches (1986, 2) interprets 'useful knowledge' in terms of 'improvement'. He illustrates the all embracing nature of these Enlightenment concerns as: the improvement of man's understanding of himself and of the natural world; the improvement of communication, physical, intellectual and social; the improvement of the environment in which man lives and works and of the processes by which he produces what he needs.

There is no doubt that as it approached its bicentenary in 1983, and influenced perhaps by the developing worldwide interest in Enlightenment studies among social and science historians, the Royal Society of Edinburgh was re-awakened to the magnitude of the challenge of its chartered objectives. When faced with the urgent questions of our day arising from such matters as population pressures and malnutrition, the need for the conservation of natural and urban resources, social justice and world peace, biomedical advance and medical ethics to mention but a few – the Society reaffirms the belief of its founders that it is only through the sum of human knowledge, feeling and understanding that they can be solved. Thus the Society recognises the obligation which its Charter lays upon it to devise ways to apply the knowledge and understanding which it has at its command for the benefit of society at large.

Its Charter also requires the Society to be aware of its responsibilities within Scotland. Phillipson considers that the emphasis on useful knowledge in the Scottish Enlightenment sprang from the desire to 'revive Scotland's fortunes in a rapidly changing post-Union world' (Phillipson 1981, 341). In some respects, our own day mirrors the intellectual environment and needs of Scotland which the founders experienced.

We live at a time when the focus of political power is becoming more remote. Just as the eighteenth-century Scot lived in the aftermath of the removal of political power from Edinburgh to London, so we see power being transferred to Brussels. As in post-Union Scotland the meaning of nationhood had to be re-examined, so in modern Europe smaller nations are seeking to rediscover their distinctive cultural identities. In Scotland this is leading to the revival of language and letters, art and music on one hand and economic enterprise on the other, and in some measure reflects the flowering of native culture in the eighteenth century. It was from such roots that the Royal Society of Edinburgh sprang and 'Scotland's premier learned society' has a chartered responsibility for learning and useful knowledge in the country's new awareness of itself among the brotherhood of nations.

In the twentieth century as in the eighteenth, Scotland experiences these political changes in a different historical context than England. Then the memories of nationhood and the continuance of the institutions of the church, law and education in Scotland led, at least for a time, to different perceptions north of the Border. The constitutional differences between the Royal Society of Edinburgh and its sister institutions in London, to which reference has been made, is one example of such differing perceptions. Scotland has over 250 years of experience of living as a less powerful part of a wider economic partnership. For 200 of those years the Royal Society of Edinburgh has sought to advance learning and useful knowledge in Scotland and may thus have helped to minimise the cultural dominance of her wealthier neighbour. England has no such experience. It is to be expected that approaches will differ between the sister kingdoms and their institutions as together they integrate with the New Europe. It may well be that lessons learned by the The Royal Society of Edinburgh, in pursuing its chartered aims in Scotland, may prove of wider interest and application in future years.

TEMPORA MUTANTUR, ET NOS MUTAMUR IN ILLIS[2]

Antiquity and past achievement are not enough to justify the continued existence of any foundation. A body which is unable to adapt to change may perish, or become a useless irrelevance. Of the Institut Française, Hahn (1971, 318) has written:

> As an arm of the state, the Institut remained for over a century the only organised unit that spoke on behalf of the scientific community and through which national policies were transmitted. Today it is a glorious relic of the past, more akin to a Hall of Fame than an Olympic Stadium. Time and the very nature of the growth of science, which the Academy had so successfully stimulated, were its undoing. Age, wisdom and ceremony now prevail where once youth, creativity and debate reigned supreme.

On the other hand, a long-established Society may adapt to changing circumstances and, in doing so, find new inspiration and opportunities. In the course of its history the Royal Society of Edinburgh has indeed changed with the times. The nature of its Fellowship had to change to reflect the

3

growth of professionalism in academic disciplines during the first half of the nineteenth century and, more recently, to recognise the importance of the contribution of women to the advancement of learning. Again, the nature of the Society's publications has changed many times to suit changing scientific needs and developing reprographic technologies. Like any body, the Society has experienced times of weakness as well as of strength but, on the whole, it has been faithful to its chartered objectives. Changing circumstances, however, have required altered means of achieving them. Thus features of the Society's activity which were once highly regarded, such as the maintenance of weather records and servicing a large research reference library, have been abandoned in favour of new activities better suited to further the Society's objectives in modern Scotland. Disengagement from such activities by the Society does not impugn their validity – weather records must still be kept and library services remain vital – but circumstances have changed outside the Society which enable them to be better done elsewhere.

THE SOCIETY'S MUSEUM

One long-since abandoned activity was maintaining a museum.

Chambers' *Twentieth Century Dictionary* tells us that, at its simplest, a museum may be 'a collection of curiosities'. More explicitly it is 'an institution or repository for the collection, exhibition, and study of objects of artistic, scientific, historic, or educational interest'. It is a 'place of study; a resort of the learned' (Geddie, 1959). The nature of a museum is determined by collecting policy and there is, therefore, almost no limit to the purposes of collection and display. Just as the nature of museums varies, so their use varies. Users may wish to be informed, impressed or simply entertained. They may approach the collection by way of reason or emotion, objectively or subjectively.

The museums which came into existence from the later sixteenth century onwards did for the natural sciences what experimentation did for the physical sciences; they allowed philosophers 'to see with their own eyes' the evidence of new discoveries and theories. In the spirit of the age they were regarded as a 'means of stimulating curiosity and inquiry' (Wittlin, 1949, 60). The contexts of their formation and use were distinct from other types of collections which then existed which were expressions of social prestige, wealth, kinship and the like. They were part of the apparatus of knowledge which Francis Bacon saw as bestowing power on humanity for the better control of nature and for developing human understanding and ingenuity. Societies, academies and institutions, dedicated to the advancement of learning, regarded the formation and maintenance of a museum as a means of furthering their purposes.

Like academies and societies, museums were a product of the European enlightenment. Principal Forbes conveys something of the intellectual excitement of the sixteenth and seventeenth centuries when he wrote that the work of Copernicus, Tycho Brahe, Galileo, Kepler and Leonardo da Vinci 'kept all Europe in a tremble of expectation for the discoveries of each succeeding year'.

> In those days when a virgin mine of natural phenomena was first opened to the intelligent exploration of mankind, the succession of inventions, discoveries, and capital theories in physical science, kept every thoughtful mind on the stretch. The comparatively recent art of printing served to disseminate rapidly both facts and doctrines ... What could men do in such circumstances but assemble with others like-minded, and see with their own eyes the facts which seemed to contradict the experience or prepossessions of ages, and either maintain or overthrow the new philosophy? (Forbes, 1866, 3)

The Royal Society of London was founded in 1660 and for over a hundred years a museum or 'Repository' played an important part in its life (Simpson, 1984). In its early years it contained miscellaneous objects which reflected the varied interests of the Society's Fellows (Hoppen, 1976, 8). The Society insisted, however, that it was for serious use and not for mere diversion (Hunter, 1981). The collection grew rapidly in the second half of the seventeenth century and the objects presented were often discussed at meetings. The first catalogue was produced by Nehemiah Grew and published in 1681. The condition of the collection deteriorated in the first decades of the eighteenth century but by 1765, after much labour, the situation had been put in order and another catalogue produced. Accommodation had always been a difficulty and in 1779 the Government offered the Society premises in Somerset House which lacked sufficient space to house the Repository. By that time, however, the rapidly growing collections of the British Museum had become of greater significance than those of the Society and it was decided that, with the exception of the scientific instruments, the Repository should be gifted to the British Museum (Weld, 1848, II, 120).

When the founders of the Royal Society of Edinburgh were negotiating for their Charter in 1783, the decision regarding the Repository of the Royal Society of London must certainly have been known to them for some were Fellows of the London Society. The Charter of 1783 required that donations of natural products be placed in the Museum of the University of Edinburgh and antiquarian objects in the Library of the Faculty of Advocates. It would be misleading to assume, however, that their decision to use existing institutions to house material donated to the Edinburgh Society was motivated by the London precedent. This arrangement was made not because the Society then had no accommodation of its own, but rather because of the powerful considerations of principal and patronage then operating within the Scottish Enlightenment. In the next chapter we shall see that these were major factors in the institutional discord between the University of Edinburgh, the Society of Antiquaries of Scotland, the Philosophical Society and the Faculty of Advocates which preceded the foundation of the

Royal Society of Edinburgh itself: a flurry in the Enlightenment dovecots which has interested many historians.

There we trace the events which led up to the Society's First Charter and the important role which the collections, made under its terms, played in the recreation of the Natural History Museum of the University of Edinburgh by Professor John Walker. In the early years of the nineteenth century museums became didactic institutions central to university research and teaching in many disciplines. Thus the nature of a museum and its collections was a matter of the utmost cultural importance.

The arrangements of the First Charter worked well during Professor Walker's curatorship but the high-handed attitude of his successor, Robert Jameson, towards the Society and its collection inevitably resulted in friction between the University and the Society. This led to the granting of a second Royal Charter to the Society in 1811 which gave it the right to own property and thus to form and retain its own museum. The Society never recovered possession of the collections lodged in the University Museum under the terms of the First Charter but, under the Second Charter, a museum was formed which reached its apogee in the mid-nineteenth century when housed in the Society's rooms in the Royal Institution.

In the period from 1859 to 1910, when its own collections diminished and eventually ceased to exist as a scientific entity, the Society's concern for museums under the care of professional curators, which were then emerging in Scotland, increased. In conjunction with other civic and learned bodies, in particular the Highland and Agricultural Society and the City of Edinburgh, it had a vital interest in the establishment of the Industrial Museum of Scotland in 1854.

The gestation of the national museum was far from straightforward. It was brought about by visionary men, many of whom were fellows of the Royal Society of Edinburgh, who used appropriate bodies – learned and civic – as their power base to persuade a reticent government of a case which finally proved irresistible. Motives were mixed, reflecting the interests of the various bodies involved and the complexity of the contemporary intellectual network in Scotland. On the government side, ideas about the new institution changed to accommodate the aspirations of the contending parties within the limited financial resources available. When, in 1859, the decision was taken by the Royal Society of Edinburgh to part with all but its geological collections to a number of other institutions, the greatest number of specimens was passed to Scotland's new national museum. It is of interest that the five men comprising the Society's committee which recommended that action had all played an active part in establishing Scotland's new national museum four years previously.

The development of the Industrial Museum of Scotland suffered a severe setback with the early death of Professor George Wilson, its Director. In the difficult period which followed, the Society was active in seeking to sustain the momentum for the building and the ultimate completion of the national museum in Edinburgh. In Chapter 4 the reasons for the volte face in government policy towards the Industrial Museum of Scotland are examined. The story is continued to the completion of the original museum building as the Edinburgh Museum of Science and Art, a changed name which reflected the changed nature of Scotland's national museum.

Why, having won the fight to maintain its own museum, did the Royal Society of Edinburgh dispose of the bulk of its collections within half a century? Specimens of fine art and ethnography were passed to the Society of Antiquaries in 1828. In 1859 the collections of biology and of technology were distributed to other institutions. In 1878 and finally in 1910 the remaining geological collections left the Society and its museum, as a scientific collection, ceased to exist. What had wrought such a rapid change in the attitude of the Society's Fellows to the museum which had been so highly prized? These are questions about which the histories have nothing to say and which this work seeks to address.

The history is a microcosm demonstrating the changes that influenced the waxing and waning of the museum of the Royal Society of Edinburgh ; it is an ideal case study because the Society reflected attitudes to museums which were held by many academics. These had widespread consequences and still influence thinking and policy making. It is of particular interest because Fellows of the Society took part in those developments in science and teaching which necessitated change and were eventually influential in effecting it in Scotland.

THE RECONSTRUCTED CATALOGUE OF THE COLLECTIONS

The present study grew out of the author's research into the nature and origins of the collections which were acquired by the Royal Society of Edinburgh. Only as that story unfolded did its wider historical implications for museums emerge.

From published and manuscript sources a catalogue of specimens, once in the museum of the Royal Society of Edinburgh, was reconstructed (Appendix I). It is certainly incomplete, because records are inadequate, and includes only items supported by documentary evidence, to which reference is made. It has been possible to identify several hundred specimens which survive in the institutions, or their successors, to which material was given. These include the Faculty of Advocates Library, the Society of Antiquaries of Scotland, the Industrial Museum of Scotland, the University of Edinburgh, the National Museums of Scotland, the Royal Botanic Garden, the Royal College of Surgeons of Edinburgh and the Hunterian Museum, Glasgow. Specimens had been transferred from one institution to another, sometimes more than once, before reaching their present repositories and in many cases infomation about the material had been lost during transfer. Where collections have been traced, Society records have enabled the provenance of the material within them to be re-established, which has greatly enhanced its value and has important implications for scholarship.

All manner of objects were added to the museum which reflected the many interests and widespread geographical concerns of the Fellows and their associates. Thus significant zoological, botanical and geological collections, from home and abroad, were accumulated. Ethnographic collections and oriental pieces were acquired and there were specimens and models of significance in the fields of technology and the history of science. The collection of scientific instruments was kept separately from the museum (see Appendix II).

The aim of this collections-research has been to provide the historical framework of the Society's collection. It has looked for the sources and donors of the objects, the content of the collection, the fate of the material and, where it survives, its present location. Informed discussion of the significance of the objects is beyond the scope of this work.

1 ... by name and title ROYAL SOCIETY OF EDINBURGH, for the advancement of Learning and useful Knowledge..., suited to the state of that part of our realm which is called Scotland.

2 Times change and we change with them

JOHN WALKER AND THE YEARS OF ACHIEVEMENT
1783-1803

One man that has a mind and knows it, can always beat ten men who havnt and dont

George Bernard Shaw

The histories of the Royal Society of Edinburgh and the Natural History Museum of the University of Edinburgh find common ground in the creative achievements of Professor Walker. He played an important part in founding the Royal Society of Edinburgh and was, from 1783 until his death, both Secretary of the Physical Section of the Society and Regius Keeper of the College Museum. Throughout this period the terms of the Society's First Charter applied whereby natural history objects acquired by the Society were housed in the Natural History Museum of the University.

John Walker (Jardine 1842, Taylor 1959, Scott 1966, Scott 1976, McKay 1980) was educated at Canongate Grammar School, where his father was rector, and at Edinburgh University, where his chief scientific interests were botany and mineralogy. He trained for the ministry and in 1758 was inducted to his first charge at Glencorse, moving to Moffat in 1762.[1] Between 1760 and 1786 he undertook six journeys into the Highlands and Hebrides to survey their natural history, population, agriculture, manufactures, fisheries and religious state. The extensive survey of 1764 was commissioned by the Trustees of the Forfeited Estates through his friend Lord Kames, and by the Church of Scotland and the Society for the Propagation of Christian Knowledge. In the course of the seven months of this journey Walker claimed to have travelled over 4,700 miles, of which he sailed 1894, rowed 420, rode 1630 and walked 792.[2] In 1771 he received a similar commission from the same bodies for another major expedition to extend his survey to other areas. His reports were lodged with the commissioning bodies but it was not until after his death that his observations from the six journeys were published (Walker 1808a). In recognition of his achievement he received an honorary MD from Glasgow in 1765 and DD from Edinburgh in 1771.

When this remarkable man became the second occupant of the Regius Chair of Natural History in the University of Edinburgh and Regius Keeper of its Natural History Museum in 1779 he had already made his choices from the intellectual wares in the cultural supermarket of the Enlightenment and, in single-minded self-assurance, applied his insights to the affairs of Church, University and Society. To Walker three things were axiomatic: Firstly, the sovereignty of God over the moral and natural world:

> Did all things happen according to a fixed order of natural causes, without any supreme direction of events, we might then indeed, be said to live in a fatherless world. But it is our happiness to know, that an invisible and over-riding power pervades and governs both the natural and moral world; and that the Almighty may powerfully interpose in both, without any infringement of those general laws which he hath established in his universe (Walker 1791).

This view is similar to that arising from the physical sciences and succinctly given by Colin Maclaurin (1748):

> ... the Deity's acting and interposing in the universe, shew he governs it as well as formed it.

Secondly, the validity of the Baconian inductive method in science:[3]

> ... we shall follow the synthetic method of enquiry and content ourselves with endeavouring to establish facts rather than attempt solutions and to try by experiments how far that method may lead us thro' the mazes of the subject.[4]

In contradistinction to Newtonian deductive methods:

> Nature consults no philosophers. They too seldom indeed consult her ... Often ... a man conceives some general fanciful idea in natural history ... then goes in quest of fact, and circumstances to support it, and probably offers this idol to the world, by the name of his Theory or his System. (Walker 1808b, 336).

Thirdly, the museum as an essential in the study of Nature:

> Many Gentlemen in our own country and others abroad have an inclination to make collections of Natural Objects but are much at a loss to know what things are proper to collect .. After the proper bodies are collected and prepared there is still another care required of the Naturalist and that is to place them in a proper and scientific manner. Such a collection is called a museum and must subsist wherever an attention to the study of Nature prevails.[5]

What was axiomatic to Walker, however, was not necessarily so to others. In this chapter we consider the intellectual and academic environment into which Walker entered in 1779 . We shall see how successful he was in recreating the Natural History Museum of the University and how jealously he guarded the type of natural history teaching within the University which he thought proper, a campaign which involved him in a creative role in the formation of the Royal Society of Edinburgh. Under the terms of the Society's First Charter, and as Keeper of the Society's Museum, Walker obtained significant collections for the Society which were housed in the Natural History Museum of the University. The chapter closes with a review of the interest and continuing significance of some of these collections.

I WALKER'S INHERITANCE

MUSEUMS, PEDAGOGY AND ENLIGHTENMENT

Emerson believes science to have provided the driving force behind enlightened thought in Europe. For him 'the enlightened' were characterized by their belief that 'rationally-grounded natural knowledge could be found, should be sought and was to be acted upon to improve the human condition' (Emerson 1988a, 338). With Chitnis (1976) he sees the origins of the Scottish Enlightenment in the enlightened thought of seventeenth century Europe rather than as a cultural reaction in Scotland to the Act of Union of 1707.[6] Indeed, in seventeenth-century Scotland virtuosi such as Sir Robert Sibbald already recognised the value of natural knowledge.

Sibbald studied at Edinburgh University and, like many of his learned contemporaries, completed his formal education on the Continent. He went to Leiden in 1660 and then to Paris, Angiers and London before returning to Edinburgh in 1662 to practise medicine. Emerson notes that Sibbald and his friends did much to institutionalize in Scotland the critical methods and empirical secular outlook with which they had become familiar and which the European Enlightenment extended to every area of thought. 'Their natural history, philosophy and mathematics, like their antiquarian and critical-historical concerns, shaped the Enlightenment in Scotland' (Emerson 1988a, 339).

Following Bacon's example, Sibbald believed that basic to the improvement of Scotland and 'advancing the Wealth of the Kingdome' was a knowledge of the country and its natural productions. To this end he initiated a survey of the coasts and collected topographical descriptions of Scottish regions. He pioneered surveys of botany and zoology in Scotland, formed a notable collection of natural productions and, with Sir Andrew Balfour, founded the Edinburgh Physick Garden (Simpson 1982). He was also anxious to create institutions in Scotland which would advance learning by discussion. With friends, he founded the Royal College of Physicians of Edinburgh, incorporated in 1681, and may have contributed to its museum (Craig 1976, 100). In 1698 he projected a Royal Society of Scotland (Emerson 1988b) along the lines of the Academies of France and Italy 'to improve and Advance all good Learning especially that of Greatest use for Human lyfe Divinity, Medicine, Law. The study of History Civil Ecclesiastical, Natural; and Experimental Philosophy and the Mathematicks' (Emerson 1988b, 48). Three or four years later he proposed a Royal Society of Scotland with a scope more akin to the Royal Society of London.

In contrast to Sibbald's inductive methods, the deductive approach was strengthened in Scotland, in the later part of the seventeenth century, by men such as James Gregory, David Gregory and Archibald Pitcairne, all correspondents of Sir Isaac Newton. Indeed the deductive approach became so established in Scotland that it was recognized as characteristic of Scottish culture by English critics (Buckle, 1861, see also Davie 1961, 189ff).

Teaching, of course, played a vital part, along with the founding of academies and the formation of museums, in the spread of enlightened thought in Europe. Birse (1994, 42-46) has drawn attention to the remarkable results in the teaching of science in Scotland between 1740 and 1865. His statistical study shows that for more than two centuries Scotland produced significantly more scientists and technologists per head of population than any other country large or small. This activity began in the second half of the seventeenth century, gathered momentum in the eighteenth century and reached a peak in 1850. Birse thus supports Emerson and Chitnis in seeing the importance of science and philosophy in the Scottish Enlightenment. He believes, however, that the cultural flowering between 1730 and 1790 was only the beginning of a wider phenomenon marked by the growth of engineering and applied science from 1750 to 1850, which he has termed The Scottish Achievement. Like Emerson and Chitnis, Birse also rejects the view that the cultural take-off was due to the beneficial effects of the Union of 1707. He attributes it to the ending of the regenting system in Scottish universities[7] and to the intellectual stimulus which was thereby opened to students to choose 'between courses given by famous professors vying with each other to attract students (and income!) by making sure that their lectures were interesting, and covered applications as well as the principles of their subjects' (Birse 1994, 46).

As part of this process many professors of the physical sciences illustrated their lectures by memorable demonstrations. Anderson has noted that during the eighteenth century in Edinburgh University James Crawford, Andrew Plummer and William Cullen had all used lecture demonstrations in Chemistry but Joseph Black's were a tour de force far exceeding those of his professorial predecessors in scope, neatness and unvarying success (Anderson 1982, 10). We know that at a slightly later date in Edinburgh Sir John Leslie, every session, showed his Natural Philosophy class nearly a thousand demonstration experiments which were mounted for him by an operator.[8] Demonstration lectures in anatomy were also popular in Edinburgh and in 1764 Alexander Monro *secundus* had a purpose-built Anatomy Theatre constructed to accommodate them (Fraser 1989, 43). Similarly museums and herbaria provided vital illustrative demonstrations in the teaching of geology, zoology and botany. In Walker's words:

> In Natural History nothing elucidates so much as a demonstration of the several species, nothing tends so much to illustrate as a view of the bodies themselves. In this science more knowledge may be obtained by the eye than can be convey'd by the ear.[9]

For Walker, the museum was not only a valuable teaching aid for his students but, as Withers notes, it had wider educational and symbolic value as a practical means of extending knowledge and making natural history useful. In a Scotland which was then concerned with the philosophy of improvement, the museum 'gave natural history an exchange value beyond the productions, lectures, or displays themselves' (Withers, 1992, 298).

Scientific research based on inductive and deductive reasoning co-existed among the improvers of the Enlightenment and their differences of approach caused dissension as to the sort of natural history to be taught and the nature of the museums to be formed. Out of that tension the Royal Society of Edinburgh was born.

NATURAL HISTORY AT THE UNIVERSITY OF EDINBURGH

The early history of the University's Natural History Museum has been summarised by A G Fraser (1989, 193-4).

Shortly after his appointment as Principal, William Robertson sought to establish the importance of natural history within the University. In 1767 a second storey was added to a building in the old university complex, dating from 1642, to house a museum.[10] Dr Robert Ramsay, physician, was in the same year appointed Regius Keeper of the Museum and first Regius Professor of Natural History by the King. It was not until 1770, however, that the Town Council enacted Ramsay's admission which permitted him to take up these offices.[11]

Previously 'the Receptacle both of natural and artificial Curiosities appertaining to the College' (Maitland 1753, 364-5) had been the College Hall on the upper floor of the adjoining building which dated from 1617. The Hall was a spacious room in which the principal and professors held meetings and students received their degrees.[12] Outstanding among the collections housed in the College Hall was that made by Sir Andrew Balfour and obtained by the Town Council after his death in 1694.[13] This had been supplemented by Sir Robert Sibbald's largely Scottish collection presented in 1697 (Craig 1976, 100). Sibbald published a catalogue of his collection which he dedicated to the Town Council of Edinburgh, the patrons of the College (Sibbald 1697). In 1711 a visitor described the collection in the College Hall as 'a vast Treasure of Curiosities of ART and NATURE, Foreign and Domestick' (quoted Fraser 1989).[14] By 1753 the Hall was also used as an overflow book store because the library in the 1642 building was full. According to Grant (1884, I, 375) 'the objects fell into disorder, deteriorated, or were abstracted. By 1770 ... the Sibbald Museum had disappeared'.

The fate of the Balfour-Sibbald collection has long remained unclear but is of concern to us, not only because of its intrinsic importance, but because its sorry history became a factor in the dispute between Lord Buchan and the University (see p 17).

Ramsay's successor, Professor John Walker, told his students in the 1780s:

His (Balfour's) museum was deposited in the College of Edinburgh, in the hall, which is now the library (ie the College Hall); and there is reason to think it was then the most considerable that was in the possession of any University in Europe. There it remained for many years, useless and neglected; some parts of it going to inevitable decay and others abstracted. Yet even after the year 1750 it still continued a considerable collection, which I have good reason to remember, as it was the sight of it, about that time, that first inspired me with an attachment to Natural History. Soon after that period, it was dislodged from the hall where it had been kept; was thrown aside; and exposed as lumber; was further and further dilapidated, and at length, almost completely demolished.

In the year 1782, out of its ruins and rubbish I extracted many pieces still valuable and useful, and placed them here (ie in the Museum in the 1642 building) in the best order I could (Walker, 1808b, 365).[15]

What event soon after 1750 could have caused the collection to have been so rudely dislodged? From Fraser's work we know that refurbishment of the College Hall, where the *Musaeum Balfourianum* was stored, took place in 1753 when an attic floor was added and the whole adapted for use as the new and larger library. The adjacent 1642 building was not refurbished to provide museum accommodation until 1767 and in 1753 was still occupied by the library. It is reasonable to suggest, therefore, that the *Musaeum Balfourianum* had to be removed by 1753 when no other suitable accommodation was available to house it. Nothing is so antipathetic to a collection of fragile objects than unsympathetic removal and inadequate storage. Such was the premium on space within the University that any accommodation which might have been available for specimens would have been used to store anatomical preparations, also dislodged from the 1617 building, since these were under the active care of academic staff. As yet, however, there was no professor of Natural History and, lacking a guardian, the *Musaeum Balfourianum* must have been unsuitably housed, if housed at all, and 'exposed as lumber' for some thirty years. Natural objects could not survive such treatment.[16]

Principal Robertson's wish to see the place of Natural History strengthened within the University had so far failed on both counts – the Balfour-Sibbald collection had been largely lost and Robert Ramsay had failed to make any impact, having held his chair as a sinecure. The situation changed when Ramsay died on 15 December 1778, for worthy candidates awaited the succession.

II WALKER'S ACHIEVEMENT

JOHN WALKER'S APPOINTMENT TO THE REGIUS KEEPERSHIP

Powerful political lobbies were mobilized in support of John Walker and of William Smellie as candidates in the contest which led to Walker's appointment in 1779 (Shapin 1974, 12-15).

William Smellie, printer and publisher in Edinburgh, 'without the aid of relations' had attended the mathematics and philosophy classes at Edinburgh and the medical classes including chemistry and botany. His writings were encyclopaedic covering politics, theology, medicine, law, Scottish history, sociology and psychology as well as natural history and Brown regards him as 'crucial for our understanding of the Scottish Enlightenment in Edinburgh and its fundamental shaping of a national intellectual temperament' (Brown 1994,4). At the time of Smellie's candidacy he was known for his proficiency in Botany having published his prize-winning *Dissertation on the Sexes of Plants* in the first edition of the *Encyclopaedia Britannica* which he edited.

John Walker was still the parish minister of Moffat when he became a candidate and had been recognised for his surveys of the Hebrides and Highlands of Scotland. He was proficient in all branches of Natural History: he had already made an extensive private mineral collection, was in correspondence on botany with Linnaeus and was known also as a rural economist and agriculturalist (Withers, 1985).

On Walker's appointment as Regius Keeper, Edinburgh Town Council, as patron of the College, required him to submit an inventory of all curiosities and rarities belonging to the University. This he did in 1780 recording 119 lots, most of which were fossils or ethnographic specimens but few zoological or botanical.[17] It confirms Walker's assertion that when he was appointed Keeper 'there was nothing to keep', and what was there was in poor condition. He reported to the Town Council that

> The greater part of it [the collection] is mere Rubbish, that never can be of any Use. Some parts of it, particularly many Birds and Fishes [ought] to be immediately thrown out, being so over run with moths & other Insects that no Animal Preparations, can be placed with Safety in the Room till they are removed. There are however many Specimens; especially of Shells & Fossils; that deserve being cleaned, dressed, and placed in better Order, but it could answer no useful Purpose, while the Room remains in its present Situation.[18]

He obtained the lower hall of the 1642 building for the exclusive use of the Museum by the agreement of Dr Black and Mr Hill to remove their classes, and in Black's case his apparatus, to other quarters. In his submission of 1780 Walker described the rooms as

> ... the largest and best Apartment in the College. It is about 70 Feet long, 24 wide & 18 high, with a Range of 10 windows to the South & well deserves to be preserved entire, for some publick Use. By its Form and Dimensions, it is excellently adapted for the Purpose of a Museum, and was it properly fitted up & furnished, no University could boast of any thing superior in that way.

While Walker remained the incumbent of Moffat, he gave no lectures. Walker was translated to the Parish of Colinton in July 1782, however, and held his professorship and his incumbency in plurality for the rest of his life. His first class-list dates from March of that year (Shapin 1974, 19).

THE ROYAL CHARTERS: THE SOCIETY OF ANTIQUARIES AND THE ROYAL SOCIETY OF EDINBURGH

A detailed account of the events which led to the granting of royal charters to the Royal Society of Edinburgh and the Society of Antiquaries in 1783 has been given by Shapin (1974, 15-35).

At the instigation of David Steuart Erskine, 11th Earl of Buchan, the Society of Antiquaries of Scotland was inaugurated in 1780 and petitioned for a Royal Charter in 1782 when its objects were defined as 'for investigating antiquities, as well as natural and civil history in general'. In 1781 John Walker's rival William Smellie was appointed Keeper of the natural history collections of the new Society and it was proposed that he should give lectures on natural history in the Society's hall (Cant 1981). Since his candidature for the university chair, Smellie's reputation in natural history had been enhanced by publication of the first edition of his nine volume translation of Buffon's *Natural History* (1780).

Writing to William Strachan at this time Smellie, now the father of nine children and feeling financially embarrassed, gave his point of view:

> I mention another project for the year 1774, my favourable friend Lord Kames suggested to me a plan for composing lectures on the Philosophy of Natural History which I highly relished. I immediately began work, and proceeded for some years collecting materials, till it received a long interruption from Buffon. After finishing Buffon, I resumed ... and shall complete the Lectures in less than twelve months.
>
> About three years ago Dr Ramsay, professor of Natural History, died. My friends applied to Lord Suffolk in my favour. But Walker's political interest was strongest and I lost the chair.
>
> At the last meeting of the Antiquarian Society, they appointed me Keeper of the Museum with a request to deliver my lectures in the hall when they were ready. This office, though no Salary is annexed to it, increased my prospect of success from the patronage of a body so numerous and respectable. But jealousy always rises in proportion to the narrowness of a country, Dr Walker, accordingly, though he has never yet Lectured himself, has taken the alarm, and is using all his influence to get my Lectures suppressed. I have indeavoured to convince his friends that no interference can ever happen. This explanation, however, has not satisfied him...[19]

At the time of his candidacy for the chair of Natural History Smellie had written to Thomas Dundas 'This science has always been my favourite study: and I have even composed a set of Lectures on the subject *because* my friend Dr Ramsay never taught a regular course' (Kerr 1811, II, 95). Smellie assured Lord Buchan that his plan to give lectures had received the approbation of Ramsay who had given him every assistance in books and advice. Furthermore,

> The adventitious circumstance of Dr Ramsay's death, and of Dr Walker's succession, no man could foresee; and on the supposition that, at some future period I should avail myself of my own labours, even Delicacy itself could have no right to complain. (Kerr 1811, II, 102-3)

Smellie's right, as an individual, to give his lectures was not contested. Walker's objection arose from the proposal to give the lectures under the auspices of the Society of Antiquaries and was stated in a letter he wrote to Lord Buchan from Moffat on 14th September 1781:

> That private [illegible word], for their own interest, should pursue plans of this sort, is not at all surprising; but surely neither I, nor the University of Edr, merit such an Opposition from any public body.[20]

The terms of the Antiquaries' petition gave offence not only to Walker and the University of Edinburgh, who saw a threat to their cultural property in the Society's natural history interests, but also to the Faculty of Advocates, because their library was the accustomed repository of documents relating to the history and antiquities of Scotland. It also upset the Philosophical Society of Edinburgh, the immediate precursor of the Royal Society of Edinburgh, in which anti-Buchan feeling had been growing (Emerson 1988c). Out of the bitter dispute which followed the Royal Society of Edinburgh emerged. Shapin (1974) has dealt with the dispute and its outcome in the context of the property, patronage and politics involved.

The weakness of the University's position in both the museum and lecture room was obvious in the face of an active policy of collecting natural history objects by the Society of Antiquaries, and the prospect of lectures being given under that Society's auspices on natural history by William Smellie. Nor were the Antiquaries slow in using the stigma attaching to the University over the loss of the Balfour-Sibbald collection to their advantage during the dispute. Principal Robertson and Walker knew that if the University's interest in natural history were to survive, Lord Buchan's ambitions, as envisaged in the proposed Charter for the Society of Antiquaries, must be resisted. They saw the foundation of a new Society as a means to undermine the Antiquaries' position. The idea of such a new Society for the Advancement of Learning and Useful Knowledge in Edinburgh, to include both the Philosophers and the Antiquaries, was proposed by Walker in 1782.[21]

The patrons who had supported Smellie and Walker as candidates for the professorship of Natural History now took sides in the ensuing institutional discord. In addition to the evident political patronage of science which Shapin has described, Withers notes differences in philosophical approach to natural history as being another important source of discord. Walker was the successor to Sibbald's Baconian views in that he believed that knowledge should be discovered through empirical study and that natural history was a utilitarian science. Smellie's natural history, on the other hand, was more theoretical and speculative although he also recognised the importance of natural knowledge as a means to economic and social improvement. The debates between them and between their respective patrons were not just a matter of which party had the 'right' to house and present nature, but also a conflict over the purposes which such displays of natural knowledge were to serve (Withers 1992, 289-90).

The Faculty of Advocates and the Philosophical Society broadly supported the University's counter-proposal based on Walker's suggestion. In the event Royal Charters in modified terms were granted both to the Society of Antiquaries of Scotland and to the Royal Society of Edinburgh in 1783. An important distinction between these charters was their approach to property. The Antiquaries had the right to hold property and so to form a museum. The Royal Society of Edinburgh had sought no such right but, as we have seen, its charter required that donations of natural productions be placed in the Museum of the University of Edinburgh and antiquarian objects in the Library of the Faculty of Advocates.

In his account of the museum in the Faculty of Advocates Library, I G Brown (1989, 175) noted that the arrangement by which objects of antiquarian interest were to be passed to the Faculty under the terms of the Society's First Charter was worked out in accordance with the wishes of the majority of the Faculty.[22] He saw little evidence that antiquities presented to the Society were in fact transferred to the Faculty. Among papers in the National Museums of Scotland, however, Brown found an inventory of coins made by Alexander Fraser Tytler, Secretary of the Society's Literary Class, which cites nineteen medieval and modern coins passed to the Advocates in June 1786. These were almost certainly the fourteen silver and five copper coins, chiefly Scottish, which were presented by Baillie James Dickson, bookseller in Edinburgh. They must have been included in the coin collections of the Faculty of Advocates which were later passed to the National Museum of Antiquities, but cannot now be recognised in the national collections.[23]

John Walker had set about re-establishing the College's collection and reputation in his own discipline. The terms of the new Royal Charters had repulsed Smellie's challenge to the University and to himself as teacher of natural history although *The Philosophy of Natural History* from Smellie's pen, published in two volumes, was yet to make a valuable contribution from a philosophical standpoint distinct from Walker's. Paragraph 9 of Walker's text of 1782 had stated:

> Any Bodies relative to the Class of Philosophy, which may come into the possession of the Society, to be placed in the Colledge of Edinr. And any Collections relative to the Class of Antiquities, to be deposited & preserved in the Advocates Library.

The adoption of this proposal in the Royal Society's charter was another means of enhancing the status of the collections in Walker's charge and his own position as Keeper. Thus he assured the future of his own position as both Regius Professor and Regius Keeper.

TOWARDS A NOBLE REPOSITORY

Walker's collecting policy was, like Sibbald's, to create a museum which would illustrate the natural products of Scotland having in mind the utilitarian nature of his science and the value of such displays to the improvers of his age. In Walker's time, however, people became more aware of Scotland's place in the wider world. In the exploration and commercial development of vast territories like India, Australasia and North America Scottish merchant adventurers and Scottish servants of the East India Company and the Hudson's Bay Company were playing an increasingly important role. Many of Walker's students were involved in these activities.

It was through Walker's extensive contacts that collections were presented both to the University and to the Royal Society of Edinburgh. His immediate contact was with his students and the instructions he gave them on what and how to collect were published for the wider use of overseas travellers ([Walker] 1793).[24] Another forum for contacting men of influence was the Royal Society of London to which Walker was elected a Fellow in 1794. Its President, Joseph Banks, had accompanied the expedition of 1769 which the philosophers of that Society had fitted out to observe the Transit of Venus and explore Australasia in the *Endeavour* under the command of James Cook. He continued to be the centre of influence in the Royal Society's interests abroad and of British exploration in many parts of the world. To him came men and collections from many parts of the world and Walker benefited from these London contacts. Nearer home Fellows of the Royal Society of Edinburgh provided Walker with a third, and influential, set of contacts through whom, as donors or as friends of donors, his museum benefited.

In a submission to the Town Council in 1785 he listed eleven 'Noblemen and Gentlemen' from whom he had received a considerable collection of natural productions for their Museum in the university and stated that

> He has also hopes of considerable additions from the Gentlemen who have attended the class of Natural History, and other Persons already abroad – As there is reason to think that there are many gentlemen in Scotland who have objects of natural history in their possession, who would present them to the publick Collection in the University if they were properly advertised that such things would be gratefully received and carefully preserved. He wishes therefore, that he was enabled to make publick Intimation that the Museum of the university is now in proper order for the reception of any Donation that may be sent to it and to defray any necessary expenses that may be incurred.[25]

The Town Council was well pleased with Dr Walker 'for his indefatigable pains in bringing the Museum to the state of perfection it is now in', authorized advertisements to appear in the newspapers and granted him up to £25 yearly on account for expenses.

Whether the office-bearers of the Royal Society of Edinburgh were as pleased with the terms of Walker's 1785 submission to the Town Council may be doubted, since all eleven noblemen and gentlemen quoted by Walker as having given collections to the Town's museum in the University had in fact given their collections to the Society – which is nowhere acknowledged in the document. This is clear from the list of donors published in the first volume of the Society's *Transactions* and from the list of articles presented to the Society and deposited in the Museum of the University which Walker had lodged with the Magistrates and Town Council of the City seven months previously.[26] While, as Physical Secretary of the Society, Walker probably played a major part in obtaining the material, as Keeper of the University Museum he should have shown greater discrimination between acquisitions through the Society and those made directly to the University Museum. As we shall see this ambivalence in Walker and his successor towards ownership of material acquired through the Society led to tension between the Society and the University.

As the collections grew under Walker's able management the lower hall of the 1642 building became overcrowded and other rooms had to be adapted for museum use. As congestion continued to increase Walker complained in 1793 that many specimens 'must remain in their present confusion huddled up in Chests and Boxes, unfit for the Public Eye, and incapable of any public Use'.[27] As Fraser has noted, these unsatisfactory conditions appear to have been tolerated by the Society throughout Walker's keepership in the hope of future improvement. The building of the new College was in prospect: Robert Adam's plan of 1789 proposed a magnificent Museum of Natural History in its south wing and in 1790 the foundation stone had been laid (Fraser 1989, fig 4, 9, p105 and p358). Walker found himself challenged to provide collections and furniture 'suitable to such a Noble Repository – As the Hall allotted for the Museum, in the New College is of great Extent & as it is to be hoped, will become one of the greatest Ornaments to the University, and to the City'.[28]

He therefore sought to purchase existing natural history collections. Alexander Weir was paid 200 guineas for the cabinets and collections of birds and animals which comprised his first museum which was placed in the College in 1786 (Taylor 1992, 155-60). Much of the cost had been raised through public subscription, a quarter of the subscribers being Fellows of the Royal Society of Edinburgh. A shortfall of £60 remained and in 1790 Walker asked the Town Council to meet this to secure 'to the University this very valuable Collection'.[29] Although the Council declined the request, the collection remained in the College Museum. On the same occasion Walker reported to the Town Council that 'For this Purpose, he has at present in View, the Acquisition of an entire Museum, amounting in Value, to several Hundred Pounds, and which he hopes to procure, without incurring any Expence to the City'.

Which museum Walker had in mind we may never know but at that time he was certainly interested in the museum at New Posso, now Dawyck. The museum was made by the second baronet, Sir James Nasmyth, an eminent arboriculturalist and botanist who had been a pupil of Linnaeus. It was in the former house of Dawyck (demolished 1830) and described by Walker as being 'in a Room and adjacent Closet fitted up entirely round with Presses, Drawers and Glass Cases'.[30] Sir James had died in 1779 and in 1786 Walker petitioned the Treasury for a grant in aid of purchase.

The late Sir James Nasmyth of Posso Bart. a Man remarkable for his Literature & Taste, formed an excellent Collection of Natural History, at a considerable Expence, which is at present offered to Sale, on Terms very advantageous to the Purchaser. The Sum necessary to make this Purchase; for transporting it to Edinr.; & for putting it up in proper Order; would amount to 400 Guineas. And could this Addition be obtained, for the Royal Museum, it would then contain a Collection, highly respectable, & greatly conducive to the System of Education, carried on in this University.[31]

Walker's petition of 1786 was unsuccessful but the future of the Nasmyth collection must still have been under consideration when he catalogued the museum on a visit to Dawyck in 1789. It could well have been in his mind, therefore, when he wrote of acquiring 'an entire museum... without Expence to the City' in his submission to the Town Council in the following year. Perhaps he had hopes of a patron purchasing the collection for the College Museum or even that the third Baron, having failed to sell the collection in 1786, might be prevailed upon to give it to the College. These hopes must have died when the Baron wrote to Walker in 1793 that he would probably have an opportunity of selling the collection that summer.[32]

DONATIONS TO THE SOCIETY, 1783-1811

Articles deposited in the University Museum under the terms of the First Charter, together with the names of the donors, are listed in the Society's *Transactions* volumes one to five.[33] Other than the Hutton Collection (see Chapter 3), the most important geological donation under the First Charter was a collection of some 400 specimens from James Hope, Third Earl of Hopetoun, given prior to his election to fellowship in 1786. This included a collection of 140 specimens of Italian marbles of which 112 are preserved in the National Museums of Scotland (G1993.34.1-112). Each specimen is backed by slate on which a label has been pasted giving the identification of genus, species and variety, eg *Phengites Onychites (n. Purpureus)*, in John Walker's writing and according to his usage, together with the letters ME (= *Musaeum Edinensis*) followed by the number allocated according to the order in which the articles were deposited in the University Museum by the Society (fig 1). Mrs Pat Crichton, Archivist at Hopetoun House, has identified this collection as among the purchases made by Lord John Hope, later Second Earl of Hopetoun, during his stay in Italy while on the Grand Tour (1725-7).[34] In a vellum-covered manuscript notebook in the Hopetoun papers occurs an entry which may well be that of the collection in question 'A Box with 100 different kinds of Marble [Price] 10 -Roman Crowns'.[35] The presence of this collection links the Society's museum with the older tradition of Cabinets of Curiosities which were the pride of many great houses, of which Hopetoun is certainly one, before the days of public or institutional museums. In contrast, most of the remainder of the Third Earl's donation consisted of mineral specimens derived from his own estates, including the

fig 1 Polished specimens of Italian ornamental marble from the geological collection presented by the 3rd Earl of Hopetoun *c*1785. Probably from 'A box of 100 different kinds of
Marble' purchased by Lord John Hope while in Italy on the Grand Tour between 1725 and
1727.
From left to right:
a. The reverse side of a slate-backed specimen of Travertine Marble showing Professor John
Walker's original Musaeum Edinensis label '*Phengites Oculatus* ME401'. The serial number
denotes the order in which articles presented to the Royal Society of Edinburgh were added
to the Museum of the University of Edinburgh. NMS G1993.34.97
b. The exhibited face of a specimen of Travertine Marble labelled '*Phengites Oculatus* ME 398'
NMS G1993.34.94
c. The exhibited face of a Fossiliferous Limestone '*Marmor Sicilio viridesceno* ME305' NMS
G1993.34.20
d. The reverse side of an unbacked specimen of Breccia Marble showing Professor Walker's
original label '*Marmor Piombino* ME315' NMS G1993.34.31

Leadhills district of Lanarkshire, where mineral extraction had long been
practised and was being actively developed.[36]

In 1783, half a century after Lord John Hope undertook the Grand Tour,
James Byres was elected to Fellowship of the Society. He was a distant
cousin, and nephew by marriage, of Joseph Black the distinguished chemist
and a leading member of the Fellowship in those days.[37] Byres was famous

among British visitors to Italy as a cicerone of Rome. He was variously described as an architect or painter and was an authority on Etruscan antiquity. His reputation as a dealer in art and antiquities was at its highest between 1766 and 1790 (Skinner 1966, 16). One of his transactions was the sale of the Portland Vase to another expatriate Fellow of the Society, Sir William Hamilton.[38] In December 1791 Byres presented to the Society's museum 'A Series of ancient Roman Weights of Basaltes or Porphyry'. Having regard to his professional reputation as a dealer, and his relationship to one of the Society's leading Fellows, it is likely that this was a donation of quality. It is regrettable that in his annotated catalogue of 1812 Sir George Mackenzie had to record this series of classic weights as 'Wanting'.

Because of their perishability and the nature of the preservation methods then available it is little wonder that few natural history specimens, acquired under the First Charter, remain. Indeed we know from Sir George Mackenzie that even in 1812 many specimens were 'decayed and thrown out'.

An important botanical collection, which survives from this period, came from Dr William Roxburgh who, from 1782 to 1793, was stationed at Samul Cattah, Madras, and in 1787 appointed the East India Company's 'Botanist in the Carnatic'. The gift is recorded as 'A Chest of Plants from Bengal and the Peninsula of India'.[39] The collection was catalogued by Dr William Wright, well-known for his work on the plants of Jamaica. His manuscript, completed in 1794, lists 230 genera and 565 species and is now in the library of the Royal Botanic Garden, Edinburgh (fig 2). A number of species are represented in the collection by more than one specimen. Wright stated that the collection had been presented to the Royal Society of Edinburgh in 1792 but the record of the donation in the second volume of the Society's *Transactions* (published 1790) suggests that it was received in 1789 or at least no later than 1790.[40]

In the year following completion of the catalogue Wright went back to the West Indies. In it he had written that it would be desirable to mount the specimens on paper and some time after his final return to Edinburgh in 1798 he borrowed the collection in order to do this. In 1812 when Sir George Mackenzie inspected the Society's property which had been lodged in the University Museum under the terms of the First Charter he recorded in his annotated catalogue that the Roxburgh collection had been 'Given to Dr Wright to be arranged and never returned'.[41] Wright wrote to Sir George on 28th April 1812 assuring him that he still had the collection which had been in disorder and had started work pasting up the specimens but would return the collection at once if required. On 13 May 1812 Mackenzie recommended to John Playfair, the Society's Secretary, that 'As he is in the course of arranging them, it may be as well to leave it in his hands for some time till he finishes the task.'[42] This he appears to have done, and he eventually lodged the Roxburgh collection in the University. In 1839-40 the herbaria of the University and the Botanical Society of Edinburgh were merged to form 'The University Herbarium' which was itself

fig 2 One of about 600 specimens from the 'Chest of plants from Bengal and the Peninsula of India' presented by Dr William Roxburgh *c*1789. The specimen is *Combretum decandrum* Roxburgh, collected in February, probably in the neighbourhood of Madras. The remounted specimen has Roxburgh's ms label in ink below the plant and, below that, Dr William Wright's ms pencil identification. It was Roxburgh's practice to make two slits in the label through which he passed the stem of the plant and these are seen as parallel lines in the example shown. The numbers 8.2 on Wright's label refer to the classification in his ms catalogue (1794) of this collection, 8 being the Linnaean Class and 2 the second taxon of that class in the collection. The sheet on which the specimen has been remounted is embossed 'Edinburgh University Herbarium'.   Royal Botanic Garden, Edinburgh

24

incorporated into that of the Royal Botanic Garden in 1863 (Hedge and Lamond 1980, 4).

In 1793 Dr Roxburgh moved to Calcutta as superintendent of the Botanic Garden where he remained until 1813 and most of the collections he gave to British herbaria date from this period. The collection which he gave to the Royal Society of Edinburgh, containing many pressed plants from the Madras region, is of scientific interest in belonging to the period of his residence at Samul Cattah. It was not until between 1791 and 1794 that Roxburgh sent to London his five hundred plant drawings. From these Sir Joseph Banks selected three hundred for publication in *Plants of the Coast of Coromandel* (1795-1820), the final parts of which were completed after Roxburgh's death.

The bone breccia of Gibraltar, a large mass of which was presented by Lord Hailes soon after 1783 (another piece was given by Lieutentant Mac-Niven forty years later) was of widespread interest in these early years and samples were sought by collectors (Durant & Rolfe 1984, 18-19). For example, a specimen 'A piece of limestone rock of Gibraltar which is every-where full of bones and parts of bones' was in James Hutton's collection (Eyles, 1970, xiii, Jones 1984, 242) and another is preserved in William Hunter's collection (Hunterian Museum V.6032). Hunter identified the bones in the deposit as those of quadrupeds (Hunter 1771). In an early paper, Colonel Imrie noted the bone breccia in his account of the geology of Gibraltar in the Society's *Transactions* (Imrie 1798).

The painting of the head and horns of an elk from a marl-pit in For-farshire, presented in 1785 by Lord Dunsinnan, was of interest as being a record of one of the first authentic instances discovered in Scotland, or indeed in Britain, of the true elk, *Cervus alces* of Linnaeus (Smith, 1873, 316). I am indebted to Dr Kitchener for bringing to my notice Dr J A Smith's paper which gives information about this 'clever painting'.[43] When a medical student attending Jameson's lectures, Smith saw the painting hung in 'The British Gallery', an upper gallery of the University Natural History Museum devoted to the illustration of local zoology. After transfer of the university collection to the nation, J B Davies of the Museum of Science and Art confirmed that the painting was stored in that museum but he could find no reference to it in their records. Smith exhibited the painting to the Society of Antiquaries of Scotland when he addressed them in 1871 and published a copy of it in his paper. It shows 'but a poor specimen of an elk, the horns being small and undeveloped'. Unfortunately the original paint-ing has not been traced in the present collections of the National Museums of Scotland.

A collection of thirty-eight coloured drawings of birds of the southern hemisphere was presented in 1783 by Dr Alexander Monro (secundus) pro-fessor of Anatomy and Surgery in the University of Edinburgh and a founder Fellow of the Society. These drawings, numbered 5-42 in Walker's list of acquisitions, are now bound in a volume entitled *Original Drawings of*

Birds from Captain Cook's 2nd Voyage which is preserved in the Archive Library of the National Museums of Scotland [MS598.2]. For the following information I am indebted to the work of Averil Lysaght (1959, 260-2) who studied this collection among other eighteenth-century bird paintings. They had been the property of William Anderson who had been taught anatomy and surgery by the donor Alexander Monro *secundus*. Anderson had sailed as Surgeon's Chief Mate on Cook's second voyage (1772-5) and as Chief Surgeon on the third voyage (1776-9), in the course of which he died. He wrote to Banks from the Cape of Good Hope describing the voyage of the *Discovery* so far, with an account of the Canary Islands, and sent seed to Professor John Hope to grow on for the Botanic Garden.[44,45] He kept a notebook, now in the Library of the Natural History Museum, London, containing descriptions of birds and other animals collected on these voyages (Whitehead 1969, 163). The bird paintings may have been the work of a midshipman but the chart which accompanies the drawings is a copy of one by Georg Forster of the track of the *Resolution* with the place names written by Anderson. Lysaght notes that companion sets are in the Print Room of the British Museum and in the Mitchell Library, Sydney.

At the same time Professor Monro presented the head and horns of a water buffalo or arnee from Bengal (RSE Museum acquisition 43), but how he obtained the specimen is not recorded. Its presence in the College Museum, however, was noted by Kerr (1792, 336, Sweet 1972, 18).[46] In his translation of the Mammalian section of Gmelin's thirteenth edition of Linnaeus' *Systema Naturae*, published in 1792, Kerr made many additions. His familiarity with the contents of Weir's Museum and the College Museum in Edinburgh enabled him to note the presence in them of interesting material. Of the two arnees of unknown provenance now in the National Museums of Scotland, it is likely that one is that presented by Munro in 1783. Kerr noted also that in the College Museum was a polar bear (Kerr 1792, 185), probably the stuffed specimen presented to the Royal Society of Edinburgh by Captain Robert Liddell of Leith in 1787 (RSE Museum acquisition 750), which had become 'Decayed' by 1812, and a musk ox (Kerr 1792, 336-7) of which there is no record among the Canadian material presented through the Society.

Through the stimulus of the Royal Society of London and Captain Cook's voyages, together with the activities of the Hudson's Bay Company, there was interest at this time, not only in the natural products of Australia, Oceania and North America, but also in the products made by the races which were being encountered. Because of its eighteenth-century origins, the ethnographic material which survives is among the most important of the extant collections presented to the Society under the terms of the First Charter.

Ethnographic pieces collected during Cook's third voyage were presented by Lord Daer and Andrew Graham. These were not the first of their kind to be seen in Edinburgh, for the famous military surgeon Sir John Pringle had given a collection from Cook's last voyage to the Society of Antiquaries

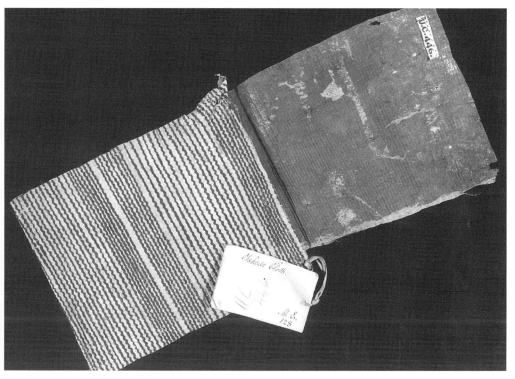

fig 3 Piece of barkcloth with painted black design and original ME label 'Otaheite Cloth'
ME128 = NMS UC446 Cook specimen presented by Lord Daer.

of Scotland in 1781.[47] The Daer material, which he presented to the Royal
Society of Edinburgh at a date between 1783 and 1785 (see Appendix I),
comprised two collections from Cook's last voyage. One collection of
seventy five items had passed to Daer from an unspecified source. The
second, of ninety seven items, was collected by William Anderson.

Basil William Douglas, Lord Daer was heir to the fourth Earl of Selkirk
and is a significant figure worthy of a digression (fig 11). He is best known
for his later political activities as an advocate of parliamentary reform and as
an admirer of the French Revolution and member of the Society of Friends
of the People. He was the first member of the peerage whom Robert Burns
met socially and, perhaps to his surprise, he found in Daer a 'brother' rather
than a lord 'Wha struts and stares, and a' that' (Ferguson 1931, II, 348). The
meeting took place at the home of Dugald Stewart on 23rd October 1786
and is commemorated in Burns' verses *On Dining with Lord Daer*.

In Shapin's view, had Daer not been the son of an Earl he would not
have been elected (Shapin 1974, 39) for other young men who sympathised
with the Revolutionary movement in France, such as the natural philosopher John Leslie, were excluded.[48] Although overshadowed by his political

activities, Daer's philosophical interests were indeed genuine. His sister, Lady Helen Douglas, was married to Sir James Hall of Dunglass, a notable Fellow and later President of the Society. While at the University of Edinburgh Daer attended Joseph Black's chemistry class and corresponded with him in subsequent years. Like his brother-in-law, Sir James Hall, he visited Lavoisier in Paris and espoused the new chemistry. Hall lectured the Society on Lavoisier's theory of combustion on three occasions in 1788 (Campbell and Smellie 1983, 22 and 79) and, in 1789, Daer brought home from Paris a copy of Lavoisier's newly published *Traité élémentaire de chimie*.[49] Two years later Daer and Hall went to France together to study the political situation.[50] Daer also attended John Walker's first course of lectures on natural history. James Edward Smith, writing to his father in 1782, sought to give the impression that the new Natural History Society of Edinburgh, which he did so much to inaugurate with Professor Walker's blessing, was attracting the interest of nobility:

> Several men of genius and rank have petitioned to be admitted as ordinary members among whom are the Earls of Glasgow, Ancrum, and Lord Dacre [sic = Daer], son of the Earl of Selkirk – three young noblemen of fine parts and great fortune. (Smith 1832, I, 44-7; Allen 1978, 487)

None of these noblemen appears in the membership lists of the Society, nor did Daer address that body (Anon 1803). As he did with Black, however, Daer continued to correspond with Walker in later years, and his presentations to the Society clearly show his active interest in ethnography.

There was some degree of order in the handling of plant and animal material collected on the Cook voyages because most of it, though not all, was channelled through Sir Joseph Banks and thereafter distributed from Soho Square to a complex network of recipients (Whitehead 1969, fig 1). Expedition members and crew, on the other hand, appear to have been free to sell any ethnographic material which they had acquired on the voyages. Whitehead notes, for example, that Johann Reinhold Forster and his son Georg sold what ethnological material they could from the second voyage. It is thus difficult to trace the provenance of known Cook ethnographic specimens in many public or private repositories. It is probable that Lord Daer was able to purchase the collection (original acquisition numbers 103-77) from a single source.

Despite the ill treatment suffered by this delicate material in the overcrowded storage conditions which prevailed in the Walker/Jameson transition (see pp 40, 46) – Sir George Mackenzie reported to the Society in 1812 that 'There are two large trunks full of South Sea Cloth & Matting, besides a number of articles which are hung up in the museum' – eleven out of the seventy five objects in the original presentation are preserved in the National Museums of Scotland and have been recognised as probably Cook material by Dale Idiens (see Appendix I). They are arrows, barkcloth (fig 3), a mat, a bag of plaited pandanus (fig 4), a flax cloak and fishhooks. In most cases

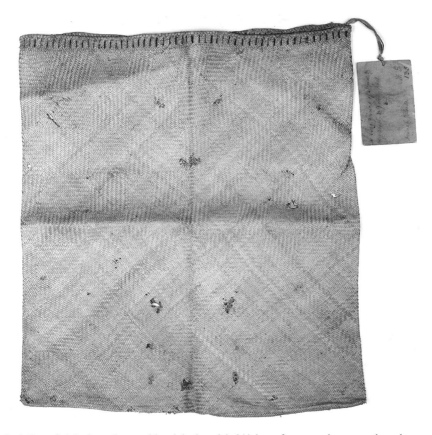

fig 4 Bag of plaited pandanus with original ME label 'A bag of straw and very neatly and firmly made. Friendly Is.' ME135 = NMS UC475 Cook specimen presented by Lord Daer.

the identification is supported by the objects being associated with Professor John Walker's original manuscript 'ME' or *Musaeum Edinensis* labels. The numbers would suggest that this collection had been made up entirely of Cook material of which the less robust items have perished.

The 'Mr Anderson, Surgeon to Captain Cook' who made the collection which comprised the second part of Daer's donation (original acquisition numbers 178-274) also formed the collection of drawings of birds of the southern hemisphere (see above). In his will Anderson left his natural curiosities to Banks, but most of his belongings to his sisters and uncle (Lysaght 1959, 260-2) Lysaght identified George Dempster MP as having helped Anderson's sisters, then living in North Berwick, to receive payment for the use made of their brother's papers. Daer would have been in a position to purchase the collection from them and so help to relieve some of the hardship which must have followed their brother's death. Dale Idiens has identified eight ethnographic pieces in the collections of the National

Museums of Scotland as Cook material from the Anderson collection (see Appendix I). In most cases, the identifications are again supported by the objects having Professor John Walker's original manuscript 'ME' or *Musaeum Edinensis* labels associated. The surviving specimens are a palm-leaf mat; a mat from Samoa; four specimens of barkcloth, one stated to be from Tahiti and one painted in red and black triangles; a flax cloak from New Zealand and a bag of plaited palm leaves with sinnet ties.

As well as specimens of ethnography, the Anderson collection had contained natural history objects which, having been presented before 1785, were probably the first natural exhibits from a Cook voyage to be seen in Edinburgh. Taylor has noted that Weir's Museum acquired specimens from the Sandwich Islands in 1789 and has suggested that these could also have been from Cook's voyage, obtained perhaps through Elizabeth Scott, Duchess of Buccleuch (Taylor 1992, 157-8). Anderson's natural history specimens, like Weir's, have perished.

Eleven specimens from Cook's last voyage were included in the collection presented to the Society by Andrew Graham in 1787 (Williams, 1983). Of these only a piece of hempen rope from New Zealand, which is associated with its original *Musaeum Edinensis* label, can be identified by Dale Idiens in the collections of the National Museums of Scotland.

The Graham Collection was not listed by Professor Walker among the donations to the Society published in the Society's *Transactions*. This is an extraordinary and unexplained omission since the presentation was a large one and made when Walker was at the height of his powers. Evidence for what was given to the Society comes from two sources. Firstly, in the Walker archive in Edinburgh University Library, there is a manuscript in Graham's handwriting consisting of three folios listing the objects presented, and sixty-four folios describing them.[51] Secondly, in the Hudson's Bay Company Archives are ten volumes of Graham's manuscript observations on Hudson's Bay 1767-91, in which his donations to the Society were noted in relevant sections throughout the work. Annotated selections of the observations, edited by Glyndwr Williams, together with a biographical sketch of Graham, have been published (Williams 1969).[52] According to these sources, the Graham Collection comprised, in addition to the eleven objects from Cook's last voyage already mentioned, twelve items of Hudson's Bay Indian material and twelve Inuit items together with twenty-eight birds and ten miscellaneous natural productions (see Appendix I). It has not been possible to trace any of the natural history objects in the present collections of the Royal Museum of Scotland.

Since Graham's donation went unrecorded by Walker, it may be asked whether it was ever received and added to the collections housed in the College Museum. The identification of the hempen rope from New Zealand, associated with Walker's original label, provides direct, although slender, evidence that the collection was indeed received. I am grateful to Dale Idiens for identifying a number of other items in the ethnographical collections of the National Museums of Scotland which, although lacking contemporary labels, she believes are stylistically compatible with the period and region of Graham's collecting and, with differing levels of confidence, might be regarded as having formed part of the Graham collection.

Identifications have been supported by comparison of the objects in the collection with Graham's detailed descriptions of them. Of greater certainty among the Hudson's Bay Indian material are four birch-bark dishes (UC303.1-4, fig 5), a pair of garters decorated with porcupine quills (UC 294 & A) two shot-pouches decorated with porcupine quills (UC297-8) and a cradle backboard (UC302). Of three leather togas decorated with porcupine quills in the collection, one (UC277, fig 6) is clearly the oldest in style and the most likely to be that presented by Graham. Although it is probable that the pair of shoes from the Graham Collection is present among the six pairs in the Museum's collection, they cannot be distinguished.

Through the work of Williams and others, Andrew Graham has emerged as an important figure for his written observations on the natural history and peoples around Hudson's Bay in the late eighteenth century. He was a Scot who joined the Hudson's Bay Company as a youth in 1749 and served at Prince of Wales Fort or Churchill, York Factory and Fort Severn. Graham's first furlough was in 1769-70 during which he obtained some of Pennant's works on natural history, probably including the second edition of *British*

fig 5 One of four birch-bark dishes NMS UC303.1 believed to be part of the Hudson's Bay Indian collection presented by Andrew Graham in 1787.

Zoology which he used as a reference. At this time also the Royal Society of London asked the Hudson's Bay Company for natural history specimens. On his return to Fort Severn, Graham and others set about collecting and sent 'Beasts: Birds: Fishes &c' to that Society each year from 1771 to 1774.[53] He completed his service in Canada as chief factor at Churchill and left the country in 1775 to live in the Edinburgh district until his death at Prestonpans in 1815. While living in Edinburgh he continued to act as agent for several of the Company's servants and, from 1786 to 1791, he was responsible for paying the Company employees in Orkney.

It was twelve years after his retirement from Canada that Graham made his donation to the Society. Even before his home visit in 1769-70 his interests were known to trading Indians who brought him bird skins from inland and it is probable that when he retired in 1775 he brought home a considerable personal collection. Even during retirement he added to his collection through his contacts with Company personnel. William Tomison, for example, spent part of his furlough of 1785-6 with Graham in Edinburgh and may have brought some of the donated material with him (Glover in Williams 1969, xxiv, note 88). From 1783 to 1790 the Company's Corresponding Secretary in London was Graham's colleague Thomas Hutchins and we know that one specimen at least was obtained through him.

'A Sample of Talc' was listed among the minerals in Graham's manuscript of his donation to the Royal Society of Edinburgh and he wrote of it:

> In a letter from Mr Thomas Hutchins who sent me the lump of Talc presented to the Learned Society, in a letter this day twenty ninth of June 1787 Writes thus: 'You desire me to Write to our friends in the Bay for more of the Talc such as I sent you formerly from Albany Fort. I have wrote to Mr Thomas for a piece of which there is a large Rock up Moose River in the road to Brunswic [sic] House'.[54]

The request for another sample of the mineral had been made by Joseph Black and it was received in 1789. Perhaps Black corrected Graham's identification of the mineral because in his later writings it is called gypsum. A further quotation is of interest:

> I presented several pieces of gypsum to George Willison Esq (portrait painter) who in return most generously sent me a Basso Relievo from it done by himself. He says he never saw any such laminated gypsum so transparent. This present was sent me Anno Domini 1790 (Williams 1969, 142).

On 8th February 1791 Graham received from George Willison 'two heads cast off from the laminated gypsum viz. Adam Smith and George Dempster'.

Although samples of laminated gypsum from Moose River are present in the mineral collections of the National Museums of Scotland, Dr Livingstone has been unable to recognize Graham's specimen. Nor is there hope of identifying the metal, crystals, pyrites and other stones from Hudson's Bay which came with it. It is of interest that Graham also 'presented many stones, crystals and pyrites to Dr Hutton of Edinburgh'.

fig 6 Leather coat of an early form made of a single unseamed piece of skin except for the sleeves (NMS UC277) probably part of the Hudson's Bay Indian collection presented by Andrew Graham in 1787.

When Hutchins was surgeon at York, Graham co-operated with him in making meteorological observations which were sent home in 1772. During his furlough of 1773 Hutchins undertook to carry out experiments for the Royal Society of London on his return to Albany Fort. One of these was on the congelation of mercury and was communicated to the Royal Society and published in *Philosophical Transactions* in 1776. In Edinburgh, Graham gave Joseph Black a copy of Hutchins' paper (perhaps that presented to the Society in Hutchins' name[55]) and, as a result, Black wrote a letter to Graham in 1779 encouraging Hutchins, through him, to undertake a further series of experiments and giving some hints on their conduct. Graham forwarded this to Hutchins and, in Graham's words, 'Dr Black's excellent letter to Mr Hutchins ... enabled him to ascertain the point exactly'. Hutchins read his paper using the results of 1781 to the Royal Society on 10 April 1783 and it was published in *Philosophical Transactions* in 1783. It won Hutchins the Royal Society's Copley Medal in December 1783 and, through Black's interest, he was elected a Fellow of the Royal Society of Edinburgh in January 1784 (Williams 1969, 363-4 and Glover in Williams 1969 xxxiii).[56]

Despite Graham's residence in Edinburgh, his dealings with Black and Walker, and his generous donation, he was never elected to Fellowship of the Society. The irony of this has become apparent through the work of Glover and Williams which has revealed that Hutchins appears to have 'appropriated the credit for observations that were wholly or mainly Graham's', some of which appeared unacknowledged in Pennant's *Arctic zoology*. They note also that several sections of Umfreville's work (1790) on Hudson's Bay 'were taken straight from Graham's manuscript journals'.

John McGowan, Assistant Solicitor of the Board of Excise and a Fellow of the Society, played a curious role in the correspondence between Black, Graham and Hutchins.[57] The letter which Black wrote to assist Hutchins, while in Graham's hands, came into the possession of McGowan who undertook to Graham to send it on to Hutchins. But, as Black explained to Hutchins:

> Mr Graham tells me he [McGowan] did not send the original letter but a Copy of it & put a direction at the bottom as if the original had been addressed to himself. The design of all this is sufficiently evident, he wished to gain a little Credit & Favour with you by it & all for the sake of obtaining Rarities of which he is so extravagantly fond.... this is a foible which his Friends easily overlook on account of his Good Humour & Social Disposition & of his being perfectly disinterested in all other matters ...Our intention is only to put you on your Guard in Case anything should fall into your hands which you may think proper to send to the Museum of the Royal Society here, that you may not send it thro' the hands of Mr McGowan.[58]

McGowan's good humour and social disposition were probably seen at their best at meetings of the Oyster Club, of which he was a member, and which Black had founded with Adam Smith and James Hutton. MacGowan's donations to the Society included a beaver, lynx and arctic fox from Hudson's Bay which were already 'decayed and thrown out' in 1812.

An Indian canoe from the Island of St John was presented by Sir James William Montgomery Lord Chief Baron of Exchequer (original acquisition 754), and a model of an Indian canoe, with the belt and pouch of an Indian hunter, was presented by Reverend Doctor Andrew Brown, Professor of Rhetoric at Edinburgh University and Minister of St Giles. Brown was born at Biggar and after his attendance at Glasgow University he became minister of the Presbyterian Church at Halifax, Nova Scotia, which he served from 1787-95. He returned to Scotland to minister at Lochmaben, then New Greyfriars, Edinburgh before being called to St Giles in 1800. It has been written of him that 'he was more interested in the history of North America than in literature' and a number of manuscripts of his writings on North America are preserved in Edinburgh University Library.[59] Brown's donation was given in 1794, probably when he first returned from Halifax and before his appointment to Lochmaben. A number of Indian canoes and model canoes are preserved in the collections of the National Museums of Scotland and though it is probable that those acquired through the Royal Society of Edinburgh are among them there is insufficient data to identify them.

To conclude consideration of the North American material presented under the First Charter, we return to Lord Daer who had continued his interest in the Society's museum by presenting a number of articles collected in the South Seas by Captain Bligh but of which no trace can now be found. In March 1790 Daer presented 'An Esquimaux Dress'. This item has not been traced either, but it is of interest that Daer continued his involvement with Canada, whether or not through servants of the Hudson's Bay Company. Daer's interest could have been aroused or maintained through his family's land on Lake Ontario, now in New York State, bought for the estate years before by an agent (Gray, 1964, 17). Daer died of consumption in 1794 and it was Thomas, the youngest and last of the seven sons of their father, who succeeded five years later as fifth Earl of Selkirk and whose name is written in the annals of Canada through the Selkirk Settlements.

1 One of Walker's Moffat parishioners is reported to have complained that 'he spent the week hunting butterflies and made the care of souls of his parishioners a bye-job on Sunday' (quoted by McKay 1980, 3).

2 J Walker to Lord Bute, 29 January 1765, SRO GD/18/5118 (quoted by McKay 1980, 231).

3 The terms inductive and deductive are used in this work as defined by Popper (1980). The deductive method proceeds from agreed first principles to facts, the inductive method, from accumulated facts to their connecting principles.

4 MS DC 10.33, Edinburgh University Archives, quoted Scott (1966, 27).

5 MS DC 10.33, Edinburgh University Archives.

6 A view advocated by N E Phillipson (1981). Although accepting that the origins of the Scottish Enlightenment were visible well before 1707, there is no doubt that the Scottish

cognoscenti were conscious of a cultural reaction to the union. While it may be an overstatement that certain societies in Scotland were regarded as para-parliaments, as suggested by Phillipson (see also 1993, 296) it is relevant to the present study to note that the founders of the Scottish Society of Antiquaries were well aware of the negative aspects of this possibility. William Smellie wrote '... in loyalty and affection to a common Sovereign, it was not, perhaps consistent with political wisdom, to call attention of the Scots to the ancient honours and constitution of their independent monarchy'. See Stevenson (1981, p 33).

7 In 1708 Edinburgh abandoned the system under which students had only one tutor, the regent, for all their studies. Within the next half century the system had ceased in the other Scottish universities.

8 *Report made to His Majesty by a Royal Commission of Inquiry into the State of the Universities of Scotland*, London 1831, Report Relative to the University of Edinburgh, 43.

9 MS DC 10.33 Edinburgh University Archives.

10 Edinburgh City Archives, Town Council Record, vol 81, 19 June 1765, pp 76-8 'Anent a museum or Repository for Natural Curiosities', and Town Council Record 15 January 1766 pp 316-8, 'Petition from Principal Robertson relative to the Museum in the College & alterations to be made thereon'.

11 See Edinburgh City Archives, Town Council Record, vol 86, 24 January 1770, pp 121-4, 'Act in favour of Dr Ramsay, Physician, as Professor of Natural History'.

12 The College Hall was over a hundred feet long, twenty-seven feet wide and sixteen feet high.

13 See Edinburgh City Archives, Town Council Record, vol 35, p 158, 10 May 1695 'Treasurer to buy several rarities from Friends of Sir Andrew Balfour' (Alternative entry) 'Several rarities to be purchased and put into a Closet in the Colledge to be called Musaeum Balfourianum' and Edinburgh University Library MS Gen 1801.6 'Musaeum Balfoureanum/ Or/ A Catalogue of the Rarities/ Which were collected by/ Sr Andrew Balfour;/ And bought from his Heirs/ by the Town Council of/ Edinburgh/ For the use & Ornament/ of their Colledge' (Identified by C P Finlayson as having been compiled by James Paterson, Keeper of the Museum 1699-1702). Paterson was a protege of Sibbald's (Emerson 1988b, 55).

14 The author confused the museums of the Royal College of Physicians and the Town's College but the quotation clearly refers to the Balfour/ Sibbald collection as contained in the College Museum.

15 A less explicit version of this paragraph appears in a number of ms notes of Walker's lectures preserved in Edinburgh University Library, one of which (DC 10.33) was published by Scott (1966, 46-7). Scott (1966, viii), misled by a note on a fly-leaf of this ms, dated it to about 1788. It was Walker's practice to summarise 'Discoveries and Improvements' in the years immediately preceding the date of his lecture. This ms summarises events up to 1790 (see also Scott p 6) so that the date in which the lecture was delivered is likely to have been 1791. The earliest version of the paragraph appears in ms summary notes (DC 2.22) in Lecture 5 which was delivered on 20 March 1782. Other versions, substantially identical to that published by Scott, appear in the ms record of Lecture 5 in DC 2.23 (1790) and Gen 50 pp 53-4 (undated c 1790). From John Douglas's notes (D 8.31) it would appear that in 1791 Walker recast his lectures omitting the reference to Balfour and Sibbald. This was certainly so by 1797 as is evident from David Pollock's beautiful ms 'An Epitome of Natural History' of 1797 (Gen 703.1-12).

16 The only known surviving specimen from the Sibbald Collection is the dried penis of a whale NMS Z1990.76 (Herman 1992, 59) recognised by Turner (1912, 140) as the 'Penis Balaenae Orcadensis. The Pisle of a Whale which came in at Orkney' (Sibbald 1697).

17 Edinburgh City Archives, Town Council Record, vol 98, p 316, Walker's ms is preserved in Edinburgh City Archives, McLeod's Bundle 16.

18 John Walker to Lord Provost; 22 March 1780 ms in Edinburgh City Archives, McLeod's Bundle 16.

19 Library of National Museum of Antiquities of Scotland, MS 593, vol 2/9. In letter from W Smellie to W Strachan, London [1781].

20 National Museums of Scotland archive Ms 594, vol 3/8.

21 'Proposal for establishing at Edinr, a Society for the Advancement of Learning and Useful Knowledge' ms by John Walker 2 March 1782. Edinburgh University Library MS La III.352/1, printed in Shapin (1974, 40-1).

22 Faculty Record 2, p 529 i cf 4, p 272, reference quoted from Brown (1989).

23 I am grateful to Nicholas Holmes of NMS for trying to locate these specimens. He concludes that 'there is no chance of being able to identify any of the coins in the NMS collections today. In most cases it is not even possible to establish which NMS coins came to us from the Faculty of Advocates, and only particularly rare or fully described coins can be traced back to the old manuscript catalogues drawn up in the eighteenth and nineteenth centuries.' (Letter of 19th November 1993.)

24 Reprinted in J M Sweet (1972, 398-400). Miss Sweet thought that an article by 'DE' (1793) might have been by David Erskine, Earl of Buchan, a frequent contributor to The Bee. If so, such an article from one of his opponents might have goaded Walker into submitting his own contribution on the same subject to the same magazine.

25 Dr Walker to the Lord Provost, Magistrates and Town Council 1785 ms in Edinburgh City Archives, McLeod's Bundle 16 and inscribed in the Town Council Record for 3 August 1785 vol 106, 324-7.

26 'A List of Articles in Natural History presented to the Royal Society of Edinr. and deposited in the Museum of the University' ms signed by Walker and dated 24 January 1785, Edinburgh City Archive, McLeod's Bundle 16.

27 Edinburgh University Library, Laing mss III, 352/2 quoted by M A Taylor 1992

28 Dr Walker to the Lord Provost & Town Council 7 December 1790, ms Edinburgh City Archive, McLeod's Bundle 16.

29 Town Council also declined the later offer by the Trustees of the late Alexander Weir who gave the City first refusal to purchase on behalf of the Community Weir's second, and much larger, collection . Edinburgh City Archive, Town Council Record for 3rd December 1800, vol 134, p 176.

30 Edinburgh University Library, Special Collections Dc 1.18 item 4, Ms 'A Catalogue of the Museum preserved at New Posso 1789'

31 Edinburgh University Library, Special Collections, La III 352/2, Ms Jas Nasmyth to John Walker, New Posso, 25 April 1793.

32 Edinburgh University Library, Special Collections, La III 352/1.

33 *Transactions of the Royal Society of Edinburgh* vol 1, 1783-1785, pp 77-80; vol 2, 1785-1789, pp 77-79; vol 3, 1789- 1793; vol 4, 1793-1797; vol 5, 1799-1803.

34 *The Diaries & Travels of Lord John Hope 1722-1727* Research Paper of the Extra-Mural Department, Edinburgh University.

35 'Books, Prints, Designs, Marbles, Intaglios and other Curiosities brought by Lord Hope in different Countrys 1722-1727' NRA(S) 888 Bundle 1657.

36 In connection with this development it is of interest that the second and third Earls of Hopetoun corresponded with Joseph Black on such matters as assays of ores and gold soil. See letters in Edinburgh University Library, Gen 873/1/28-32 and Gen 873/1/40-42, 51-52.

37 Personal communication from J Jones.

38 Byres' interest in Hamilton's activities was not confined to the commercial. In a letter of 4 July 1783 Sir Charles Blagden FRS (1748-1820) tells Sir Joseph Banks that it was Byres who first informed him of Sir William Hamilton's observations on Vesuvius.

39 *Transactions of the Royal Society of Edinburgh*, ii, 1785-9, p 79.

40 I am grateful to Dr Leonard Forman, Royal Botanic Gardens, Kew, for advice concerning the Roxburgh Collection. Dr Forman's work on Roxburgh's collections is currently in press.

41 NLS ACC 10000/386.

42 MS letter of 28 April 1812 of W Wright to Sir George S Mackenzie and MS letter of 13 May 1812 by Mackenzie to John Playfair are at NLS ACC 10000/386.

43 Dr John Alexander Smith (1818-1883) MD, FRCPE, archaeologist and ornithologist was elected a Fellow of the Royal Society of Edinburgh in 1863.

44 MS Letter of William Anderson to Banks from Cape of Good Hope, 24 November 1776, Webster Coll. Kew: BC 1.58-59.

45 MS Letter of John Hope to Banks, 16 August 1779, telling him that he has an evergreen shrub with orange flowers, grown from seed sent by Anderson.

46 Kerr (1755-1813), the biographer of Walker's rival William Smellie, trained in medicine in Edinburgh attending Munro's anatomy classes in 1774 and 1776. He had practised as a surgeon in the city, and was elected to Fellowship of the Royal Society of Edinburgh in 1788.

47 Pringle, when president of the Royal Society of London, had presented Captain Cook with that Society's gold medal, and the collection had been given to Pringle by Cook's widow (Stevenson, 1981, 43-4).

48 Despite the bitterness this engendered in Leslie he was eventually elected to Fellowship in 1807.

49 Edinburgh University Library, Special Collections Ms Gen 873/111/153-4, T C Hope to J Black, Glasgow 14 July 1789.

50 NLS MS 6329, Hall's journals.

51 Edinburgh University Library, Special Collections DC.1.57 IV 'The following curiosities presented to the Edinburgh Royal Society with a true Account of them by ANDREW GRAHAM, late Factor to the Honble. Hudson's Bay Company. January AD 1787'.

52 In this work Glover notes that volume E.2/5 in the Hudson's Bay Company Archives gives Graham's account of his donation to the Royal Society of Edinburgh.

53 Edinburgh University Library, Special Collections MS DC 1.57.VI, eight folios, 'List of Beasts: Birds: Fishes &c sent to the Royal Society by Andrew Graham & others AD 1771:2: 3 & 4'.

54 Graham MS ibid, folio 59.

55 See *Transactions of the Royal Society of Edinburgh*.I, History of the Society, p 80.

56 Hutchins wrote to Black on 4 March 1784: Mr McGowan has informed me of the Obligation I am under to you for the obliging manner in which you interested yourself in procuring me the distinguished honour of being elected a Member of the Royal Society of Edinburgh. (Edinburgh University Library, Special Collections Gen 873/11/163)

57 See Edinburgh University Library, Special Collections, Gen 875/11/162F draft letter to Thomas Hutchins from Joseph Black, 1 March 1784, Gen 873/11/163-8, letters of Thomas Hutchins to Black, 4 March, 5 March and 10 April 1784.

58 Edinburgh University Library, Special Collections Gen 875/11/162F.

59 Edinburgh University Library, Special Collections Gen 154-159 include 'History of North America', parts 2-4, 'French Settlement in Canada',' Settlement of Virginia' and 'Acquisition and settlement of the middle colonies'. See also Hunter (1867, 21-4); Fasti Ecclesiae Scoticanae, I, 72; Christison and Christison (1885, I, 46); Rice and McIntyre (1957, 23); Meikle (1945, 95-7).

CHAPTER THREE

WHAT SORT OF A MUSEUM?
1804-1859

Never glad confident morning again!
Robert Browning

For John Walker, the Natural History Museum of Edinburgh University was central to the teaching of his subject and it remained so for his successor, Robert Jameson. As we shall see in Chapter 5, however, during the fifty years of Jameson's professorship the relationship of museums to university teaching underwent radical change. When Jameson became the Professor of Natural History the provisions of the Society's Charter proved irksome to both the Society and the University. The impasse was resolved by the granting of a Second Charter in 1811 which allowed the Society to hold property and so to keep its own collections. Museum acquisition, however, brought with it problems of accommodation, curation and policy which the Society was slow to resolve. Displayed in the privacy of the Society's premises, collections could no longer serve the educational role which they had when housed in the university. What then should be the purpose of the Society's museum? Here we review these events and trace the changing role of the Society's museum from education to research. We shall see how a policy gradually emerged to make that museum firstly a source of material for description and experimentation and secondly, a repository for specimens described in papers published by the Society. At first collecting continued to be general, reflecting the eclectic nature of the fellowship. As the number of collections grew, however, so did problems of accommodation and curation and the need for specialization became apparent. At the same time the fellowship became biased towards science as the 'Physical Section' of the Society strengthened at the expense of the 'Letters Section'. Thus, as the policy of museum specialization was implemented, collections of art, antiquity and ethnography were the first to be housed in other institutions.

DISSOLUTION

During the last six or seven years of Walker's life he was blind and he died on the last day of 1803 with many of his hopes unfulfilled. The 'noble repository' in the new College building, to which he had looked forward and for which he had worked, had not been built. Two years after the laying of the foundation stone in 1789 its architect, Robert Adam, had died and, with the outbreak of the Napoleonic Wars in the following year, building had come to a halt. Many of the specimens Walker had collected for display in the promised new museum remained in 'confusion, huddled up in Chests and Boxes, unfit for the Public Eye'. As Walker's health had deteriorated and the congestion of museum collections increased, zest for collecting diminished and fewer and fewer specimens came from the Royal Society of Edinburgh.

The fortunes of another Edinburgh museum waxed as those of the College Museum waned. After the sale of his first collection to the College in 1786, Alexander Weir had amassed a second, larger and more important collection of natural history objects from home and abroad which he exhibited first at addresses in the South Bridge and latterly at 16 Princes Street (Taylor 1992). The importance of this collection is evident from the fact that in his notes to his translation of *The Animal Kingdom*, Kerr cited eight mammals of special interest in Weir's museum and only three from Walker's museum (Kerr 1792).[1] Weir died in 1797 and three years later his representatives offered his collection of natural history to the community, only to be refused by the City Fathers.[2] How different the answer might have been had Walker still enjoyed health and vigour and had there still been some prospect of the opening of the new College Museum.

In 1792 an anonymous author had written:

> A few years ago there was not in this place [Edinburgh] a single collection of specimens of natural history, public or private, that deserved to be noticed. Since Dr Walker was appointed professor, and read lectures on the subject, things have taken a great change. His own museum, for a private collection, contains a great variety of beautiful specimens in high preservation, of animals, vegetables and minerals (Anon 1792, 132).

The writer here speaks of Walker's museum as a *private* collection and it is known that the Professor had used his personal collection in the university to assist his class work. From the age of fifteen Walker had collected minerals. As a student he had found William Cullen's chemistry class an inspiration and had sometimes accompanied Cullen on his collecting trips. His *elementa mineralogiae*, based on his own collection and that of the University, was already extensive by the 1750s and later grew to 323 genera (Scott 1976, 132). An indication of the size of his private collection was given by Walker himself who reckoned the number of his mineral specimens to exceed 3138. These, however, were 'extracted from the general register of my museum, which contains many minerals that, for want of examination, could not be inserted in their proper places in the catalogue' (Walker 1822, 94).

It was therefore a matter of consequence that, following Walker's death, his trustees claimed much of the material in the Natural History Museum as the personal property of the late professor and removed it.

It was in 1797, during the unhappy time of Walker's incapacity, that James Hutton, the 'father of modern geology', died and his sister and heiress presented his whole collection of stones and fossils to Joseph Black who in turn, and under certain conditions, presented it to the Society.[3] Under the terms of the First Charter, it was eventually placed in the University Museum, the last major collection to be so lodged. It was the fate of the Hutton Collection that brought matters between the Society and the University to a head. Its subsequent loss provides a striking illustration of what can happen to an important and famous collection when its context ceases to be respected.

Jones has established the nature and significance of the Hutton Collection and has documented the history of its neglect and loss in the College Museum (Jones, 1984). Its importance lay, not in its monetary value nor in its representativeness of rock or mineral types or of the geology of the country – the accepted objectives of most other contemporary geological collections – but in providing proofs and illustrations of Hutton's *Theory of the Earth*. John Playfair's description of the collection is revealing:

> They who expect to find, in a collection, specimens of all the species, and all the varieties, into which a system of artificial arrangement may have divided the fossil kingdom, will perhaps turn fastidiously from one that is not remarkable either for the number or brilliancy of the objects contained in it. They, on the other hand, will think it highly interesting, who wish to reason concerning the natural history of minerals, and who are not less eager to become acquainted with the laws that govern, than with the individuals that compose, the fossil kingdom (Playfair 1805, 88).

Hutton constantly made deductions about Earth processes from hand specimens of rocks and minerals and gives many examples. His theory that subterranean heat was the agent of rock consolidation was based on a descriptive analysis of a series of hand specimens. Similarly

> He also used hand specimens to illustrate the results of other processes which were an integral part of his theory of cyclicity but which, like consolidation, could not be observed either because of their situation or because of their time scale; for example, the formation of sedimentary rocks by erosion and consolidation, the subsidence and subsequent elevation of land, and the secondary nature of mountains usually held to be primitive (Jones 1984, 224).

Two further examples may be given here to show the significance of Hutton's hand specimens. A sample of graphic granite, showing a eutectic intergrowth of quartz and felspar, convinced him that this rock could have been formed only by crystallisation from a cooling melt. He required no further proof of the igneous origin of granite than was provided by the hand specimen. To discover the history of granite intrusion, however, he required to make field visits to granite sites. In Glen Tilt, where he saw granites of different ages in an exposure where later veins cut earlier ones, he found evidence of that history. Granite could therefore no longer be thought of as 'Primitive' as supposed by geologists such as Werner, that is as a crystalline precipitate from a primeval universal ocean (the Neptunian view), but had crystallised out of fluids formed at different times by the fusion of pre-existing rocks (the plutonist view). He collected boulders from the site which illustrated this phenomenon. Thus in his cabinet he could show specimens providing 'proofs' of both the origin and the history of granite.

By brilliant scientific deduction Newton had provided a perspective of space previously unsuspected. In the same way the world learned of the immensity of time through the work of Hutton. The Huttonian paradigm was perfected by generations of geologists and significantly advanced only by another brilliant piece of deductive science, the Plate Tectonic Theory. That a cabinet of specimens should provide proofs of, and to some extent have inspired, such a significant advance in human understanding was remarkable.

Such an intimate relationship of museum specimens with scientific theory is not common. As Withers has implied, had Smellie been able to form a natural history museum according to his own lights it would have been very different from Walker's. We may suppose that with Smellie's philosophical approach to the processes of zoology it might have resulted in a collection of zoological specimens illustrative of theory akin to Hutton's in a different branch of science. A parallel may be found, however, in some of the anatomical preparations of Hutton's contemporaries in Edinburgh. Alexander Monro *secundus* and John Gregory, following Robert Whytt and William Cullen, provided proofs and illustrations of the importance of the nervous system as the means of effecting the integration of bodily functions which bridged the Cartesian gulf between soul and body (Shapin 1993, 276-7). Hutton's work on rocks which opened a new perception of the immensity of time, like the work on nerves with its new perception of man's response to his environment, was of profound importance to wider Enlightenment thought in fields such as moral philosophy and social theory.

It might have been supposed that a vulcanist like Faujas would have enthused over such a collection but, when he saw it in Hutton's house in 1784, he confessed 'I therefore had much more pleasure in conversing with this modest philosopher than in examining his cabinet which presented me with nothing new'. Faujas reserved his praise for Walker's collection in the University Museum which he found well ordered and, so far as rocks and minerals were concerned, representative of all occurrences in Scotland which it has been possible to procure (Faujas 1797, 264-6). It is extraordinary that even Faujas was so entrenched in the context of representative collections that he could not see the significance of the 'proofs' which Hutton's cabinet displayed.

Walker's former student and successor, Robert Jameson, inherited his master's empiricism and had been influenced against Hutton's *Theory of the*

Earth by the writings of Richard Kirwan.[4] He established his anti-plutonist credentials in two papers read before the Royal Medical Society in Edinburgh in 1796 (Sweet and Waterston 1967). He was elected to fellowship of the Royal Society of Edinburgh in 1799 and in the following year went to Freiberg to absorb Neptunianism from the fountainhead. He was a student of the Bergakademie under A G Werner until his father's death in 1802 necessitated his return to Edinburgh. He then assisted the now incapacitated Walker in his museum and teaching duties and was in a favoured position to be appointed Walker's successor in 1804.

The difficulties which arose between the Society and the University following Jameson's appointment had three main causes. The first was his refusal to allow certain Fellows access to the museum to see collections, particularly the Hutton Collection, lodged there by the Society under the terms of the First Charter. As we shall see below he even tried to deny access to members of a committee, under Sir George Mackenzie's convenership, which the Society had appointed to report on the state of these collections. This may have been due to the young, and as yet insecure, professor's wish to hide the deplorable condition of the museum in his charge, but for which he bore no blame. As we have seen, it resulted from years of congestion and muddle towards the end of Walker's life and, after his death, by the removal of his large personal collection by his trustees. When Jameson was asked by the Commissioners in 1826 whether a considerable proportion of the Museum had been formed since his appointment, his reply was: 'The whole I may say.'[5] Like his predecessor, Jameson felt that there was little to curate when he assumed the keepership 'the museum was so inconsiderable, that the whole of the articles were contained in a few cases'.[6] However Jameson may have overemphasized the depleted state of the museum he inherited. The present study has identified many specimens from the Royal Society of Edinburgh collections which, with others donated directly to the University, have survived from Walker's keepership. Secondly, Jameson's intransigence in refusing access to the Hutton Collection was interpreted as Wernerian prejudice (Chitnis 1970). A third reason, which dismayed the Society, was Jameson's failure to keep the Hutton Collection together and so maintain its scientific integrity.

Curatorial experience suggests that Jameson's failure in his guardianship of the Hutton Collection may have been even more insidious than muddle or even malice but lay rather in his inability to respect the intellectual context in which it was formed and in which it was intended to be used. Because this failure provides an object lesson relevant to the wider arguments of this work, it may be well to enlarge upon it.

For Bacon, knowledge was power and we have seen that Sibbald followed that view in his belief that knowledge of the country and its natural productions was basic to the improvement of Scotland. Walker also believed that natural history was a utilitarian science and that knowledge of it should be discovered through inductive empirical study. He therefore did his best to assemble a collection which would be representative of the natural productions of Scotland. Jameson was not only trained in Walker's perceptions but inherited responsibilities for collections formed in this intellectual context. He is rightly praised for the quality and representative nature of the mineral collection which he later assembled in the College Museum following these precepts. As we have seen the Hutton collection was formed in an entirely different intellectual context and for different purposes – the context was deductive science and the purpose was to provide proofs in support of theory.

In practice the methodology of the science which produced these collections was not as clear cut as many historians have suggested but was often more a matter of emphasis. In Leveson's words the normal tradition was that of 'observations suggesting hypotheses, and hypotheses suggesting observations' (Leveson 1996, 75). Thus both types of collection were valid when judged within the context of their collecting policies, in that both allowed the viewer to 'see with his own eyes the facts'. In Walker's museum the viewer could see a range of the natural products of Scotland and could judge for himself the application that might be made of them for the improvement of the nation. In Hutton's museum the viewer saw evidence illustrative of that philosopher's theory, without travelling many miles to examine the field relationships, and could judge for himself the validity or otherwise of its various propositions.

The contemporary polarity between these views on the presentation of natural history could be summed up in the question 'What is the best sort of collection?' For the curator, however, such a question is invalid since no such value judgement should be made. A representative collection is neither more nor less virtuous than a collection of proofs of theory because both have value within their own intellectual context and, with contextual sensitivity, it is possible to maintain and value both. What is not possible, without an immediate loss of value, is to make a collection made in one context conform to a collection made in a different context. It is probable that Jameson attempted to do this by extracting from Hutton's collection such specimens as would enhance the representative collections of the college – perhaps a good agate or jasper for the mineral collection or an interesting piece of fossil wood for the fossil collection – but, taken out of context, these specimens would be ranked *pari passu* with any other mineral or fossil. Where there was no locus within the existing reference collection for specimens speaking in another context – such as a specimen exhibiting successive granitic veins – it would be regarded as worthless and consigned, with other similar specimens, to a storage box if not actually discarded. It is known that in 1826 the bulk of the Hutton Collection was indeed kept in boxes 'in a garret or spare room where it cannot be seen'.[7]

In January 1807 the Society's Secretary, Professor John Playfair, moved and carried a motion, after amendment by Henry Mackenzie, 'that it is the opinion of the Society that it is expedient to have their Charter free from

44

any restriction respecting the disposal of their property of whatever kind'.[8] When the Society next met a committee was appointed to draw up the terms of a new Charter and of the petition for obtaining it. Under the convenership of the Solicitor General Lord Meadowbank, one of the Society's Vice-Presidents, the draft was completed in 1808.[9] At first there was resistance from the Senatus of the University which favoured Jameson's proposal that a room be allocated to the collections of the Society, including the Hutton Collection, in which the specimens should be arranged by a Keeper to be appointed by the Society and under the Society's control. Jameson, as Professor of Natural History, would have right of access to this room but not to exhibit objects to his class without permission of the Society. He envisaged that the Society would meet in it but another room should be provided for its usual meetings if it was unsuitable.[10]

Resistance to the New Charter was overcome, however, and it was sealed in 1811.

SIR GEORGE MACKENZIE'S ENQUIRY

A draft of the Second Charter, printed in *Transactions* in 1808, includes the following:

> As it was not meant that the new charter should have any retrospect, the Huttonian Collection, with a great number of other articles, the property of the Society, still remain in the University Museum.[11]

For many years the Society continued to regard as its own property specimens deposited with the University or the Faculty, although it had renounced the right of recall.

The condition of articles deposited in the University Museum under the terms of the First Charter, was as we have said the subject of an enquiry by a Committee set up by a General Meeting of the Society on 11 November 1811 under the convenership of Sir George Mackenzie[12]; this reported on 23 December 1811[13]. Although Jameson at first refused the committee access to the Museum and subjected it to a frustrating series of letters declining to provide the information for which it asked, a manuscript catalogue of the articles so deposited, annotated by Sir George Mackenzie, was produced.[14] The Committee reported that, although receipts had apparently not been obtained from Walker for articles deposited, he, as Secretary of the Society's Physical Class as well as Keeper of the Museum, was official giver and receiver, and transfers may have been made without attention to formality. Members were satisfied that the lists of transfers made between 1783 and 1789 and published in *Transactions* volumes I to V should be accepted as proof of receipt by the University since they had been drawn up by the Society's General Secretary 'under the eye of Professor Walker himself'. It is of interest that Walker probably forwarded these lists to the Town Council. His manuscript of the first list, signed on 24 January 1785 and corresponding to that printed in the first volume of *Transactions*, is preserved and the statement subscribed, which may indeed be interpreted as a receipt, is as follows:

> This Day the above Articles were presented to the Royal Society of Edinr. and were ordered by them to be deposited in the Museum of the University. They also appointed the above Catalogue of these Articles to be lodged with the Magistrates & Town Council of the City.[15]

In a note added in May 1824 by Sir George Mackenzie to his Report on the state of the Society's property in the University Museum given in 1811 (see below) he states:

> the Keeper showed them (the Society's Committee) some chests or boxes lying under the seats of the Class room which he said he believed contained some things belonging to the Royal Society & he added that it was impossible to find room for displaying everything...[16]

THE MUSEUM AT 40-42 GEORGE STREET 1811-26

The first meeting of the Society on 23 June 1783 was held in the old College Library which, according to the minute, was found inconvenient and a committee was formed to find more suitable accommodation (Moncreiff 1884, 458). The times presented formidable challenges, however, and twenty-three years later meetings were still being held in the College Library. Redevelopment of the College had been spoken of since 1767 but in 1789 subscriptions were invited for the new building and the Society responded with the promise of 500 guineas on the understanding that it would receive rooms in the building. Such rooms were indeed proposed in Robert Adam's plans of 1789 and 1791 (Fraser 1989, 105, 111, 212). As we have seen, building stopped during the Napoleonic Wars and it was not until 1815 that work was resumed.

Brewster wrote that in the closing years of the eighteenth and the first decade of the nineteenth century the Society was in a very languid condition. But, with the election to Council of enthusiasts such as David Brewster, Sir George S Mackenzie of Coul, James Skene of Rubislaw and Thomas Allan, arrangements were made 'that a paper should be read at every meeting, and in this way a more numerous attendance was obtained' (Brewster 1866, 321). The desire for better accommodation grew more urgent and in 1810, with the walls of the new College Building still standing neglected and the outcome of the Peninsular War in the balance, the Society moved into 40-42 George Street which it had purchased in December 1809 (Waterston, 1996, 84). This coincided with negotiations for the new Charter which, if granted, would require additional space for the Society's Museum.

After that Charter was sealed in 1811, Thomas Allan, a banker and an accomplished geologist and mineralogist, was elected the Society's first 'Keeper of the Museum' and served in that capacity until 1819 (fig 16).[17] He was responsible also for the Society's growing library and in 1819 this was

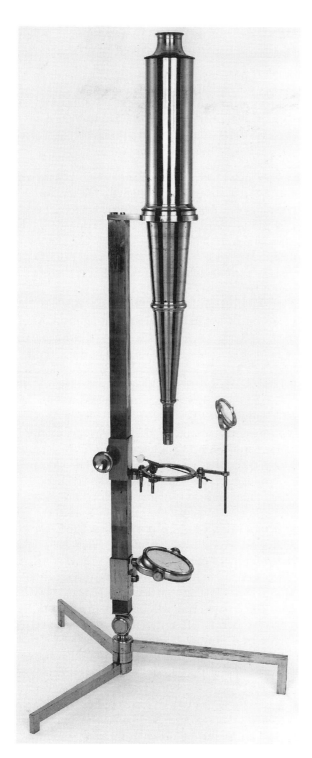

fig 7 Large polarising microscope ordered for the Royal Society of Edinburgh in 1823 at the request of its General Secretary David Brewster from Alexander Adie (FRSE 1846). By the time the instrument was delivered in 1829 the clumsy polariser of parallel glass plates, used in the instrument, had been superseded by the Nicol prism (William Nicol FRSE 1838) which makes use of the double refracting properties of the calcite crystal. NMS T1982.90

47

recognised when he became 'Curator of the Museum and Library'. Allan believed that all geological papers should be accompanied by specimens for the Society's museum:

> I consider it of very great importance that every geological paper should be accompanied with specimens, in order that if the former be found deserving of publication in your Transactions, those who may peruse the description may know, that the specimens referred to, are to be seen in the repositories of this establishment (Allan 1812, 411, see also Allan 1815a, 133).

Allan was succeeded as Curator in 1820 by James Skene of Rubislaw, an advocate and one of Sir Walter Scott's closest friends (fig 16). He was widely travelled and his interest in geology had been encouraged by his friend G B Greenough, first President of the Geological Society of London, who had accompanied him on journeys in Europe.

Geology remained an active interest of Fellows of the Royal Society of Edinburgh and with geologists as curators while the museum was housed in 42 George Street, it is not surprising that, of the 26 donations which the Society received during the period, nineteen were geological. Among the earliest donations under the Second Charter were significant collections of Scottish rocks illustrating published papers by Thomas Allan on the geology of the Edinburgh District (Allan, 1812), and by Lt Col Ninian Imrie on the geology of the Grampians (Imrie 1812). To these was added the collection made by John Playfair and Lord Webb Seymour illustrating their paper on the geology of Glen Tilt (Seymour, 1815); ground made famous for its granite-schistus contact and granitic veins by their mentors James Hutton and John Clerk of Eldin. The Museum's first geological model was received from its president, Sir James Hall, in illustration of his account of the granite contact phenomena of Windy Shoulder near Loch Ken (Hall 1815a). Thomas Allan, the Society's enthusiastic curator, widened the scope of the geological holdings by making collections in Northern Ireland and Cornwall. Flint formation was another source of interest and collections of English flints were received from Dr John Kidd MD, FRS, MWS, Professor of Chemistry and Physics at Oxford, and from Edward Grimes Esq RN.

The extensive suite of Icelandic rocks made by Sir George S Mackenzie during his travels there in 1810 was the first of the museum's overseas collections (Mackenzie 1811 and fig 8).[18] Having seen Iceland, Mackenzie was anxious to study the rocks of the Faroes and was accompanied there by Thomas Allan who, true to his own beliefs, presented rocks in illustration of his paper (Allan, 1815b). Mackenzie presented minerals collected on this occasion to Glasgow University and 27 specimens of zeolites, chalcedony etc from the collection are recognised in the Hunterian Museum (Laskey, 1813, 47; Mackenzie 1815).

Captain Basil Hall RN, was interested to observe contact phenomena and veining in far off-countries, similar to those described by Hutton and Clerk in Glen Tilt and Galloway. His collection of rocks from Table Mountain illustrated his geological description sent to the Society's secretary John Playfair, who prepared it for publication (Playfair, 1815). Hall described a junction of granite with 'killas' and, higher in the hill, a junction of the same granite with sandstone: 'the contact was the finest thing of the kind I ever saw; the Windy Shoulder itself not excepted'. No doubt he was familiar with his father's description and model. Captain Hall later sent specimens collected during the voyage of HM sloops *Alceste* and *Lyra* in 1816 and 1817, under the command of Captain Murray Maxwell, to Macao, Hong Kong, Great Loo Choo Island (now Great Ryukyu or Okinawa) and the West Coast of Korea. Hall published an account of the voyage in 1818 containing an appendix listing the geological specimens and also sent a manuscript list to the Society with the specimens but it is difficult to know whether the whole collection was received or a selection from it.[19] He comments that 'These specimens have no interest except what arises from their being authentic samples of the rocks in countries heretofore unvisited, and which are not likely to be again examined' (Hall, 1818).

fig 8 Slaggy Basalt from Mount Hekla, Iceland, one of a collection of some 300 specimens presented by Sir George S Mackenzie of Coul in 1811. The collection formed part of that made by Mackenzie, with Richard Bright and Henry Holland, during their expedition to Iceland in 1810. The contemporary label 'C 35' refers to the catalogue of this collection printed as Appendix III in Mackenzie's *Travels in the Island of Iceland...*(1811). GLAHM R386
Hunterian Museum, University of Glasgow

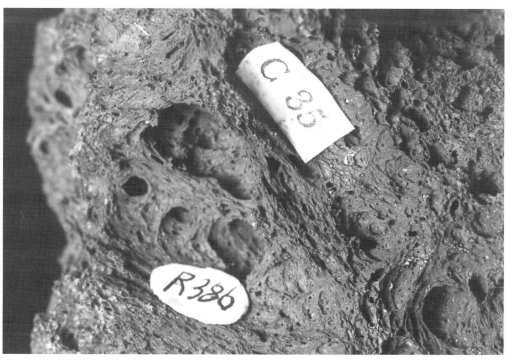

49

Of particular interest to Hall, and no doubt to Fellows, were specimens from a small island off the West coast of Korea at latitude 36 10'N, longitude 126 13'E which Captain Maxwell named Hutton's Island 'in compliment to the memory of the distinguished philosopher whose theory has been used to explain the curious phenomena which it exhibits'. These were, according to Hall, a granite in the east, schistus at the centre and breccia to the west with a dyke of porphyritic granite cutting the schistus. Today's Admiralty Chart shows an unnamed reef at 36.9' N, 126.11' E, south east of Oeyeon Do island, which appears to be all that remains of 'Hutton's Island'.[20] Another serving officer, Lieutenant MacNiven of the 26th Regiment, sent specimens of bone breccia collected from near Rosia, Gibraltar.

Since its earliest days Fellows of the Society had been interested in glacial and post-glacial phenomena and the opinions of Hutton, Playfair and Jameson on the more extensive spread of Alpine and Scandinavian glaciers in the past, and Jameson's belief in the possible former land glaciation of Scotland, had earned Edinburgh a recognised place in glacial studies (Cunningham, 1990, Chapter 4). Sir James Hall did not agree with the glacialists and attributed smoothed and striated surfaces found on rocks in the neighbourhood of Edinburgh to 'attrition of stones carried along by a great current of water' (Hall, 1815b). Corstorphine Hill was one locality where Hall had noted striated surfaces and in 1825 he presented a plaster cast, taken from a rock surface there. Finds from post-glacial deposits (*Bison scoticus* found in a peat-moss on the Duke of Buccleuch's estate in Roxburghshire and a stag's horn from clay in Dunbartonshire) had formerly been passed to the University, but Sir George Mackenzie started the Society's own collection by presenting a whale's vertebra from the Blue Clay of Hilton, near Strathpeffer.

Only three zoological specimens were presented during this period of which two, a madrepore from Bermuda 'of unusual magnitude, ... supposed to be the finest in the kingdom' (Anon, 1821) and the snout of a Saw-Fish, were from the Marchioness of Huntly.[21] This lady was an acquaintance and correspondent of the Society's secretary, David Brewster.[22] Lady Huntly's chief interests were mineralogy and conchology but she was also well able to understand and appreciate Brewster's optical experiments (Gordon, 1869, 106).

The wish of the Society's curators to see the association of museum specimens with published work was fulfilled with the third zoological donation. Dr Alexander Kennedy, a physician in the service of the East India Company, had drawn attention to a parasitic worm found in the eyes of horses in India. He thereafter procured a specimen for the Society which was described and named *Ascaris pellucidus* by Captain Brown (Kennedy, 1823).[23]

A number of interesting miscellaneous items were added to the Museum while in George Street. Francis Simpson Esq presented four 'Sculptures of Indian idols' in 1819 through W A Cadell who described and illustrated them in *Transactions* (fig 9). William Archibald Cadell FRS was an amateur

fig 9 One of four 'Indian Idols' presented by Francis Simpson through W A Cadell in 1819 and figured by Cadell in *Transactions of the Royal Society of Edinburgh* 14, pl xxiv, fig 3. The siltstone Avalokitesvara of the Pala Period, 11-12th century AD, is from the Bengal/Bihar region of North-East India.   NMS A1956.565

mathematician and published in the journals of the London and Edinburgh societies. He had recently returned from his travels on the continent which had included some time as an internee in Napoleon's France, from which he had escaped as a supposed Frenchman, such was his fluency in the language. Francis Simpson of Plean had married Cadell's sister Jane Sophia in 1804.[24] These sculptures were probably passed to the museum of the Society of Antiquaries in 1828 under the agreement then reached with that Society (see below) and are now preserved in the Eastern collections of the National Museums of Scotland.

In 1824 (Sir) John Robison presented 'The Door of the Bookcase of Sir Isaac Newton.' His father, Professor John Robison, the Society's first General Secretary, had been such an admirer of Newton that he confessed to James Watt his 'superstitious veneration for every relick of that wonderful Man' (Robinson and McKie, 1970, 272). He had visited Woolsthorpe Manor, Newton's birthplace, and obtained the small oak door of a cupboard from the occupiers of the house. At the same time he commissioned the artist J C Barrow to make a number of drawings of the room, showing the position of the cupboard together with a plan and views of the exterior (Keesing, 1991). A letter of Sir John Robison to Professor J D Forbes of 11 October 1834 throws light on these events:

> I beg leave to offer you a set of sketches of Sir Isaac Newton's house which my Father employed an Artist to take when he visited the place in the Summer of 1797, on which occasion he obtained from the persons then inhabiting the house, the small oak door of the press at the side of the fire place of the room in which Sir Isaac was born, & which he usually sat in while living there; & in which press he kept his books. This door is now deposited in the Museum of the Royal Society.[25]

While the Royal Society was thus regaining momentum, the Society of Antiquaries had fallen on bad times. After a period of debilitating illness, its able secretary, William Smellie, had died in 1795 and the Society lacked support. Between 1808 and 1813 only two papers were read and 31 donations received (Stevenson 1981, 55). Sir George Mackenzie, president of the Physical Section of the Royal Society, having returned from his travels, rejoined the Society of Antiquaries in 1812 and with Thomas Allan, who also joined that Society, negotiated with the Antiquaries to rent two rooms on the bedroom floor of the Royal Society's house in George Street into which that Society moved, with their museum, in 1813 (Stevenson 1981, 56). This allowed them to realize capital by selling their own house and so relieve a financial crisis.

James Skene, the Royal Society's second Curator, was also a member of the Society of Antiquaries. As well as attending to his Royal Society duties, Skene continued with the cataloguing and arranging of the Society of Antiquaries' collection in 42 George Street, where a third room was later made available to that Society.

fig 10 Ulodendroid stem from the Craigleith Sandstone (Lower Oil Shale Group, Dinantian) of Craigleith Quarry, Edinburgh, presented by Thomas Allan in 1821. The specimen, *Lepidodendron veltheimi* (= *Megaphyton allani* Jongmans) was described and figured by Allan in *Transactions of the Royal Society of Edinburgh*, 9, 235-7, pl XIV. NMS G1995.3.1

The house in George Street was a domestic building having a basement and three storeys. Number 40 was a shop at street level in which John Urquhart carried on his hairdressing and perfumer's business. Access by number 42 was to a common stair which led to the Society's rooms on the first floor and to those of the Antiquaries on the floor above. Although rented by the Antiquaries specifically for their collections, after the material had been moved in *en masse* in 1813, little attention was given to it until a number of prominent members of the Royal Society such as Mackenzie, Dalyell, Allan, Jardine, Brewster and Skene, who were also Antiquaries, helped with its arrangement.

THE MUSEUM AT THE ROYAL INSTITUTION 1826-59

As plans were made for work to resume on the College Building, rooms for the Royal Society of Edinburgh were included in William Playfair's competition plan of 1815 and again in his amended plan of 1816. While financial restraints had required the size of the new College building to be

53

reduced, increasing student numbers made greater demands for space and it became evident that the Society could no longer hope for rooms there. In 1817 the Society informed the College Commissioners that it would give up the right to have rooms if an appropriate remission of their original subscription could be agreed (Fraser, 1989, 172 and 212).[26] It was therefore interested when, in 1821, an approach was made to it and other bodies by the recently founded Institution for the Promotion of the Fine Arts in Scotland (later known as the Royal Institution) with a view to a new building being erected to provide gallery space for the Institution and for the common use of a number of learned bodies. On the Society's initiative the Board of Manufactures was approached and it was agreed that the Board, which was financed by a grant from Central Government, would erect the building and occupy part of it and lease accommodation to the Royal Society of Edinburgh, the Society of Antiquaries and the Royal Institution. Work began on William Playfair's classic building at the foot of the Mound in 1823 and it was occupied in 1826. A tenancy then began for the Society with the Board of Manufactures which was to last for eighty years (Waterston 1996, 86).

THE ROYAL INSTITUTION, FIRST MUSEUM 1826-35

In 1826 the Society of Antiquaries and the Royal Society of Edinburgh moved to the Royal Institution and their Museums were housed in adjacent rooms of equal size (thirty-two by twelve feet) on the first floor of the new building (plan p 55). These rooms were lit by skylights. Access to the Royal Society's Museum was by way of a stair to the south of the Meeting Hall on the ground floor, which could also be reached from the exterior by way of a southern doorway. Access to the Antiquaries' Museum was by way of the west staircase at the north of the building and through their Meeting Hall.

James Skene continued as curator of both museums until 1833. In 1828 agreement was reached between 'the Antiquarian and Royal Societies in this place' to transfer 'to the Museum of each whatever articles might be in their possession but more particularly adapted to the Enquiries of the other'. Skeletal evidence for animal species in early Scotland was excepted by the Antiquaries from the natural history material handed over to the Royal Society at that time. According to Stevenson 'Burmese idols in marble and other articles came to the Antiquarians, but the full list then made has not been traced ' (Stevenson 1981, 69-70). Two gold coins of the time of James I and James II presented to the Royal Society by the Barons of the Exchequer in 1817 should have been transferred under this agreement but are listed as having been passed to the Society of Antiquaries in 1859.[27] It seems likely that few transfers were actually made as a result of the 1828 agreement.

A feature of the Society's museum at this time was the receipt of specimens, often from overseas, which were used by Fellows in their research.

54

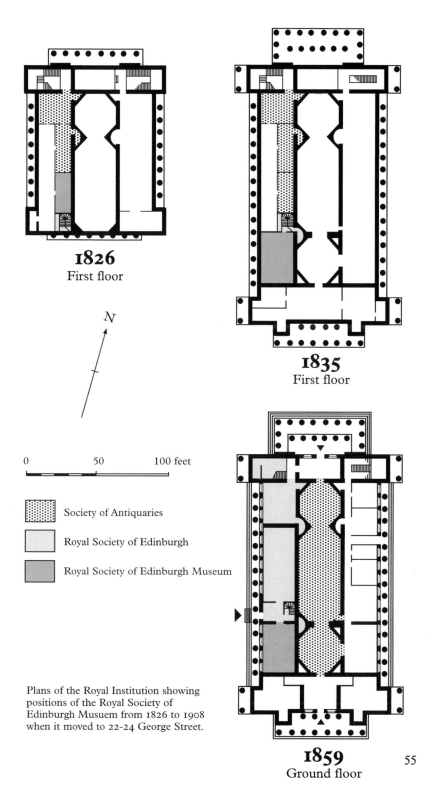

1826
First floor

N

0   50   100 feet

Society of Antiquaries

Royal Society of Edinburgh

Royal Society of Edinburgh Museum

Plans of the Royal Institution showing
positions of the Royal Society of
Edinburgh Musuem from 1826 to 1908
when it moved to 22-24 George Street.

1835
First floor

1859
Ground floor

55

Between 1826 and 1829 a notable donor of such material was George Swinton, Secretary to the government in Calcutta. Because of the importance of Swinton to our story, and because no biography of him has been published, some details of his life are given here.

George Swinton was the fifth son of John Swinton, 27th of that Ilk, Senator of the College of Justice as Lord Swinton, and his wife Margaret Mitchelson of Middleton (fig 11). He was a second cousin of the Society's President, Sir Walter Scott.[28] In 1793/4 he was a pupil at the Royal High School in Edinburgh and after attending the University of Edinburgh, like many of his family, he served with the East India Company. He arrived in India in 1802 and retired from the Bengal Establishment in 1833 (Prinsep, 1844, 369).[29]

During a long and distinguished career with the East India Company he gained wide experience, serving at various times in the Persian Secretary's Office and in the Secret, Political and Foreign Department under which he accompanied the British expeditionary forces in the First Burmese War (1824-6) and Henry Burney to Siam in 1825.[30] In 1826 he was Officiating Superintendent of the Botanic Garden at Calcutta and clearly had some interest in botany since he collected plants for N Wallich and was commemorated by Griffiths in his plant genus *Swintonia* (Desmond, 1994, 668). At the time of the donations Swinton held the influential office of Acting Chief Secretary and then Chief Secretary to the Government in Calcutta and, through his contacts with Company and Army Officers at many outposts, was in a position to respond to requests by Fellows for objects of natural history or manufactures from Bengal, Assam, Burma and Persia. He wrote to Brewster on 29 December 1826: 'As Secy. of the Royal Society you might draw up a list of what is wanting to complete the several Genera of the 3 Kingdoms in the Society's Museum & this would enable me to send you in reply what is required.' And again on 25 March 1827: 'I shall always be happy to receive from you lists of desiderata & to endeavour to procure the articles or information required'.[31] He was elected to membership of the Society for Promoting the Useful Arts in Scotland in March 1827 and, on the proposal of David Brewster, to Fellowship of the Royal Society of Edinburgh in May of the same year.

That research material was sent in response to requests is evident from the inclusion in a consignment addressed to Brewster on 9 February 1827 by the ship *Symmetry* of 'Bottle with Eyes of Elephant, Deer & Tiger' at a time when Brewster was working on the lenses of animal eyes. Brewster acknowledged Swinton's help in the supply of material (Brewster, 1833 and 1836). Swinton sent donations to other societies such as the Society of Antiquaries of Scotland[32] and sometimes included material intended for other bodies, such as the Society of Arts (which did not then have a museum) and the Royal Botanic Garden, along with consignments for the Royal Society of Edinburgh. On more than one occasion, he invited Brewster 'if you have any collections of your own, or wish to oblige any friends, you can take what

fig 11   Some major donors to the Museum of the Royal Society of Edinburgh.

Basil William Douglas, Lord Daer (1763-94, elected 1785). Paste medallion by James Tassie 1794.   Scottish National Portrait Gallery (PG1263).

Charles Murray Cathcart, Lord Greenock, later 2nd Earl Cathcart (1783-1859, elected 1833). Portrait by Sir John Watson Gordon. Courtauld Institute of Art

George Swinton (1781-54, elected 1827). Portrait in oils by John Hayes.   AIC Photographic Services, Private collection

Professor Charles Piazzi Smyth (1819 - 1900, elected 1846).   © 1987 Royal Observatory Edinburgh (8704101)

you please'. Brewster took advantage of this offer and, after working on the material, published a number of papers in his *Edinburgh Journal of Science*, often including descriptive notes which Swinton had sent from Calcutta on the material in the consignments. Papers on Indian varnishes and the properties of Tabasheer appeared and in the latter the following acknowledgement is made:

> This collection I owe to George Swinton Esq., Secretary to the Government at Calcutta, whose liberality and unwearied ardour in the cause of science and the arts is well known to all public institutions of his native country. (Brewster, 1828c)

Skene was unhappy about the looseness of these arrangements and, when John Robison succeeded Brewster as the General Secretary in November 1828, he asked Robison for clarification. Robison sent Skene what lists he had of Swinton's donations and promised to help Stark, then assisting Skene in the museum, with any enquiry into details by 'searching for them in Mr Swinton's letters, many of which Dr Brewster has left with me.'[33]

The volume and diversity of material sent by Swinton was an embarrassment to some in the Society who felt that a collecting policy for the Society's museum was required. Thomas Allan suggested to Council that many of the objects were not appropriate for the Society's museum.[34] A few days earlier Allan had made clear his reservations to Brewster:

> I am quite aware that you have appropriated little or none of the large consignment sent by Mr Swinton to this country but on the contrary have distributed it among various and sundry public bodies and manufacturers for the purpose of advancing science and the arts and the Royal Society among others have recovered a heterogeneous collection of things of very little use to them and almost destitute of notes or memoranda to render them in any respect interesting coupled besides with the necessity of a great outlay of money to bring them into any kind of use as for instance 5 Guineas charged for putting together ⅔rds of the skeleton of a Boa, not worth 5/- when all is done.[35]

Council thought otherwise, however, and 'as a mark of their sense of gratitude for his repeated valuable & interesting donations of objects for their Museum' agreed to send Swinton a complete set of the *Transactions*.[36] Robison, as General Secretary, made a statement to Council in clarification:

> ... in his letters (which accompanied the objects of Nat. Hist. & Art which he had transmitted from India [Swinton] had uniformly expressed his desire that the articles he sent should be disposed of in such a way as to prove as generally beneficial & instructive as possible. He added that many of the articles which Mr A(rchibald) Swinton had been authorized by his brother to entrust to him (Mr. R.) were originally intended for the Museum of the Society of Arts, but as that Society has no Museum, it was his intention to lodge them in that of the Royal Society provided it should be understood that he should be at liberty to apply portions of them to be distributed among scientific men & Artists for examination and experiment.

Dr Graham also stated that he had received a letter from Mr Swinton, Calcutta, authorizing him to select specimens of certain gums & vegetable juices for examination.

The Meeting considered these statements & expressed their wish that Mr Swinton's liberal & patriotic views be followed out, and authorized the Secretary to apply the necessary portions of the specimens in the way directed by Mr Swinton, taking care to engage all persons undertaking such examinations, to make full written reports to the Royal Society of the results of their experiments.[37]

The unusual animals sent to the Society by George Swinton were of great interest, particularly to Dr Robert Knox the anatomist who was consulted 'as to the disposal and arrangement of the anatomical and zoological presents to the Society' (Knox, 1831, 390). Knox dissected and described a number of them and acknowledged their donor as 'that distinguished patron of Natural Science Mr Swinton'.[38] Authentic dugong material, for example, was then hardly represented in European collections and Knox

fig 12 Skull of Indian Dugong presented by George Swinton in 1827, bisected by Robert Knox and described by him in *Transactions of the Royal Society of Edinburgh* 11, 1831, 389-416. NMS Z1996.83.6

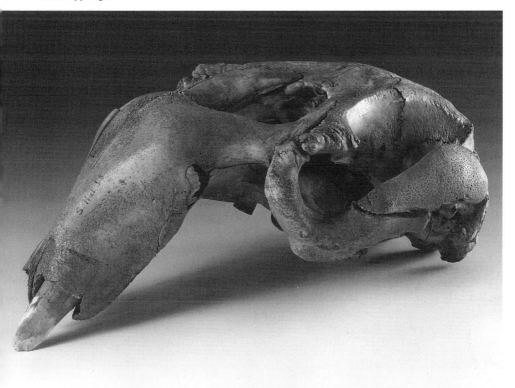

published a description of the dentition of the animal based on the head sent by Swinton in 1827 (Knox 1829, 1830 and fig 12). The importance of this specimen was recognized by Council and, on Robison's suggestion, the Treasurer, Thomas Allan, was requested to have a cast made for dispatch to Europe's leading comparative osteologist Baron Cuvier in Paris.[39] Knox prepared a number of Swinton's specimens and presented them to the Society, 'free of charge'[40] and the *Billet* for that day records that these were the cranium of the dugong and cast of the same, the skeleton of the long-armed gibbon, the skeleton of a boa constrictor, the skeleton of an iguana, two lizards, one alligator and twenty seven specimens of ophidian reptiles. Other dissections and preparations made from material sent to the Society's museum by Swinton were retained by Knox in his personal collection. These were acquired for the Anatomical Museum of the University of Edinburgh and a number of them have been recognised in material since presented to the National Museums of Scotland by the Anatomy Department (for example, Knox Collection Nos 107-109, 116 and 121, listed Turner, 1912, 146-147, 151). Since 1825 Knox had been conservator of the museum of the Royal College of Surgeons where his brother, Frederick John Knox, was taxidermist and responsible for many fine preparations (F J Knox 1836). From Thomas Allan's letter, quoted above, we know that the Society had spent money in having natural history specimens prepared, such as the boa constrictor mentioned, and it is likely that this was done by Frederick Knox on Robert Knox's recommendation. In his list accompanying the consignment sent by the *Louisa* in 1829, Swinton had noted 'Two jars containing a large and small long armed Gibbon from Assam – mother & son'.[41] These were described by Knox in 1829 and proved to be two females (Knox 1829). Robison had requested Knox 'to prepare them in whatever way [he] thought most beneficial to science'.

In 1830 oils were sent to Professor Christison for analysis. Christison described this event:

> When Sir David Brewster was secretary of the Royal Society of Edinburgh, the late Mr George Swinton, while secretary to Government at Calcutta, sent to the Society several novel natural productions, which seemed to him to deserve investigation. Sir David, probably seeing no source of optical interest in any of them, consigned them all to repose in a dark closet. His successor in office, Sir John Robison, a great lover of order, discovered them in a general 'redding up' of the Society's premises; and being interested in every product of India, where he had spent most of his early life as an engineer in the Nizam's service, asked me to look at them. I singled out Gurjun oil, Indian caoutchouc, Persian naphtha and Rangoon petroleum (Christison, 1885, I, 393).

In due course he reported his findings on petroleum from Rangoon and naphtha from Persia (Christison 1836). In the Rangoon specimen he discovered what he believed to be a new 'compound inflammable principle' which he termed *Petroline* but which, in an Appendix to his paper, he acknowledged to be the same as *Paraffine* described in August 1830 by Reichenbach. To Swinton's surprise his Persian naphtha turned out to be pure turpentine, a substitution having taken place apparently in India. William Gregory re-examined the petroleum from Rangoon and confirmed that it contained paraffine and eupione (which had been described from tar by Reichenbach in 1831). He was aware of the value of these substances which burn without smoke or smell and with a purity of light equal to wax. He also examined other genuine specimens of naphtha from Persia and reported the results of his work in a paper immediately following Christison's (Gregory 1836). He concluded that the naphtha from Persia and the petroleum from Rangoon were products of destructive distillation and 'It remains for the geologist to ascertain the sources'. That the potential of Burma and Persia as sources of industrial fuel oil should have been recognized at this date and in this way is remarkable. It was to be over twenty years before a geological survey of the oil seepage areas of Burma was undertaken by Oldham and not until after 1900 that the search for oil became a serious geological enterprise.

In concluding our consideration of George Swinton reference must be made to the dispute between David Brewster and Robert Jameson which he unwittingly caused.[42] What was probably the first of Swinton's donations to the Society was a case containing a number of 'Burmese idols' which he sent by the ship *Jane* of Calcutta addressed to 'Edinburgh Royal Museum, care D Brewster Esqr'. It arrived in the warehouse of Messrs Bazett Farquhar Crawford & Co in London in December 1825 and was forwarded by Mr Davidson, Edinburgh University's agent, to Leith by the smack *Venus* in January 1826 where it was exempted from duty and delivered to the University Museum. In Brewster's words:

> They were sent to Prof Jameson who opened them, took out their contents, and gave me no notice. He detained the property a year and a half altho' threatened with prosecution by Messrs Bazett and by Mr Swinton's Bankers in London. I applied to Jameson by letter, and thereon, I received no answer, but was at last told that the Barons of Exchequer could alone authorise him to give them up as they were Royal Property.[43]

Having been assured by Henry Jardine and Clerk Rattray, both Barons of the Exchequer and Fellows of the Society, that the Barons had nothing to do with it and that Jameson was entitled to give up the property, Rattray advised Brewster to apply to the Sheriff court to recover the property and he did so. While petitions and answers were in process with the Sheriff, however, the Barons ordered Jameson to return the case to Brewster which was done in July 1827. On 21 January 1828 the Sheriff Substitute found 'that the article in question having been now delivered up to the pursuer it is unnecessary to give any judgement in so far as regards the merits of the case'. Further, however, he ruled that Jameson, being only the keeper of the museum of which the administrators were the Barons of Exchequer, was not the person to be called in the action and required Brewster to pay the professor's legal expenses of £23-12-2.[44] Despite Thomas Allan's strong objections as Treasurer, Council decided that, since Brewster had undertaken the action as the Society's secretary to recover property belonging to it, the expenses should be met from Society funds.[45]

The flint of Brewster's irritability and the steel of Jameson's obstinacy, when struck in contention, produced sparks. They had already fallen out over the management of the *Edinburgh Philosophical Journal* in 1824. The arguments in the case of the Burmese idols need not concern us here but the papers make entertaining reading. Brewster did not agree that the College Museum could appropriate a case addressed to him at 'Edinburgh Royal Museum' since it was not entitled to be called Royal. It was referred to in the Royal Society's own royal charters simply as 'Musaeo Academia Edinensis'. He wrote:

> In the first place it might have been expected that the Defender should at least have pointed out the acts or Statutes or Warrants which authorised the assumption for the College Museum of even the name of the Royal Museum, for it is clear that the mere unauthorised assumption of that name could carry no greater privileges to the soi disant Royal Museum than it does to the Royal Hotel.

In referring to the College Museum as 'The Royal Museum' Jameson was following a precedent set by Walker forty years previously.[46] Indeed Jameson's grounds for so doing were firmer than Walker's. As part of the settlement over the Royal Society Museum following the Second Charter, and in response to an application by the University for the improvement of its museum, a government grant had been made by Lord Castlereagh. Furthermore, by his commission as Regius Keeper of the Museum in 1812, Jameson could claim to have received official recognition from the Crown. He had also received 'a royal request that servants of the government and others in foreign parts should collect and send suitable objects to the University Museum' (Fraser, 1989, 194), in furtherance of which he issued his own instructions to collectors in 1817. He also supplied naturalists, many of whom were his own students, as medical officers on government and other expeditions. Through these official and other contacts he was notably successful in obtaining many valuable acquisitions for his museum (Sweet, 1972). In his evidence to the Commissioners, given at the time of his altercation with Brewster, Jameson had said:

> Application being made, Government issued an order, commanding that all packages addressed to the Keeper of the King's Museum here should come duty-free.[47]

The use of the titles Royal Museum or King's Museum remained unchallenged by the commissioners.

Between 1821 and 1828 the title of Skene's office had been 'Curator of the Library and Museum' but his attention was more and more preoccupied by management of the library and exchanges of periodicals. In 1829, perhaps because of the large number of objects recently received from George Swinton, Skene suggested to Council the need for a descriptive catalogue of the contents of the Museum to be prepared and 'understood there was a member of the Society whose aid might be obtained in effecting so desirable an object'.[48] At the next meeting the Secretary was asked to request Mr Neill to assist the Curator. It would appear that it was Patrick Neill who Skene had in mind as his assistant. At the next Annual General Meeting, however it was John Stark FRSE who was elected 'Assistant Curator'. Neill was already heavily involved in the work of other societies as secretary of the Wernerian Society and of the Caledonian Horticultural Society. He probably suggested Stark, his friend and fellow printer, as suitable for the assistantship which he was unwilling to take on himself. Stark's interest in the care of the Museum continued until his death twenty years later.

John Stark of Huntfield is another Fellow whose contribution to the Society's museum was signficant but about whom little has been published. He was born at Blyth's Muir, Peeblesshire, in 1779, the son of James Stark and Elizabeth Lawson. From an early age he owned a printing works at Old Assembly Close and was the author and printer of a number of compilations of considerable local interest. He wrote of Lord Kames as one 'who had from nature an insatiable appetite for information of every kind', words that could well describe Stark himself. His *Biographia Scotica* ... was published in 1805 and his most successful *Picture of Edinburgh....* first appeared in the following year. This was favourably reviewed in the *Scots Magazine*[49], and, in six editions and many impressions long remained in print. In this work the section on natural history was contributed by Patrick Neill. On page 427 of the first edition Stark acknowledges his indebtedness to Neill, 'a young gentleman whose knowledge and abilities in investigations of this kind will render the present article particularly interesting'. The 'young gentleman' in question was three years older than Stark who was then twenty-seven!

Among the notable books printed by Stark was Thomas Brown's *Illustrations of the Conchology of Great Britain and Ireland* (1827), a quarto work with fifty-three coloured plates drawn by Brown and engraved by W H Lizars. Stark became a competent naturalist himself and published a number of scientific papers. In 1834 he found *Dreissensia polymorpha* in the Union Canal (Jackson 1945). He was elected to Membership of the Wernerian Society in 1821 and to Fellowship of the Royal Society of Edinburgh in 1826 following the communication by David Brewster, in March of that year, of his paper on *Pholas* (Stark, 1826). In 1828 he published *Elements of Natural History*, a two volume work of which he was not only author and printer but, with Adam Black, also publisher.[50]

Stark's first duty was to prepare a report on the Society's Museum which was duly submitted to the General Secretary and, as one of the few existing contemporary descriptions of the Museum, is quoted *in extenso*:

To John Robison Esq.

15 Brown's Sqr 2nd Janry 1830

Dear Sir

I have gone over the articles in the Museum generally, and named many of them, particularly the Serpents on the Board put up by Dr Knox. There are, however, a good many more reptiles to be put up, for which tubes and preparation glasses will be required (fig 13). The Museum is indeed rich in Indian Serpents, and a few donations of American ones would make the collection very complete.

The *Mammalia* are few in number, but the specimens are interesting. Of *Birds* there are very few. Of *Fishes* from 20 to 30, put up in preparation glasses, but not named. These are from the East Indies I presume: but I should be glad to know their proper locality from Mr Swinton's notes before attempting to name them, if they can readily be found.

The *Shells* are few in number, and none of any rarity; but Dr Brewster mentions his having some wh[ich] he is to give to the Society the selection, and I can contribute a good many of the Native Species. The *Madrepores* from Mr Swinton are pretty good specimens.

I observe a quantity of *Bones* similar to the Kirkdale ones. If these are from Professor Buckland, or otherwise, perhaps you could indicate where I might find the list, for the purpose of labelling them.

The Miscellaneous articles seem in good order, and the Mineral and Geological specimens, by Mr Allan's care, properly disposed in drawers.

As the articles at present in the Museum, many of wh[ich] are interesting and valuable, can only be considered as the beginning of a collection, wh[ich] the influence of the Royal Society and its members abroad will no doubt materially increase, to the advantage of Science, it is quite necessary, for proper preservation of the specimens, that the whole, as far as possible, be protected from dust and handling, by glass, & properly labelled with their generic & specific names, & the names of the donors. At present it might be necessary to complete the cases on one side of the room. A central table, covered by glass, the under part of which might be drawers for geological specimens, insects etc. would hold all the smaller articles, such as shells, corals etc. displayed in the best mannner for examination – But this is for the consideration of Council.

Dr Christison has kindly undertaken the analysis of, and to make experiments on, some of the varnishes, oils, etc. in the Museum, of wh[ich] the results will be communicated to the Society.

I beg to apologise for my unintentional intrusion at the Meeting of Council, of which I was not at the time aware that I did not, ex officio, form an adjunct - and am

Dear Sir

Your most humble Servant

John Stark [51]

Stark's embarrassment at his 'intrusion' at a Council meeting was soon overcome because he was present, *ex officio*, at the meeting of 4 January 1830 and continued a faithful attender until his death. His concern for the

fig 13 Indian snakes presented by George Swinton (1827) and bottled in spirit by the Society's museum curator John Stark. The specimens now form part of the collection NMS Z1859.21 and are preserved in the original bottles with the original Royal Society of Edinburgh museum labels.

65

Museum was expressed at the next meeting of Council when he stated that many of the more delicate and valuable articles in the Society's collection were suffering from exposure to dust and external injury and suggested that glass doors to the shelves should be provided for their protection.[52] He was asked to report on what he considered essential with information on probable cost and on 1 February gave Council his view that £20 would be required for the work. At the time, however, the Society was still in dispute with the University on the future of their specimens in the University Museum and Council postponed action on Stark's suggestion until the outcome was known.

The Society's archive contains a number of notes requesting Stark's services in identifying or arranging specimens.[53] Thomas Allan sends the Atacama meteorite to Stark's printing house with the request that he take it to the Society as he is unable to do so himself. Robison sends him two black lizards received by Dr Brewster from George Fairholme Esq for identification. Again, 'Mr Robison will feel obliged to Mr Stark if he will have the goodness to get from Mr Neill an early proof of the circular for the next meeting ... Mr Stark will have the goodness to have them (a great number of preparations by Dr Knox) laid out previous to the meeting in such a way as to shew them to advantage without putting them in danger of accidents'. In these and many other ways Stark willingly obliged.

It is unfortunate that Stark is remembered more as the butt of Robert Knox's invective than for his service to Knox and others as the Society's curator. At what has been described as 'the most memorable and liveliest meeting ever held in the Society's rooms' on 4 December 1837, Stark read a paper entitled 'Notice on the Food of the Herring and Salmon'(Campbell and Smellie 1983, 25). He claimed that a number of authors had preceded Knox in observations on the vendace and herring which the anatomist had given in an earlier lecture (Knox 1834). Sir Thomas Makdougall Brisbane occupied the chair and an account of the meeting has been given by Lonsdale, a student and admirer of Knox, who quotes his hero's words thus:

> Is it necessary for me, Sir Thomas, the friend and companion of Baron Cuvier, to defend myself in the society of my compeers against the base and personal scurrilities of a mere dabbler in science? (Lonsdale, 1870, 191)

'And in this strain' observes Lonsdale '*avoiding the merits of the question at issue*, he continued to pour out in the most fervent style the vials of his wrath on Mr Stark. His speech came like a flood of invective and wit'; a flood which engulfed also such respected figures as the Rev Dr John Fleming and Professor T S Traill. At the time of this meeting Knox's reputation, except among his anatomical students, was already in eclipse. It was nine years since the 'West Port tragedy' which had stained Knox's reputation among the people, but it was rather his habit of invective, from which he spared neither friend nor foe and which Stark had to endure in 1837, which turned his scientific colleagues against him.[54] Six years before his abuse of Stark, he

fig 14 Palaeoniscus robisoni Hibbert [*Elonichthys robisoni* (Hibbert)], From the collection of fossils from the Dinantian limestone of Burdiehouse, Edinburgh, made in 1834 under the direction of Sir John Robison, the General Secretary of the Royal Society of Edinburgh, and Dr Samuel Hibbert. Specimen figured by Louis Agassiz 1833-43, Tab 10a, figs 1-2. NMS G1878.18.8

had resigned his conservatorship at the Royal College of Surgeons through a quarrel with the distinguished surgeon James Syme (Creswell 1926, 83-4). Stark might well have agreed with Sir Robert Christison's view of Knox that he was 'a man of undoubted talent, but notoriously deficient in principle and in heart' (Christison 1885, I, 311).

With the founding of the Geological Society of London in 1807, and the establishment of flourishing geological schools, in Oxford under William Buckland and in Cambridge under Adam Sedgwick, Edinburgh and its Royal Society had become a backwater for geological debate. Geological battles which had once been fought out within the walls of the Society were now conducted, largely by exiled Scots, in London (Forbes 1866, 17-18). A passive popular interest in the subject continued among the Society's Fellows. Passivity changed to an active concern among these gentlemen in 1826 when fossil fishes were discovered in the Caithness Flagstones and excitement reached fever pitch in 1833 when one of them, Dr Samuel Hibbert, discovered what he believed was a saurian reptile in the limestone of Burdiehouse. Systematic collecting to conserve what was recognized to be a finite research resource, and involvement of the best available scientific talent in the description of the resulting specimens, was organized by the Society's Secretary John Robison to give a new dimension and relevance to the Society's museum. Andrews (1982, 12-18) has written a detailed account of the formation of the Burdiehouse collection during the winter and spring of 1833-34, its impact on the deliberations of the British Association which met in Edinburgh in September 1834 attended by Louis Agassiz, who subsequently described the fish fossils, and the production of Hibbert's monograph on Burdiehouse (Hibbert 1836 and fig 14).

Another Fellow who was an active collector of fossil fishes in the local Carboniferous strata at this time was Lord Greenock. Charles Murray

fig 15 Model of the second Eddystone Lighthouse NMS T1859.414.B3, one of the collection of models and papers connected with the Eddystone Lighthouse presented by the Countess of Morton in 1828.

Cathcart was the second son of the first Earl of Cathcart and was styled Lord Greenock on the death of his elder brother in 1804 (fig 11). He had a distinguished military career and from 1837 to 1842 commanded the forces in Scotland and was Governor of Edinburgh Castle. In 1841 he was promoted Lieutenant-General and in 1846 left Scotland to become commander in Canada, having succeeded his father as second Earl of Cathcart in 1843 (Neaves 1862). Lord Greenock had become interested in geology while at the Royal Staff College at Hythe where he had taken an interest in the museum formed by the Royal Staff Corps which he commanded. When he came to Edinburgh in 1830 he attended Professor Jameson's natural history class and it was to Jameson's Wernerian Society in February 1833 that he communicated his discovery of fossil teeth in the Lower Carboniferous rocks of Paxton, Berwickshire. In that spring also he discovered fish-bearing ironstone nodules at Wardie and specimens which he donated to the Society's museum were later described by Agassiz. It was Jameson who recommended him for Fellowship of the Royal Society of Edinburgh to which he was elected on 2 May 1833. He immediately became active in its affairs and communicated his paper on the Castle Hill in December of the same year (Greenock, 1836a). In the following March he moved that £50 be paid from the funds of the Society towards the expenses of the British Association which, at the invitation of the Society, was to meet in Edinburgh in September 1834. It was to the British Association that he presented his paper on the Coal Formation of the Midland Valley (Greenock, 1836b). He was elected to Council as a Vice-President in November 1834 and, with the exception of the year 1845-6, retained that office until 1848-9.

In 1828 the Countess of Morton presented a major collection of models and papers connected with the erection of the Eddystone Lighthouse, the content and origins of which have been described by Rowatt (1924-5). It had been formed by Mr Robert Harcourt Weston, principal lessee of the lighthouse, who presented it to Lord Morton 'for the manner in which he had interested himself with regard to Mr Weston's affairs.'[55] George, 17th Earl of Morton was one of the sixteen peers who were then elected by the Scottish peerage as their representatives in the House of Lords and was thus in a position to assist Weston. He died childless and his widow presented the collection two months later. The collection is preserved in the National Museums of Scotland having been donated by the Society in 1859. The earliest item is an engraving published in 1699 of Winstanley's lighthouse (1698-1703). There are seven objects relevant to the second lighthouse (1709-1755) which was built by Rudyerd (fig 15) and twenty-five relevant to the third lighthouse (1759-1882) built by John Smeaton. With the collection is preserved also a contemporary label reading 'the lead found in the body of Wm Hall, Edystone Lt Keeper'. This was removed from the stomach of a Keeper after the fire of 1755 and described by Edward Spry, Surgeon at Plymouth (Spry 1756).

In 1831 the Board of Manufactures engaged W H Playfair to extend the Royal Institution building by sixty feet southwards to provide much-needed extra accommodation. Following its completion in December 1835, the Society was provided with a new and enlarged Museum (thirty-four by twenty-four feet) on the extended first floor to the south of the access stair (plan p 55). A new external door to this stair was then made in the west side of the building, that to the south having been lost in the extension. The room vacated by the Society's museum was added to the suite of rooms occupied by the Society of Antiquaries (Stevenson 1981, 72).

With the cessation of Skene's joint curatorship the museums of the Antiquaries and the Royal Society went their separate ways. In 1836 he was succeeded as Curator of the Antiquaries' Museum by Alexander Macdonald of the Register House staff who had for some years been his assistant. In 1834 Skene had handed over the curatorship of the Royal Society's Library and Museum to Professor Thomas Stewart Traill who, two years earlier, had been appointed to the Chair of Medical Jurisprudence in the University of Edinburgh (fig 16).

Council had become concerned that scientific instruments, acquired by the Society to facilitate the work of Fellows in such tasks as surveying and the keeping of meteorological records, should be properly cared for. In response to a request by Council in 1839, Traill prepared a catalogue of the Society's instruments (see Appendix II below)[56], many of which are now preserved in the scientific collections of the National Museums of Scotland. As was his predecessor, Traill was concerned to an ever greater extent with the rapidly expanding library and responsibility for the museum devolved more and more to Stark as his assistant. The position was formalized in 1841 when Traill was elected 'Curator of Library and Instruments' and Stark was promoted from Assistant Curator to 'Curator of Museum'.[57] This arrangement continued until Stark's death in 1849.

A number of important collections were added to the Society's museum at this time. Outstanding among these were three collections of preserved fishes presented by Dr Richard Parnell who made extensive collections of fish and grasses (Jack et al, 1982). As an ichthyologist, he is best known for his major study of the fishes of the Firth of Forth. The collections which he presented to the Society in 1836 and 1837 consisted largely of specimens from the Firth of Forth but some were from other localities. Mr Swinney, curator of fishes and amphibians, has recognised twenty-seven of these specimens in the National Museums of Scotland collection. Since the collection was passed to the national museum most, but probably not all, of the specimens have been remounted though some of the backing sheets still carry Parnell's signature (fig 17). The National Museums of Scotland have two other collections of Dr Parnell's fishes, one which he presented to Professor Jameson who gave it to the Natural History

fig 16 Early Honorary Curators of the Museum of the Royal Society of Edinburgh.

Thomas Allan 1812-19. From the portrait bust by Samuel Joseph. City of Edinburgh Museums and Galleries, Lauriston Castle Collection

James Skene of Rubislaw 1820-33. Detail from wash drawing by an unknown artist. Scottish National Portrait Gallery (PG2051)

Thomas Stewart Traill 1834-54. Detail of portrait in oils by Alexander Mosses. Scottish National Portrait Gallery (PG1851)

Sir Douglas Maclagan 1856-78. From an engraving by G. Aikman of an original portrait in oils by Sir George Reid. Scottish National Portrait Gallery (B5207)

Crenilabrus rupestris
Goldsinny
Brixham September 1836

B Parnell

fig 17 Skin of *Crenilabrus rupestris* taken at Brixham in September 1836 and mounted by Dr Richard Parnell. Dr Parnell presented extensive collections of fish from the Firth of Forth and elsewhere in 1836 and 1837. This specimen is preserved in the collection NMS Z1859.23.

Museum of the university (NMS Z1834.8), the other a large collection bequeathed by the collector's widow (NMS Z1888.12).

A collection of historic importance to freshwater science was that illustrating the growth of the salmon which was presented by John Shaw of Drumlanrig in 1839. It was a series of specimens from the ovum to the smolt, and included the ordinary and transitionary state of the parr which illustrated Shaw's famous account of experimental observation on the development and growth of salmon fry (Shaw 1840). Until this time salmon parr were considered to be a different species from adult salmon. It was not until Shaw's classic experiments that young were reared from the eggs and sperm of adult salmon and shown to be indistinguishable from the salmon parr of rivers. A similar collection illustrating his paper on the development of the sea trout of the Solway was presented by John Shaw in 1843 (Shaw 1844). These collections were given to the national museum in 1859 but unfortunately they cannot now be traced in the collections of the National Museums of Scotland.

Mr Heppel, curator of molluscs at NMS, has recognised a number of shells from conchological collections presented to the Society in this period which are now preserved in the National Museums of Scotland. On 16 March 1840 Professor Traill exhibited to the Society a collection of African shells which had been collected and presented by J O M'William Esq,

Surgeon RN. Of these, specimens from Isle of Princes, Mozambique and Simon's Bay, Cape of Good Hope are in the NMS collections (fig 18). Of British land and fresh-water shells presented to the Society in 1844 by the Hon Mrs Cathcart, Mr Heppel has recognised eight specimens of *Theodoxus fluviatilis* in the NMS collections.

The fossil collection of Rev David Ure, author of *The History of Ruther-glen and East-Kilbride* (1793) was presented to the Society by John Stark himself in 1843. The collection is of great interest for the history of paleontology because, although Ure was a pre-binomial author, many common Scottish Carboniferous fossil species were illustrated in his well-known work of 1793. John Fleming, who described and named a number of Ure's fossils in his own *History of British Animals* (1828), claimed that Ure had 'an acquaintance with organic remains unequalled in the work of any contemporary author of the United Kingdom'.[58] Ure started his collection when an assistant minister at East Kilbride between 1784 and 1790 (Burns 1993,

fig 18 Achatina reversa presented in 1840 by J O M'William Esq RN from Isle of Princes, Africa. NMS Z1959.24.3

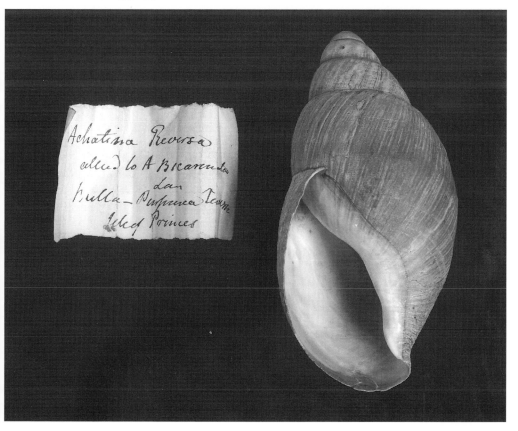

fig 19 Spirifera striatus Martin, a Carboniferous lamp shell, figured by David Ure in his *History of Rutherglen* of 1793 at Pl 15, fig 1. A specimen from the Ure Collection presented by John Stark in 1843. GLAHM L11095 Hunterian Museum, University of Glasgow

262-3) and appears to have continued his field interests during a peripatetic period when he was involved with Sir John Sinclair's *Statistical Account* and then in the charge of Uphall, to which he was presented in 1795 by the Earl of Buchan, the principal heritor of the parish. It is not known when or how John Stark gained possession of the Ure collection but it is possible that some of the labels, which accompany the specimens, may have been written by him. In later years, however, the Society was criticised for the state of the collection (Gray 1865, 46-7). Over 2000 specimens remain in the Ure Collection which is preserved in the Hunterian Museum, Glasgow, to which it was given by the Society in 1910 (fig 19).

J D Forbes presented a number of collections illustrating his geological work at home and abroad. Had they survived, the rocks showing striation and polishing by glacier flow which he presented in 1843 would have been of historic interest. Forbes collected them to support his theory of glacier flow which was illustrated by the model which he had made, described and presented three months before. The specimen from under the ice of the Glacier de la Brenva he collected in July 1842 when he was still developing his theory prior to publication of his famous work on the Alps (see Cunningham 1990, 125-6, Forbes, 1843). In 1851 Forbes' friend John Ruskin presented rocks from artificial sections near Chamonix.

74

Although the Professor of Fine Arts at Oxford is better known for his writing on the arts, Ruskin had studied geology under Buckland when an undergraduate at that university and had been convinced of the truth of Forbes' theory of glacier motion on first reading Forbes' book in 1843. Ruskin knew Chamonix well and had met Forbes there in 1846. In a letter to George Richmond, written on 30 August, he tells how Forbes had set his friend Dr Henry Acland 'on a nasty, useless, ugly, bothering glacier walk' leaving Ruskin to entertain Mrs Acland (Cook & Wedderburn, 1909, 63). An unsavoury battle between John Tyndall and Forbes over the latter's claim of precedence for his theory of glacier flow ensued which was continued by Forbes' Scottish supporters even after their champion's death. Ruskin's support of his late friend in *Fors Clavigera* (letter 34, October 1873) was quoted in their cause (G Forbes 1874).

A committee, under the convenership of that vigorous and able Vice-President Lord Greenock, to consider the fitting up of the museum was appointed by Council in 1842, and their report gives a good idea of the appearance of the museum at that time.[59] Lord Greenock was an active member of the Highland and Agricultural Society and his committee consulted that society on museum cases before commissioning John Leslie to make a large table case for the display and storage of geological specimens. This was placed in the museum with its long axis to north and south, and the glass covered display case, painted white internally, was divided into east and west sections.[60] Leslie was commissioned also to make wooden boxes for the storage of specimens.[61] Over the old ranges of drawers, which had been brought from the previous museum room and fitted up along one side of the new museum, Leslie fitted side cases with glass doors. These would no doubt have been used for the display of natural history specimens. The total cost of Leslie's work had not exceeded the £100 which Council had allowed Greenock's committee to spend, and in addition removable screens had been fitted to the skylight, the only natural lighting of the room. Lord Greenock and the curator (John Stark) had arranged a good number of specimens in the cases, both those formerly in the Society's possession and those more lately presented, and had labelled such as were known with the names and the donors. Greenock felt that there was sufficient accommodation in the new drawers and cases so that specimens presented to the Society in future would be easily accessible to Fellows, and through them to all scientific investigators. He recommended to Council, however, that 'at as early a period as the State of Funds will admit' the opposite side of the Museum should be fitted to correspond with the side already completed.[62]

To inform Fellows of their work a 'List of the principal Donations to the Royal Society, and which may now be seen in the Museum' was printed and distributed with the *Billet* of 6 February 1843. This lists twenty-three geological collections, nine natural history collections and five others, including the Eddystone Lighthouse collection. Although a number of important acquisitions were yet to be made, this may be regarded as the high water mark in the fortunes of the Society's Museum.

John Stark died at his home in Rutland Street on Christmas Eve 1849 and the General Secretary reported in November 1850 that Council was urgently considering the Curatorship of the Museum 'occasioned by the death of Mr Stark who so long and usefully filled that office'. Their choice was James Wilson of Woodville, who was appointed curator of the museum in 1850 and continued as such until his death.

Wilson of Woodville was a younger brother John Wilson, Professor of Moral Philosophy at Edinburgh University and better known as 'Christopher North' of the *Edinburgh Review*. James was a man of independent means but took classes at Edinburgh University with a view to becoming a lawyer and was one of Robert Jameson's students in natural history. In 1816 he travelled in Holland, Germany and Switzerland and then spent some time in Paris working at the Jardin des Plantes, where the bird collections were of special interest to him. He played an important role in the acquisition of the collection of Louis Dufresne of that institution by Edinburgh University in 1819 and, on his return from Paris, helped Professor Jameson to arrange the Dufresne birds in the College Museum (Sweet 1970). While visiting Sweden in 1819 he was diagnosed as suffering from pulmonary tuberculosis. Following his marriage in 1824, he settled at Woodville, in the Morningside district of Edinburgh, where he devoted himself to gardening and the study of natural history. He published fourteen papers on natural history in the scientific journals as well as many articles in Blackwoods, *The North British Review* and the *Quarterly Edinburgh Review*. Among other books, his *Illustrations of Zoology* was published in 1831. A remarkable accomplishment, however, was his authorship of nine articles on natural history subjects published in the seventh edition of the *Encyclopaedia Britannica* (1842) and a further two in the eighth edition (1853) comprising, in all, 900 pages. Such was his reputation as a naturalist that in 1854 he was offered the chair of Natural History at Edinburgh University, made vacant by the untimely death of his friend Edward Forbes, but this he declined. Although still busy in authorship his health was failing.

Wilson was a valuable member of Council and acted as the Society's General Secretary during J D Forbes' prolonged illness in 1850. Although a more distinguished naturalist than his predecessor as curator of the Society's museum, there were few significant donations during his curatorship which he may well have treated rather lightly. Certainly, during the last few years of his life he was physically unable to do much work for the museum.

1 Kerr noted the following mammals in Weir's museum – polar bear, common badger, variegated mole, white mole, unknown deer, many-horned sheep, arnee, and musk-ox.

2 Edinburgh City Archives, Town Council Record, vol 134, p 176, 3 December 1800.

3 MS Letter from Joseph Black to John Robison, Secretary of the Royal Society of Edinburgh dated 2 December 1797 NLS ACC 10000/386.

4 Hutton's famous work was largely identified with the Royal Society of Edinburgh, his zeal for which had encouraged him to write it, and which provided the forum in which it was delivered and the Transactions by which it was communicated to the world (Playfair 1805, 51 and Campbell and Smellie 1983, 63).

5 *Evidence, Oral and Documentary, taken and received by the Commissioners ... for Visiting the Universities of Scotland*, Vol 1, *University of Edinburgh*, London 1837,142.

6 Evidence of Robert Jameson, ibid, 1, 176.

7 Evidence of Robert Jameson, ibid, 1, 543.

8 NLS ACC 10000/15 Extract Minute of Society meeting of 26 January 1807 held in College Library.

9 Members of the committee were Dr Wright, Alexander Keith of Dunottar, Henry Mackenzie, James Bonar the Treasurer, Mr Farquarson and Professor Playfair the Secretary.

10 Extract minute of meeting of Senatus Academicus of 28 April 1808, NLS ACC 10000/386.

11 *Transactions of the Royal Society of Edinburgh*, 6, 1804-1811, II, 1-2.

12 Members were Lt Col Ninian Imrie, Thomas Allan and Thomas Thomson.

13 NLS ACC 10000/390, date obtained from 'Inventory of Papers relating to the claim of the RS to be admitted to College Museum' NLS ACC 10000/386.

14 NLS ACC 10000/386.

15 Edinburgh City Archive, McLeod's Bundle 16.

16 NLS ACC 10000/390.

17 Thomas Allan formed one of the finest collections of minerals in Scotland which, in his later life, was displayed in his house, Lauriston Castle, Edinburgh and which his son Robert sold to the Greg family of Manchester in 1860. It is now in the Natural History Museum, London (Farrar and Farrar, 1968).

18 Mackenzie had been accompanied to Iceland by two young friends, Henry Holland and Richard Bright, both of whom became distinguished physicians (Kark and Moore 1981). They both gave accounts of their journey to the Geological Society of London before publication of Mackenzie's book. 'Sketch of the Mineralogy of Iceland' by Holland was read in his absence by Bright on 17 May 1811 and Bright read his own paper 'On the Obsidian & other Mineral Products of Iceland' in July 1811. Both papers exist in manuscript in the Mineral Department of the Natural History Museum, London as does the manuscript 'Catalogue of Mineral Specimens collected in Iceland by Richard Bright Jnr 1810 and arranged by him at Ham, Green 1812' Bright presented the collection to the Geological Society of London. Mackenzie divided his Icelandic collection between the Royal Society of Edinburgh and the Edinburgh University Museum. He told the University Commissioners (1826) that 'he had not had a chance to label the specimens at the time of the donation and that Jameson had never let him do so. His collection supported views other than those of Jameson'. The specimens presented to the Society, on the other hand, were named and a catalogue of them published as Appendix III of his book (Mackenzie 1811, 435-56).

19 NLS ACC 10000/389 (watermarked 1818).

20 Chart 913, Korea – West Coast 1984.

21 Elizabeth, Marchioness of Huntly and 5th Duchess of Gordon, was the daughter of Alexander Brodie of Arnhall and the Burn. His older brother James Brodie FRS, who had succeeded his kinsman as 21st Brodie of Brodie, is well known as a botanist and supplied

a number of fossils to James Sowerby who described them in his *Mineral Conchology*. Elizabeth shared her uncle's scientific interests and Elizabeth Grant of Rothiemurchus wrote of 'a very fine collection of shells and minerals ... left by Lady Huntly to her cousin [William] Brodie of Brodie', grandson of her uncle James Brodie FRS (Grant, 1898, 381). Lady Huntly's mineral collection is now preserved in the Nairn Museum. In 1813 she married George, Marquis of Huntly (1770-1836), who succeeded his father as 5th and last Duke of Gordon in 1827.

22 Brewster may well have become known to Lady Huntly while she was staying with her famous mother-in-law, the Duchess of Gordon, at her Speyside home at Kinrara. Brewster was engaged in the business of his sister-in-law's nearby estate at Belleville, Kingussie.

23 Captain Thomas Brown was elected a Fellow in 1818 but left the Society after about ten years (Jackson, 1945). Although best known as a conchologist, Brown developed his interest in equine disease and published a larger work on the subject seven years later (Brown 1830).

24 I am grateful to Mr Patrick Cadell (letter to CDW 22nd November 1995) for information on Francis Simpson and his relationships to W A Cadell and the possible motivation for his voyage to India in 1800.

25 NMS, History of Science Section: NPM Catalogues and Inventories, item H, at p 79, re No 2185. I am grateful to Dr A D C Simpson for drawing my attention to this letter. He writes that there is some confusion about the date of John Robison's visit to Woolsthorpe, and it may be that it was in 1796, perhaps repeated in 1797: he is understood to have been in the area promoting Watt's engine improvement. He believes it plausible that Barrow was commissioned by Robison to survey the site and produce perspective views as a result of an initial visit in 1796. Simpson has traced a number of Barrow's sketches, four at St Andrews University Library, three now in the Royal Museum of Scotland and a plan of which there is a copy at Grantham Library, Art Gallery and Museum.

26 The matter remained a vexed question between the Society and the Commissioners until 1832 and no settlement was ever agreed.

27 NLS ACC 10000/20, Council Minute of 21 November 1859.

28 Scott's maternal grandmother, Jean Swinton, was a sister of George Swinton's grandfather John Swinton of Swinton, Advocate (Swinton,1877, 1883). Scott wrote 'my heart always warms to the Swinton connection, so faithful to old Scottish feeling' (Scott, 1891, entry for June 6 1826).

29 Swinton wrote to David Brewster that a ball of indian rubber 'will stot better than any ba' at the High School' (NLS ACC 10000/389, Memorandum for Dr Brewster 9 Feb 1827 on the contents of boxes by the ship *Symmetry*) and again 'Mr Livingston I remember well as he was at the Rector's class with me' (NLS ACC 10000/392 Letter from Swinton to Brewster of 26 October 1826). I am grateful to Mr R C T Green, archivist at the Royal High School of Edinburgh, for confirmation that these references are indeed to that school. The school's Library Register for session 1793/94 shows that Swinton was enrolled in the rector's class for that single session. The famous classicist and teacher Alexander Adam had been rector since 1768 and under his able tuition and example Swinton finished his schooling.

30 Letter to CDW from Oriental and India Office Collections of British Library, 14 December 1993.

31 NLS ACC 10000/389 extracts from Swinton's letters by J Robison.

32 See *Antiquaries' Society Transactions* vol III, 1831 List of Donations Appendix pp 119 and 138, where gifts of Burmese sacred figures and gold and silver coins from Assam are recorded.

33 John Robison to James Skene, undated but watermarked 1828, NLS ACC 10000/291.

34 NLS ACC 10000/17 Council Minute of 25 March 1828.

35 T Allan to D Brewster 21 March 1828, ms copy in NLS ACC 10000/394.

36 NLS ACC 10000/17 Council Minute of 15 January 1829.

37 NLS ACC 10000/17 Council Minute of 2 February 1829.

38 NLS ACC 10000/292 ms 'Additional observations on the Anatomy of the Dugong'

39 Allan, as we have seen, was not enthusiastic about the Swinton material and three months later Council took the unusual step of 'instructing' him 'to proceed immediately in getting the mould made'(NLS ACC 10000/17 Council Minutes of 14 November 1828 and 2 February 1829). This was done and in the following year it was Allan who got Council to agree that a cast should be sent to the Royal Academy of Turin (NLS ACC 10000/17 Council Minutes of 18 January 1830).

40 NLS ACC 10000/17, Council Minutes of 21 December 1829.

41 NLS ACC 10000/389.

42 In 1820 George Swinton had married his cousin Anne Elizabeth Swinton who later inherited the Swinton estates. Their three youngest sons, George Keith, William Bentinck and James Samuel, died on active service in the Indian Army and their eldest, Archibald Adam, served in India with the Bengal Civil Service. There was another son, Allan, and two daughters. After retiring from the Bengal Civil Service in 1833 George Swinton resided at Atholl Crescent, Edinburgh where he died on 17 June 1854 and was buried at the Dean Cemetery. A memorial window in the North Aisle of St John's Episcopal Church, Princes Street, is dedicated to his memory.

43 D Brewster to T Allan 17 March 1828 NLS ACC 10000/394.

44 The papers concerning the proceedings of Brewster v Jameson are at NLS ACC 10000/392.

45 Correspondence between Brewster and Allan on this matter is at NLS ACC 10000/392. See also Council Minutes for 25 March and 7 April 1828 NLS ACC 10000/17.

46 See for example Edinburgh University Library, Special Collections, MS La III 352/2

47 Evidence of Robert Jameson, op cit, note 5, 142.

48 NLS ACC 10000/17 Council Minutes of 2 and 16 February 1829.

49 *The Scots Magazine* 1806, pp 604-8.

50 John Stark should not be confused with his son, Dr James Stark MD FRCSE FRSE, Statistician to the Registrar-General and a pioneer in the application of Vital Statistics (obituary, *Proceedings of the Royal Society of Edinburgh* 18, 1890-91, 3) who was appointed Curator of the Museum of the Royal College of Physicians in 1839 and was still active at the College in 1854 (Craig, 1976, 102-4).

51 NLS ACC 10000/391, J Stark to J Robison, 2 January 1830.

52 NLS ACC 10000/17 Minute of Council meeting of 18 January 1830.

53 NLS ACC 10000/391.

54 William Hare, at his lodging-house in the West Port of Edinburgh, had assisted William Burke in suffocating at least sixteen people over a period of two years and sold the bodies for dissection. They were arrested in November 1828 and Knox was implicated because the last of the bodies was found in his rooms. Lord Cockburn's opinion was that 'our anatomists were spotlessly correct, and Knox the most correct of them all' (Cockburn 1872, 395). Fellows of the Royal Society of Edinburgh had found him guilty, at most, of 'blamable carelessness'.

55 Letter of 21 September 1827 from Susan Elizabeth, Dowager Countess of Morton to Sir Walter Scott, President of the Royal Society of Edinburgh (Rowatt 1924/5, 16).

56 NLS ACC 10000/18, Minutes of Council of 18 January and 25 November 1839.

57 Printed Billet for 22 November 1841.

58 Account of meeting of 5 February 1849 in *Proceedings of the Royal Society of Edinburgh* 2, 219.

59 NLS ACC 10000/18, Council Minute of 22 April 1842.

60 Below the display case were forty-two drawers on each of the east and west sides. The drawers were made of American ash, glass topped, with brass label holders and two knobs at the front of each. They were enclosed within the case by glass doors and flush bolts with good brass locks. The carcase and framing of the case was of American pine and the exterior was finished with four coats of copal varnish. The cost of the table case was £54.

61 NLS ACC 10000/389.

62 NLS ACC 10000/18, Council Minute of 16 December 1842 and NLS ACC 10000/389.

CHAPTER FOUR

THE INCEPTION
OF A
NATIONAL MUSEUM FOR SCOTLAND

We are the music-makers,
And we are the dreamers of dreams...
Yet we are the movers and shakers
Of the world for ever, it seems.

A W E O'Shaughnessy

There can be few places where the influence of men of vision was better exemplified, or a time when it was so clearly acted out, than in the compact cultural milieu of victorian Edinburgh. An example is provided by the inception of Scotland's national museum. It was brought about by a small number of visionaries using appropriate learned and civic bodies as their power base to persuade a reticent government of a case which finally proved irresistible. Because many of these men were Fellows of the Royal Society of Edinburgh, and because of the profound effect the establishment of the national museum had on the Society's view of museums, not least of its own, we must trace the events, and introduce the ideas, which led to the establishment of the Industrial Museum of Scotland in 1854 before returning to conclude the history of the Society's museum in the following chapter.

As we have seen, John Walker and Robert Jameson referred to the Natural History Museum of the University of Edinburgh as 'The Royal Museum' or 'The King's Museum', and for long it had been Jameson's ambition that the College Museum would become Scotland's national museum. As early as 1826, in his evidence to the Royal Commission, his case had been clearly stated:

> I am anxious that new accommodation should be speedily provided for the Royal Museum, which is not to be considered as a private department of the University but as a public department connected in some degree with the country of Scotland; it is the National Museum of this country.[1]

Nothing can detract from Jameson's personal achievement in re-creating the Natural History Museum of the University as one of the finest of its type in Europe. But entry for members of the public was not easy, not only because of the admission charge, but because entry depended, to a large extent, upon Jameson's whim. As the Royal Commission reported:

> the whole arrangement is brought too much under the control of one individual who acts according to his own opinion and discretion. In the present case, his private interests interfere with the management of a great public institution.[2]

Despite Jameson's aspirations, neither his museum, nor any of the many other museums then existing in Scotland, with the exception of the Hunterian Museum, could be regarded as freely available to the public.[3] Most existing museums, like those of the Royal Society of Edinburgh and other learned bodies such as the Royal Colleges of Physicians and of Surgeons, were private collections formed to promote the aims of those institutions.

The story of the creation of Scotland's national museum begins in England and Ireland for it was in these sister countries of the British Isles that relevant precedents were set. The British Museum, Britain's first national museum, was founded in 1753 with the purchase of Sir Hans Sloan's library and art collection with funds from the National Lottery. In 1759 the collections were transferred to Montagu House in Bloomsbury and in 1779 the Royal Society of London gifted its 'Repository' to that museum (Weld, 1848, II, 120), only the scientific instruments being retained (Simpson, 1984). The Society's decision had been prompted by lack of space in the accommodation then being offered by Government in Somerset House, and recognition that their museum, which for over a century had played an important part in the Society's life, was now overshadowed by the rapid growth of the British Museum collections. It was not long, however, before even the ducal palace of Montagu House became overcrowded and in 1845 Sir Robert Smirke's classic building was completed.

In 1835 the Geological Survey of Great Britain had been established, within the Ordnance Survey, to produce geological maps of the country based on Ordnance maps as they became available. As part of that enterprise the Museum of Economic Geology was founded at Craig's Court, London, to house the collections formed by the Survey. In 1844 the British Geological Survey became answerable to the Commissioner of Her Majesty's Woods, Forests, Land Revenues, Works and Buildings. In 1845 the same department of government inaugurated the Irish Geological Survey with its adjunct, the Irish Museum of Economic Geology in Dublin. It became clear, however, that the Irish Museum of Economic Geology would not have the same relationship with the Geological Survey as did its London counterpart. The distinguished Irish chemist Robert Kane (Gilbert 1892), who had been appointed chemist to the Irish Survey and was director of the Museum, was, later in 1845, made answerable to the First Commissioner of Works and Buildings and not to the Director of the Geological Survey.

Kane wished to widen the concerns of his museum from economic geology to encompass all aspects of Ireland's economic life. His book *The Industrial Resources of Ireland*, had been published in 1844, and a second edition was published in the following year. His view prevailed with the First Commissioner and the Museum was restyled The Museum of Irish Industry. It was with this independent and reconstituted Museum that the Irish Geological Survey shared 51 St Stephens Green from 1847 (Davies 1995).[4]

The significance of the precedents set by these national museums, and particularly by the Museum of Irish Industry in Dublin, was quickly understood in Scotland. In April 1847 a paper was submitted to, and approved by, the Faculty of the University of Glasgow proposing that a memorial be sent to the Treasury 'with regard to the establishment of a museum of Economic Geology in Glasgow proposed to be transmitted on behalf of the Lord Provost and Magistrates, the Principal and Professors of the University and public bodies of the City'.[5]

Only a month after Thomas Oldham and his colleagues of the Irish Geological Survey had completed their transfer to 'The Green' in Dublin, a letter appeared in the Edinburgh press from *Arachnophilus* advocating the establishment of a national museum in Scotland. The writer was an Edinburgh man, Adam White[6], who had been an officer in the Natural History Department of the British Museum since 1835 (fig 20).[7] This was the first shot in a fusillade of letters which White wrote on the subject in a campaign which he conducted over a number of years. It was addressed 'To the Right Hon Adam Black and the Town Council of Edinburgh, the Provost and Town Council of Leith, and the three Burgesses representing these two towns in Parliament'. After citing the existing museums in Edinburgh he wrote:

> These do not, however, form a National Museum, which, to succeed, must be open to every passer by, without 'let or hindrance', excepting disorderly behaviour.
>
> The want of such a museum is felt by numbers of your fellow citizens; and seeing that an Act of Parliament, carried these many months, enables municipal bodies, far inferior to yours, to found and support such museums, is Edinburgh to be behind other towns... in this respect?...
>
> Never, never, if her children unanimously call out for it. My views are those of hundreds of your townsmen, of thousands of your countrymen, of every Scot, man, woman, and child, who has ever seen a museum like the British Museum, one of the chief attractions, if not the greatest ornament, of London.
>
> A National Museum must not be confined to Natural History; let it be co-extensive with art and science, – let it be a nucleus to which the spirited sons of Scotia may give and bequeath pictures, statues, specimens, books, and MSS, – let it be a place to which your hard working sailors, soldiers, merchants, and medical men in active foreign service, may delight to send specimens of Natural History, or curiosities connected with rude and less civilized nations, – let it contain a large collection of casts from the antique artists and architects to copy and study, – let it contain models of the geological structure of your country, which, in itself...is almost "an epitome of the world" – let us have specimens like those in the Museum of Economic Geology in London, to illustrate the mineral structure of the country, – let us have a place where students might delight to study, and afterwards instruct the world in those most useful remunerating sciences, mineralogy and geology, – let us have our young Scotchmen a Museum of Zoology, open as the British, where, with book in hand, they may learn for themselves, – let us have a place for manuscripts, for paintings, for antiquities, and they will come sooner than is imagined.[8]

White here introduced ideas of egalitarian education which were to become central in the debate leading to the establishment of Scotland's national museum. It was not in genteel Edinburgh, a city of professionals and academics, that these ideas had been promoted but in the burgeoning industrial city of Glasgow.

John Anderson, who occupied the chair of natural philosophy at Glasgow University between 1757 and 1796, gave *anti-toga* lectures to foremen, craftsmen and mechanics who could read and write. These were well supported – there were 200 students in 1791 – and from them can be traced the origins of the mechanics' institutes, one of the great educational movements in British history (Kelly 1957). By Anderson's will the Andersonian University in Glasgow was established and George Birkbeck appointed a professor. Birkbeck later moved to London where he founded the London Mechanics' Institution. The movement grew rapidly and by 1841 there were some 50,000 members in more than 200 institutions throughout Britain.

Not only was the idea of the mechanics' institutes pioneered in Glasgow, that city did much to prove to Scotland the efficacy of the free exhibition. There, in March 1846, a joint committee was formed to stage 'an exhibition of Models, Manufactures, Works of Art, etc.' in the city. The exhibition had been proposed by Bailie Andrew Liddell to the Philosophical Society of Glasgow, of which he was treasurer, and supported by the Corporation of Glasgow. The joint committee, convened by Bailie Liddell, was assisted in collecting items by representatives of the University of Glasgow, Anderson's University, the Mechanics Institution, and the sheriffs of the county. The exhibition took place during the Christmas and New Year holiday 1846-7 and was a remarkable success. During periods of free admission people entered at the rate of 2000 per hour. The experimental nature of the exhibition was freely admitted:

> It is well known to many, that the primary object of the original projectors of this Exhibition, and of the Philosophical Society and the Town Council in promoting it, was to amuse and instruct the working classes during the New Year holidays; and by giving gratuitous admission, insuring a numerous attendance, to determine the disputed point as to whether they would conduct themselves with propriety when admitted indiscriminately, and in large numbers, to such a place, where valuable articles must necessarily be laid out openly, and comparatively unprotected. The result has shown that they can conduct themselves with propriety in such circumstances; and that they are worthy of the trust we put in them, for not one article, during the entire period of the Exhibition, was displaced or injured by the visitors...
>
> The Exhibition we are now describing, may thus have laid the foundation of a museum which may become gigantic in extent, and more useful to the great bulk of the community, than even the Philosophical Society itself, which being purely scientific in its aim, must necessarily communicate instruction or amusement direct to a comparatively small number. (Liddell 1848)[9].

When, as *Arachnophilus*, Adam White wrote his letter to the Edinburgh press, he was clearly aware of the success of the Glasgow Exhibition in the previous winter, and hoped that the City of Edinburgh would finance Scotland's national museum through the rates.[10] In 1845 three Radical Members of Parliament, William Ewart (Liverpool), Thomas Wyse (Waterford City) and Joseph Brotherton (Salford), had introduced a Bill to enable municipal boroughs of over ten thousand to erect and maintain buildings for museums of art and science for which the rate level was not to exceed one halfpenny in the pound. Admission charges for such municipal museums were not to exceed one penny per person. The Bill was opposed by the government because Peel and his ministers had other budgetary priorities, but it passed in both houses and received the Royal Assent on 21 July 1845.[11] It was 'the first Act by which Parliament gave local authorities the power to provide cultural facilities' (Minihan 1977, 92).

As Minihan has noted, members of parliament who spoke in the debate expected much of these new municipal museums. Through the edification of children and working people by education in public museums, they expected other social results such as the reduction of crime and the improvement of conduct.

A further communication to the Lord Provost from Adam White was considered by the Town Council of Edinburgh at its meeting of 16 January 1849.[12] This letter made two important additional points 'By a National Museum, is meant a museum in a capital city open to the public gratuitously' and 'This museum must be commenced altogether apart from, and independent of private, collegiate, or society museums' (White 1850, 9-10). Councillors 'bore testimony to the very beneficial results of such museums being opened gratuitously to the public' but 'thought it impossible, considering how they were taxed in Edinburgh'. The City Treasurer remarked 'that if the Council could be provided with the funds, it would be a most admirable manner of disposing of them'.[13] As patrons of the University, the Council was aware that it was unable to find resources for the required expansion of the College Museum and, even with the possibility of a charge on the rates, it was a forlorn hope that it could finance a national museum for Scotland.

A powerful voice was raised for the establishment of a national museum when Professor John Fleming gave his presidential address to the Royal Physical Society in Edinburgh on 14th November 1849.[14] The address was widely publicised through *The Witness* in which Hugh Miller, its influential editor, not only gave a full report of Fleming's address but drew attention to it in his leading article under the heading 'National Museums'.[15] Fleming reviewed the state of science museums in Edinburgh – the University's Museums of Natural History and Comparative Anatomy, the Museums of the Royal College of Surgeons, the Highland Society, The Royal Society and New College – and concluded that:

> Edinburgh is pre-eminently deficient in a general collection. The materials for the formation of such a [national] museum are numerous and valuable. They are scattered through the apartments of our different public bodies, in some cases inaccessible, too frequently ill arranged, and in general imperfectly labelled...

We may contemplate the formation of a collection of specimens illustrative of the treasures of Scotland in botany, zoology, mineralogy, geology and palaeontology, as an attainable object.

In referring to Fleming's review, Hugh Miller wrote of Edinburgh's museums:

They serve to show, that with respect to these storehouses of science which render knowledge tangible, and speak so powerfully to the mind through the eye, the capital of Scotland lags behind the capitals of all the other civilized countries of the world.

Miller cited such large English towns as Newcastle, York, Manchester, and Birmingham, and small ones such as Dudley, as having museums; and public collections in provincial Scottish towns like Montrose and Elgin as more than equal to those of Edinburgh. Institutions of popular education such as the philosophical and mechanical institutions, schools of arts, lectureships and book clubs 'render imperative the establishment of public museums on a scale worthy of an enlightened country and age'.

The institutions to which we refer, – so characteristic of the present day, – are telling largely on the public taste; and a Museum worthy of Scotland has become essential, in consequence, to public progress.

Fleming envisaged a new museum to be built by public subscription, perhaps on the west side of the Mound or, which failing, to appropriate the Royal Palace of Holyrood House 'to a better purpose'! Among other fanciful suggestions for the museum's location were Heriot's or Donaldson's hospitals, and the castle 'where a massive building, in a style of architecture (Saxon or Norman) in harmony with the site would be an improvement'. More telling points were made by a correspondent 'x' who considered that Scottish institutions were entitled to a share of government funds in view of the liberality with which these had been spent on museums in England and Ireland.[16] 'A Naturalist' suggested that the geological collection of the Highland Society would be an acceptable donation to a new national museum. It was his view that:

The rapid increase in the number of museums in the provincial towns of England. – the local assessments for their support – and the positive use made of them by the working classes, must be reckoned among the best signs of this age.

The establishment of a museum for the zoological and geological productions of Scotland will give the greatest satisfaction to scientific men in every country, who are astonished at the list of our species, and return home grieved to find such a miserable exhibition in our public cabinets.[17]

The influence of the Prince Consort and the success of the Great Exhibition of 1851, in which the products of many Scottish enterprises were shown, prompted a renewed and widespread interest in the industrial arts.

In the last of six articles describing the exhibition *The Scotsman* challenged the complacency of its Edinburgh professional readers thus:

[The Exhibition] impresses the spectator with a sense of the dignity of labour. In this most commercial of countries, and especially in Scotland, and especially in this city of Edinburgh, there is a tendency to regard any labour but that given to 'the professions' as mean or sordid, unelevating and unintellectual. Look round here on the products of the loom, the lathe, the anvil, the chisel, the crucible, and think if intellect cannot be employed as worthily and usefully here, as even in groping and guessing and pretending amidst the mysteries of medicine, or making the worse appear the better reasons through the intricacies and chicaneries of the law...[18]

The Exhibition also inspired letter writers to the Scottish press. 'An Auld Toun Callant' wrote 'The variety of articles from Earth's remotest bounds exhibited here, is peculiarly adapted to delight and instruct youth'.[19] 'A W' (Adam White) wrote that, on revisiting Edinburgh, he admired its many new public buildings:

But where is your Museum?...Any American, Frenchman, German or Englishman, must miss such a building. Have any of the numerous Scottish people who have visited London this year, not been struck with the vast educational and moralising influences of an open Museum like the British Museum? If they are convinced of these influences, let each one advocate the foundation of a similar institution in the Capital of Scotland...[20]

Such press comment and correspondence have led some to conclude that the popular interest in the industrial arts which the Great Exhibition engendered in 1851, led to the foundation of the national Industrial Museum of Scotland in 1854 (Allan 1954, 5). While it must have influenced opinion, not least with government, we have seen that other factors were at work which long pre-dated the Great Exhibition which finally brought matters to a head. It was precedents set in the 'useful and most remunerating' science of geology which provided the leverage which eventually prized a national museum from government. Geological surveying had proceeded in England, Wales and Ireland but, by 1851, there had been no activity by the Geological Survey in Scotland and no national museum existed north of the border.

On 17 September 1851 a leader appeared in *The Scotsman* commenting on the recently published parliamentary report on expenditure incurred to the 1st day of January 1851 for the Museum of Practical Geology in London and the Museum of Irish Industry in Dublin. The writer notes the generosity of the outlays made for these institutions and welcomes the establishment of the School of Mines which had recently been conjoined to the London museum.

In our own country such a school is especially wanted; and, as the first step to it, a national collection of the mineral produce and industry of our country. Till this is granted us, we must again ask, as has already been more than once done, why London and Dublin should have their Museums of Mineral Wealth and Industry, richly furnished with specimens of the rocks, minerals and fossils, of the respective kingdoms, and of the useful and ornamental works prepared from the native productions of their soil – museums, too, open without fee or reward to all their inhabitants – whilst in Edinburgh and Scotland there are no such public institutions, and our people are deprived of the valuable knowledge they might there acquire!

The writer further comments on the work of the Geological Survey in the sister kingdoms and the lack of it in Scotland.

Two months later the Highland and Agricultural Society, took the initiative to promote both the Geological Survey and a national museum in Scotland. Why was this?

Between 1822 and 1847, twenty six geological maps of Scottish districts had been published by three learned societies in Scotland, the Royal Society of Edinburgh, the Wernerian Society and the Highland and Agricultural Society. Others had been published by the Geological Society of London and by commercial publishers. Of these, no less than nineteen had been published through the patronage of the Highland and Agricultural Society's Coal-District Surveys and Prize Essays (Boud 1988, 1989, 1993). It was a condition of these surveys that specimens, illustrative of the geology of the mapped district, be lodged with the Society and a significant collection of Scottish rocks and fossils had been built up over the years. This, together with models of agricultural implements and machines and other material, was exhibited in the Museum of the Highland and Agricultural Society which was displayed on the first and second floors of the Society's building on the corner of George IV Bridge and Victoria Street, Edinburgh, which was opened in 1841 (Anon 1841). The museum was popular and between 1st May 1849 and 1st May 1851 it was visited by 31,474 persons.[21]

With its record of concern for the geological mapping of Scotland it is not surprising that it should have been the Highland Society which took the initiative in approaching other learned and public bodies to memorialise the government for the commencement of geological surveying in Scotland and the creation of a national Museum of Economic Geology in Edinburgh on similar lines to those already established in London and Dublin. A meeting was held at the Highland Society's Chambers on 25th November 1851 attended by The Hon Francis Charteris MP (later Lord Elcho and then Earl of Wemyss), Dr Anderson (? Thomas Anderson FRSE), Professor Robert Christison FRSE, Professor J D Forbes (General Secretary, Royal Society of Edinburgh who took the chair), Dr John Fleming FRSE, Captain James RE (later Sir Henry James, first local director of the Irish Geological Survey (1845-6) and then superintendent of the Edinburgh Office of the Ordnance Survey who had been called to give information about the Museum in Dublin), Dr Douglas Maclagan FRSE, Mr Murray of Henderland, Mr Charles Maclaren FRSE (until 1845 editor of *The Scotsman* and possibly behind the article of 17 September), Mr Hall Maxwell[22] (Secretary of the Highland Society, fig 20) and Mr William Wilson. Letters of support were received from Sir William Johnstone, Professor J Hutton Balfour FRSE, Mr

Grainger (? Thomas Grainger FRSE), Mr Robert Chambers FRSE. John Fleming advocated Adam White's view that the museum should be independent of collegiate interests. On the other hand, and in the light of subsequent events it is of interest, Professor Christison said that the University hoped to apply to Government for the erection of a new building to extend the Natural History Museum, with the view of rendering it a national one for Scotland, open to the public. He suggested that the object of the meeting would be better attained by connecting the proposed Geological Museum with a Natural Museum, as it was unlikely that Government would provide accommodating for two geological collections in Edinburgh. The meeting considered the Dublin precedent of first importance – as had the Glasgow faculty four years earlier – and, on a proposal by Francis Charteris MP, seconded by Murray of Henderland, the following resolution was unanimously adopted:

> The Meeting are of opinion that immediate steps should be taken to obtain from the different public and scientific Bodies Memorials, addressed to the Lords of the Treasury, setting forth the importance of Establishing a Geological Museum in Scotland, and praying for a Grant of Money for the purpose of providing accommodation in Edinburgh for the valuable materials already existing for such an Institution; and further, soliciting, on behalf of it, such portions of the English and Irish Geological Collections as have been made in triplicate. The meeting are further of opinion that the extension of the Geological Survey to Scotland is of the greatest importance, and should be pressed on the attention of Government.[23]

The terms of the Highland Society's memorial were agreed by the Directors on 12 December 1851 and reported to the General Meeting held on 13 January 1852 and given in full in *The Scotsman* of the following day.

> ... there does not exist in Scotland any Museum of Economic Geology and Chemistry, and that the establishment of such an institution would be of great public benefit, by affording the means of obtaining definite and correct information with regard to the mineral wealth of Scotland; its ores and coals; its building, paving and ornamental stones, granites and marbles; and localities and composition of its soils; the qualities of its different clays for brick, tile, or ware; and of its limestones for building purposes and manures; and generally, – by developing the industrial resources of its territorial products.
> ... That the importance, in a national point of view, of an industrial Geological and Chemical Institution has been recognised by Government in founding the Museums of Practical Geology in London, and of Irish Industry in Dublin
> ... [We] would more particularly refer to Ireland, and, without questioning the propriety of the numerous grants of money in aid of the establishment of that country, they would venture to compare with them the limited allowances appropriated for similar purposes in Scotland. Your memorialists are aware that the circumstances of the two countries differ, and that much may be necessary for the one, which the other cannot look for; but this, in their humble opinion, gives to Scotland the stronger claim, for any institution equally applicable to

either country, which has been granted to Ireland but not to Scotland. That your memorialists are of opinion that an establishment such as that of the Museum of Irish Industry in Dublin would admirably answer the purposes required.

...that while the geological survey has been actively prosecuted in England and in Ireland, no part of the annual grant for the purpose has yet been expended in Scotland. Circumstances may hitherto have prevented the commencement of the survey there, but these, it is understood, are now removed; ...[they] hope that the geological survey of Scotland will forthwith be commenced, as an indispensable accompaniment to such an institution as is now sought for, and as a measure of justice to this part of the empire...[24]

One of the circumstances which had prevented the commencement of the geological survey was the tardiness of the Ordnance Survey in producing suitable base maps. For many years the Highland Society and other public and scientific bodies in Scotland had urged progress (Boud 1986). The Ordnance Survey had now published the map of Wigtownshire on the six inch to one mile scale and surveys to the same scale were in progress in Kirkcudbright, Midlothian and East Lothian which gave them grounds for optimism that the geological survey could follow.

What is not mentioned in the Highland Society's memorial, however, is anything of the fire which, on 20 November 1851, had damaged their own museum and partially destroyed its contents.[25] The Society's coal district premiums had been suspended in 1843 and the last coal district map (Charles Forsyth's West Lothian) published in 1846. The county geological premiums were also suspended in 1843, the last county map (James Nicol's Roxburghshire) being published in 1847. When re-arrangement of the museum was first being considered, following the fire of 1851, the Society no longer felt able to afford to maintain its geological collection and decided to dispose of it. If a national Museum of Economic Geology could be established would it not provide a home for the unwanted geological specimens?

Although their emphases differed, the memorials sent by other learned bodies such as the Royal Society of Edinburgh, the Royal Scottish Society of Arts, and the Royal Colleges of Physicians and Surgeons, followed fairly closely the Highland Society's lead.

The Royal Society of Edinburgh appointed a committee in November 1851 to draw up a memorial seeking first the speedy prosecution of the Geological Survey of Scotland and then establishment of a Museum of Economic Geology in Edinburgh.[26] The memorial was approved at an ordinary meeting of the Society held on 5 January 1852 and, after signature by Sir Thomas Makdougall Brisbane as president, was dispatched to the Treasury in February 1852.[27] The Royal Scottish Society of Arts sought first the establishment of a Museum of Economic Geology for Scotland.[28]

These developments were of acute concern to one old man, Professor Jameson, Regius Keeper of the Natural History Museum, who was required to report on the state of his museum to the Senatus Academicus by the end of January. In the course of the month he wrote at least three urgent letters in preparation. Firstly he asked for a copy of the Highland Society's memorial and received it 'within a few hours'. Secondly, he made the same urgent request to the Royal Society of Edinburgh but was annoyed that that Society 'requires weeks to give an answer to a simple request'.[29] Thirdly, he wrote to the Lord Provost of the City of Edinburgh.

The Senatus met on 31 January but illness had confined Jameson to his bedroom and his written report was read for him. In it he reminded Senate that on a number of previous occasions he had warned that want of accommodation had slowed the rate of museum acquisition but,

> The time, however has now arrived for the Senatus of the University addressing the Lords of the Treasury on Museum extention, as some influential parties in Edinburgh are attempting to preoccupy the ground, by obtaining from the Treasury pecuniary means for establishing in Edinburgh a New School of Geology and Practical Chemistry – with Buildings for these purposes – and a staff of Professors etc.
>
> This project I consider hostile to the University because there are already in our Establishment, Professors of Geology, and Practical Chemistry, provided with most extensive Museums of Practical and Theoretical Geology and of Practical Chemistry. I may further add that this project is prejudicial, as it interferes with our more legitimate claims for pecuniary aid for the extension of the Museum Buildings.[30]

The Senatus wisely remitted the matter to a committee under the convenership of Professor T S Traill, then the Royal Society of Edinburgh's Honorary Curator, with Professor Robert Christison and Rev. Professor Philip Kelland to consult with Jameson and report. This they did on 28 February when, with Professor John Hutton Balfour added to their number, they were asked to prepare the Memorial in terms of their report.[31]

The Memorial to the Treasury, which was approved by Senate on 13 March 1852, was the masterpiece of diplomacy which one would expect from such authors. Gone was the sense of threat expressed by Jameson and in its place was a realistic assessment of the University's inability to provide the museum extension for natural history which all recognised was necessary. The importance of the collection was such that 'Next to the British Museum, that of the University of Edinburgh is by far the most extensive and complete in the United Kingdom'. Extension was required so that the University might continue as a noted school for instruction in natural history and to fulfil 'the just expectations of the public in regard to a collection which has hitherto been the only substitute for a National one in Scotland'. The Memorial continues

> The Senatus Academicus are the more encouraged to lay their considerations before their Lordships, that a movement has been lately made in various quarters for promoting the interests of Natural History in Scotland, and with which the measures contemplated by the Senatus completely coincide.
>
> A great desire has been expressed in many parts for Establishing in Edinburgh a National Museum of Natural History for Scotland, which shall be freely open

to the public of all denominations. It is clear, however, that Edinburgh cannot support two great collections of this kind, nor could it be reasonably expected that Government should supply the means for both. But there can be no difficulty, as the Senatus think, in uniting the two into one – in other words, in converting the University Museum into a National one for Scotland ...

The Senatus Academicus, however, will cheerfully meet the desire at present so strongly felt, and pressed in other quarters, for the multiplication of the means of rational recreation, and instruction for all ranks of Society in this country, and particularly the working classes of the community, by now proposing to contribute all the available resourcers at their command for converting the University Museum of Natural History into a National and open one.

... nothing more is wanted than a more extensive building. The materials already brought together for a great National Museum, are ample in every branch of Natural History. They are sufficient, if properly exhibited, to occupy a building at least four times as extensive as the present one...

The Senatus Academicus, therefore, trust it will be thought, that as a large and valuable part of this collection is the property of the Senatus, and as the University has hitherto enjoyed the undivided use of the whole, they make no inconsiderable offer to the public, when they consent to the Natural History Museum being laid open as a National one...

The Senatus Academicus trust they may be allowed to annex, as the only conditions they would attach to the change – That the new building shall constitute an addition to, and part of the present University Buildings, but with an independent entrance for the public... by extending the University Buildings to the West. – That the principal keeper shall be, as now, both Regius Keeper, and Regius Professor in the University – And that the Lectures, and other systems of instruction connected with the National Museum shall continue to form part of the system of Tuition in the University...[32]

Jameson's letter to the Lord Provost was of similar vein to his report to Senate and was referred to the Lord Provost's Committee on 13 January 1852. (Much of Jameson's correspondence on the establishment of a national museum for Scotland was copied into the Daily Report Book of the Natural History Museum vol xii, October 1851-April 1852, NMS archive.) A letter from the Secretary of the Highland Society 'regarding the proposed establishment of a Geological Museum for Scotland in this City' had already been referred to that Committee on 2 December 1851. A draft memorial on the subject to the Lords of the Treasury, prepared by the Committee, was approved by the Magistrates and Council and signed by Lord Provost M'Laren on 16 March. It was directed that this should be printed and transmitted to the Members of Parliament for Scotland and others, requesting their support.[33]

As patrons of the University the Magistrates and Council gave the proposal for a Museum of Practical Geology their cordial support. The City's memorial follows closely that of the Senate being 'of opinion that the establishment of a Geological Museum could be most effectually promoted, and with the greatest benefit to the Public and the smallest expense to the Treasury, by connecting it with the Museum of Natural History already existing in the University'. It pays particular attention to the site:

> As regards the Site, the ground immediately to the west of the present Museum is admirably adapted for the proposed extension. Part of the ground belongs to the University, [it was acquired in 1820] and the Memorialists will be happy to have it appropriated to this object without any expense to the Public being incurred; part of it is occupied by a Dissenting Chapel, and part of it by the Trades' Maiden Hospital ... an area of about three-quarters of an acre. The Memorialists have reason to believe, that the two properties referred to could be purchased for about £7000 in all, a price greatly under what a Site of equal extent could be purchased for in any other suitable locality within the City.[34]

To judge from a later report by Murray of Henderland, seconder of the original proposal for a Museum of Economic Geology for Scotland made in November 1851, the wider scheme proposed by the City and University at first caused difficulty with the Highland Society

> The Society, as the body with whom the movement had originated immediately represented that this would not satisfy the object in view, and that it had asked not for all that may be curious in the Natural History of the world, but for an economic and industrial institution, exclusively devoted, through the appliances of geology and chemistry, to developing the agriculture and mineral wealth of Scotland. The Society farther impressed upon Government the inexpediency of making such an institution subordinate to any particular class, and the advantage of placing it under the direct supervision of an officer responsible to Government, as is the case in London and Dublin.[35]

The Lord Provost accepted the importance of this view but insisted on the need for additional accommodation for the College collection. The Highland Society accordingly united with the Town Council in urging Government to acquire a site sufficiently extensive for both purposes. On the 27 March 1852 a number of deputations from Scottish public and scientific bodies, along with four Members of Parliament – Sir George Clerk, the Hon. Francis Charteris, Sir William Gibson-Craig and Charles Cowan saw the Chancellor of the Exchequer, Benjamin Disraeli. '... all the Deputations left the room with the conviction that Mr D'Israeli was very favourably disposed to the proposal' but nothing more was heard of it. Hall Maxwell took the opportunity to impress three MPs with the importance which the Highland Society attached to 'the Industrial and Practical Character which such an Institution would possess'.[36]

In February 1853, the Lord Provost of Edinburgh and the Secretary of the Highland Society both wrote to Disraeli's successor enclosing their original memorials and pressing for a vote in parliament for money to purchase a site for the new Museum. The Lord Provost suggested that a grant of £10,000 should be made during the present session of Parliament to defray the cost of the site and begin the work. He continued:

> The Highland Society and other Public Bodies who greatly feel the want of that portion of the Museum which it is proposed to devote to objects of a Practical and

Industrial Character, under special supervision, as in the two Institutions in London and Dublin already referred to, are also most anxious for a Speedy commencement of the Work, in order that Scotland may soon enjoy the advantages which have already been conferred on the Sister Kingdoms, by the Establishment of these Museums; and in this desire the Magistrates and Council fully participate.[37]

The Highland Society's letter concluded:

The Directors of this Society, while urging the paramount importance of the industrial and practical objects contemplated in the Society's memorial, are of opinion that the site suggested by the Town Council is admirably suited for the purpose, and that it is most desirable the proposed institution should be so extended as to open to the public the advantages of the valuable collections illustrative of natural history in its different branches, which are now in a great measure lost from want of accommodation.[38]

When inviting the Secretary to read the letter to the General Meeting of the Highland Society in July 1853, however, Mr Pringle of Whytbank noted that the matter was now in the hands of the Board of Trade and he moved that the Directors be authorized to renew their application in that quarter.

The new government department concerned was the Department of Science and Art, a very small, but select, administrative unit in which the senior administrators appear to have had considerable influence on policy. It is hard for individuals to exert personal influence in larger administrative departments but, in such a small establishment, personal enthusiasms may colour the advice given to ministers. Because negotiation for a national museum in Scotland henceforth would have to be conducted through the Department of Science and Art, we must look more closely at that Department and its personnel.

The Great Exhibition had encouraged the fine arts and practical sciences and, in 1852, Government decided to give expression to the country's awakened appreciation of their value by creating a new administrative Department of Science and Art. This had come into being in 1853 as a department of the Board of Trade but was later transferred to the Education Department of the Privy Council. Subsumed within the new department was the Department of Practical Art of which Henry Cole (Anon 1887) had been appointed secretary in January 1852. Cole, whose lifelong interest had been in the arts, came to the Department of Science and Art as 'Secretary for Art'. Initially he worked in tandem with Lyon Playfair who had been appointed 'Secretary for Science' (fig 20). Cole and Playfair had worked together for the Great Exhibition and, without the unique contribution of each, there is little doubt that the Exhibition would not have taken place.

Lyon Playfair had attended school and university at St Andrews. In 1835 he went to Glasgow to study chemistry with Thomas Graham at the Andersonian Institution and when, two years later, Graham became Professor of Chemistry at University College, London, Playfair moved with him as one of his assistants. He returned to Scotland to study medicine at Edinburgh but a breakdown in health forced him to give up the course. He spent 1839-40

94

fig 20 Furthering a National Museum in Scotland

Adam White (1817-79), a member of staff of the Natural History Department of the British Museum, who urged the establishment of a national museum for Scotland in Edinburgh. Trustees of the British Museum

Dr Lyon Playfair, Lord Playfair of St Andrews (1818-98, FRS 1848, FRSE 1859) of the Department of Science and Art. Detail of original in oils by H W Pickersgill. Portrait Collection of the University of Edinburgh

John Hall Maxwell Esq of Dargavel (1812-66) from 1846 secretary to the Highland and Agricultural Society. Detail from lithograph by Hahnisch after Hahnisch. The British Museum 136620

George Wilson (1818-59, elected 1845) first Director of the Industrial Museum of Scotland and Professor of Technology, University of Edinburgh.

95

with Liebig in Giessen and, in 1843, became Professor of Chemistry at the Royal Institution, Manchester. In 1845 he was appointed chemist with the Geological Survey, afterwards becoming professor at the newly established School of Mines, Jermyn Street. It is significant that this Scot, with experience of both the Scottish and English education systems, an admirer of the new practical teaching methods which he had seen in Germany, who had experience in manufacturing industry, and who was known for his support of the Prince Consort's enthusiasm for the promotion of the arts and applied sciences should, on the creation of the new Office of Science and Art, be appointed its first secretary for science.

During the summer of 1853 representatives of the City and the Highland Society met the President of the Board of Trade, Mr Cardwell (Smith, 1887), to urge the establishment of the Museum of Practical Geology and Chemistry on the site beside the College. Hall Maxwell reported to his Directors:

> that he had endeavoured to impress Mr Cardwell [of] the importance of making the practical part of the Institution distinct from the college, and at all events to provide accommodation for it should the Magistrate's scheme appear to be too expensive.[39]

In January 1854 Murray of Henderland reported that it was still not known what course Government was likely to take. Mr Cardwell had stated, however, that if Government should ultimately grant this Museum, neither the College nor the Town Council, its patrons, should have any control over it.[40]

A new initiative was now taken by the Highland Society's indefatigable secretary Hall Maxwell which he reported to his Directors on 10 February 1854. Following a meeting with Lord Elcho (formerly Francis Charteris) a week previously, at which the idea may have been hatched, he had written to Elcho on 10 November 1853 and he now reported that his letter had since been passed to the President of the Board of Trade. Since the Magistrates and Senatus had raised the issue of the University's Museum and Chair of Natural History in relation to the proposed national museum, would it not be appropriate for government to consider, in the same context, the future of the extensive existing agricultural collections in relation to the chair of Agriculture?

> As an Institution meant to develop and promote the industrial resources of the Soil, it will, in its Geological and Chemical features, have much affinity with the objects of the Agricultural chair in the University, and, on that account, it would be desirable to provide within the new Building suitable accommodation for this class, and for the Museum of Models and Paintings connected with it. We have but one chair of Agriculture in Scotland, and I need not say how much its Value will be increased, could the Students acquire, within the same Establishment, a knowledge of Geology and applied chemistry – Sciences now so intimately connected with Agriculture.
>
> The advantages of such an addition to the proposed Museum would be felt, besides, in a much wider sphere than that of the mere Student. I have frequently

had occasion to observe the readiness with which Farm Servants, Country Mechanics, and others, avail themselves of Models for making themselves acquainted with Improvements in Implements. Many who cannot comprehend Drawing nor follow the Details of Scientific Specification, are capable of at once appreciating the purposes and peculiarities of a Machine in Model; and I am convinced that a well selected Assortment of Models illustrative of the most approved Implements, and the most recent Inventions and Improvements, would be of great Service as a means of practically conveying instruction to the agricultural operative – whether his Vocation be in the field or the Workshop.

Beyond the cost of the requisite accommodation, the expense of the new Institution would not be much increased. The Chair of Agriculture is already endowed, and connected with it, there is a vast collection of Agricultural Models, and of Paintings illustrative of the different Breeds of Animals. The Highland and Agricultural Society has also a Collection of similar character, which, I doubt not, would be transferred to Government, and, out of the two, a valuable and instructive Museum might be formed...[41]

Later in February Lord Provost M'Laren again visited London to press on Ministers the need to include a sum in the estimates, soon to be brought before parliament, for the purchase of the Trades' Maiden Hospital and the Independent Chapel, for the demolition of the latter and for the new building to be rapidly proceeded with. A grant of £15,000 was sought in the coming session and £10,000 in the next. On 1 March he wrote to Hall Maxwell with his opinion that the Prime Minister and the Chancellor of the Exchequer appeared favourably disposed to making a grant but that the President of the Board of Trade was less favourable. He urged the Highland Society to send a deputation to London at once 'as it might decide the question in our favour'.[42]

It was so decided and Hall Maxwell went to London on the evening of the 8 March to make the necessary arrangements for the deputation to meet Edward Cardwell, President of the Board of Trade.

With a view of neutralizing the efforts that have been made to induce Government to prefer Glasgow as the proper place for the proposed Museum, [Hall Maxwell] thought it desirable to secure the attendance of some of the leading Peers and Members of Parliament connected with the Western Counties. The following Noblemen and Gentlemen were accordingly requested to join the Deputation – The Dukes of Hamilton, Montrose, and Buccleuch; The Earls of Dalkeith and Eglinton; Mr Lockhart MP for Lanarkshire; Sir A Campbell MP for Argyllshire; Colonel Blair MP for Ayrshire; Mr Hume MP for Montrose Burghs; Mr Cowan MP for Edinburgh, and Sir George Clerk.

On the 14th, the Deputation with the exception of Messrs Lockhart and Hume who were prevented from attending; waited on Mr Cardwell; and the Duke of Hamilton generally explained the nature of the object in view. Mr Cardwell stated that strong representations had been made to him as to the propriety of establishing the Museum in Glasgow instead of Edinburgh and requested the opinion of the Deputation on that point.[43] The Duke of Hamilton, the Duke of Montrose, and the Earl of Eglinton as Lords Lieutenant of the Counties connected with Glasgow, expressed themselves to the effect that the Institution was one of a National Character and should therefore be established in the Metropolis...[44]

The delegation went on to offer the Society's collection of agricultural models to government, in addition to its rock collections, on condition that the new museum should be built in Edinburgh. Until Hall Maxwell had suggested otherwise, the Highland Society had intended to use some of the insurance compensation, which it had received in respect of fire damage to its museum, to update and repair its collection of agricultural models. The models had been made from premium-winning drawings, were all innovative and many were patented. Could a parallel have been drawn in the minds of officials with developments in London? They must have been aware that, in the previous year, the Prince Consort had suggested that a museum should be formed in connection with the Patent Office. The Patent Office Museum was indeed established in the following year (1855) under the Commissioners for Patents at Southampton Buildings, London, but soon became the responsibility of the new Department of Science and Art. The collection was formed by Bennet Woodcroft, first Superintendent of Specifications at the Patent Office, and was moved to Kensington Palace in 1856 and then to the 'Brompton Boilers' in 1857. It retained its identity until it was absorbed into the South Kensington Museum in 1883 to take its place with the other scientific collections (Anderson 1995, 214-6).

When Professor J Hutton Balfour, as Curator, addressed the General Meeting of the Highland Society in July 1854, he had the satisfaction of reporting the success of the delegation:

> Up to this period Government was uncommitted, and some difficulty was felt as to whether the institution should be fixed in Edinburgh or Glasgow. The result of the Society's deputation was conclusive and satisfactory; and it was immediately followed by the mission of Dr Lyon Playfair to Edinburgh for the purpose of making the necessary preliminary arrangements.[45]

Following the Highland Society deputation's meeting with the President of the Board of Trade, Lyon Playfair, who as 'Secretary for Science' already had departmental responsibility for the Museum of Economic Geology in London and the Museum of Irish Industry in Dublin, hurried to Edinburgh in person to negotiate with the parties for the establishment of a national museum in the Scottish capital. While in Edinburgh he wrote to the Lord Provost on 1 April setting out his draft recommendations to the Board of Trade for the establishment of the new museum and sought the approval of the City and the Senatus for what was proposed before minuting the Board of Trade. The Museum would encompass the economic and industrial interests as advocated by the Highland Society and the natural history interests advocated by the University and City. Both sections of the museum would have Keepers, appointed by and responsible to the Board of Trade. However, vital connection with the University would be maintained by the Professor of Natural History being the Keeper of the Natural

History collections and the Keeper of the Industrial collections being the occupant of a new Chair of Technology to be created within the University.

Playfair's proposals as they affected the natural history museum, which were considered by the Senatus on 4 April 1854, may be summarised thus

1. The Independent Chapel and Trades' Maidens Hospital and gardens should be purchased for £7000.

2. 'Should Parliament in a future year vote money for building a Museum on the site purchased, it is to be understood that it will be as entirely under the charge of the Board of Trade as the Museum of Economic Geology in London, or the Museum of Irish Industry in Dublin'.

3. 'The principles upon which these Museums are founded recognize the importance of using the specimens in them for instructional purposes to the fullest extent compatible with their security and preservation, and the same principles would be applied to the proposed Museum. Though the Patrons of the University would have no controlling power in the management of the new Museum, the Board of Trade would no doubt think that the Museum was used in the best possible way for the advantage of the public, if the Professors of the University employed its collections in the illustrations of their courses with the consent of the Director of the Museum'.

4. There should be no separation of specimens acquired from the university from others to be aquired by the new Museum. 'As the future Museum will be entirely the property of the public, I would propose that your Lordship should recommend that the specimens now belonging to the University should be given to the Government without any further conditions than those implied in the instructional use above referred to.'

5. The Professor of Natural History in the University should be the Keeper of Natural History in the new Museum, but not as regards its technological application. 'This Office of Keepership of the Natural History part would be viewed as being directly responsible to the Government, and not in any way to the Patrons of the University who would be asked to concede to the Crown any rights that they may have had to appoint a Keeper of the present collections, and it must not be considered as interfering with the due responsibility of any General Director of the Museum who may hereafter be appointed.'

6. Provision for the use of the Museum by the public, free of charge, will be made: 'two or three days in each week may probably be reserved, on which a small fee for admission may be charged, in order to enable students and Men of Science to study the collections without the inconvenience of crowded assemblages of persons.'

7. The Industrial part of the Museum will not be confined to the Application of Geology, but will extend to general Technological purposes.[46]

Subject to necessary conditions Jameson had achieved his ambition in the settlement – the natural history collections of the University would form the foundation of the national collections which would be housed in a new building and, unless otherwise determined at a later date, come under the charge of his successors in the Chair of Natural History. Fifteen days later he died.

On 20 July 1854 Lyon Playfair wrote to the Lord Provost informing the Council that Parliament had voted a sum to purchase the Museum site and that the money would be spent on receipt of certain legal assurances from the City. At the sederunt of 8 August 1854 the Town Council therefore enacted as follows:

> On the report of the College Committee, and in furtherance of the proposed establishment, did and hereby do renounce all right of property in and management of or control over the Collections forming the Museum of Natural History in the University of this City, belonging to them as Patrons and Guardians of the said University and in favor of the Lords of the Committee of Privy Council for Trade.[47]

They further ceded to the nation the piece of land which they held for the University on the proposed museum site and agreed to concur with any plan for the widening of the approach to the Museum by North College Street and to cede so much of the property on the north side of that street, which belonged to them as Patrons and Guardians, as might be necessary for that purpose.

Parallel affirmations were sought and received by Playfair from the Highland Society in respect of its geological collection and agricultural models. The only conditions attached to the gift were firstly, that stated by Playfair, that the collection should be used for the advantage of the public by being displayed in a Museum which would be open to the public on certain days of the week free of charge. Secondly, that stated by Hall Maxwell, that the Industrial Museum should be strictly public, under Government superintendence, and independent of any local control.[48]

Before the sunny recollections of the Great Exhibition of 1851 had faded at home, the skies darkened abroad with the threat of war. In June 1853 the British Fleet lay off the Dardanelles, in the following February Czar Nicholas recalled his ambassador from London and by the end of March 1854, even as Dr Lyon Playfair was negotiating in Edinburgh for the creation of Scotland's national museum, the Crimean War had begun.

After the dreadful winter of 1854-5, with the army in a wretched state at Sebastopol through illness and mismanagement, Lord Aberdeen's coalition government fell in January 1855 and he was succeeded as premier by Lord Palmerston. In the same month the Royal Scottish Society of Arts appointed Dr George Wilson to convene a committee to try to expedite the commencement of the collection of objects for the 'Great Economic Museum for Edinburgh'.[49] Although not public knowledge, for about a year George Wilson's name had been mentioned in connection with the post of Director of the Industrial Museum but it was not until February 1855 that he received notification of his appointment. In Anderson's words, 'With strong scientific, historical and pedagogic interests, Wilson was ideally suited to the job for which Playfair had selected him' (Anderson, 1995, 221). Wilson had graduated in medicine at Edinburgh but his interest in Chemistry led him in 1838 to the laboratory of Professor Thomas Graham at University College, London where his fellow assistants were Lyon Playfair, a colleague of student days, and James Young. He graduated MD in 1839 and became well-known in Edinburgh as an extra-mural lecturer in chemistry (fig 20).

An example of the expectations of the new industrial museum which were now developing is provided by the Highland and Agricultural Society. The chemical interests of the museum's new director raised hopes of service from the Museum to the Society. Hall Maxwell reported to his directors:

> I had a satisfactory meeting at Marlborough House with Dr Lyon Playfair, in reference to the extent to which the Museum will be made subservient to the purposes of Agriculture, and it is not improbable that, when the Institution is brought into working order, the call on the Society to maintain a Chemical Department may be superseded.[50]

To sustain the Russian War, ever increasing demands on government resources were made. Despite this, and after further legal process [51], the site for the new industrial museum was secured for £7000 under the Edinburgh Lands Act of 30 July 1855 which enabled purchase of the Dissenting Chapel and the Trades' Maiden Hospital and the ceding of the university land adjoining West College Street.[52]

George Wilson's appointment to the new Regius Chair of Technology followed in August 1855. The influence of his friend Playfair in these appointments must have been well known to Wilson when he wrote

> The Queen of England in her might
> She made a wondrous Chair;
> She beckoned to a Scottish wight,
> And said, 'Ho! sit thou there!'
> The Scottish wight, he bowed his head,
> And stammered an apology;
> 'Nay! sit thou there!' the Queen she said,
> 'In my chair of Technology.'

> ([Wilson] 1866, 282)

Clause three of Lyon Playfair's letter to the Lord Provost of 1 April 1854 had promised an association of teaching with the new Scottish national museum. The association of collections with teaching was part of Playfair's strategy for the encouragement of the practical sciences. In 1854 also, on the other side of the Irish Channel, his department had added a teaching function to the existing Museum of Irish Industry by attaching to it the new Government School of Science applied to Mining and the Arts. In London schemes were afoot on a grand scale for the association of the collections of what was to become the South Kensington Museum, which had been established in Marlborough House in 1852, and the Royal College of Science.

The new Edinburgh Professor of Technology was an enthusiastic advocate of this policy. Wilson addressed his students

> With the Industrial Museum this Chair stands in organic connexion, My office as Professor of Technology, is to be interpreter of the significance of that Museum, and expositor of its value to you, the Students of this University (Wilson, 1855).

The Treaty of Paris, which ended the Crimean War, was not signed until March 1856. In Edinburgh it was accepted that while the war continued there could be no expectation of further money to build the new museum. In the war years, however, Wilson had been busy collecting, as the industrial specimens now crowding the Dissenting Chapel and Trades' Maidens Hospital testified. In these years also Wilson's ideas concerning the aims and requirements of the Industrial Museum of Scotland had matured. The Keeper of Natural History at the Museum was now George James Allman who had become Regius Professor at Edinburgh in 1855. The Chair and Keepership had become vacant on the sudden death of Edward Forbes, who had succeeded Jameson in May 1854 but had died only six months later.

In July 1856 Wilson and Allman answered a request from Lyon Playfair stating what space would be required in the new museum for the exhibition of industrial and natural history specimens. They note that the 33,000 square feet of the purchased site would be reduced by upwards of 400 square feet if the breadth of West College Street were increased from nineteen to twenty-five or thirty feet 'so as to maintain the free access of daylight to the University Halls, and provide for its admission to the New Galleries'. They judged that the requirement of the natural history and industrial galleries would be about equal at 15,000 to 20,000 square feet of floor area. To this allowance was made for lecture rooms, library, laboratories and subsidiary apartments comprising office and preparation rooms for the Natural History Museum, Industrial Museum and Geological Survey together with provision for the domestic establishment – housekeeper's apartments, attendants room, and so on. They envisaged a museum building in the form of a quadrangle of three floors measuring 155 feet from east to west and 190 feet from north to south. It would comprise gallery blocks to east and west with connecting blocks to north and south which would accommodate the rest of the stated needs. Although this arrangement was not adopted in the final building two suggestions by Wilson and Allman were carried out:

> The Upper Gallery in the Eastern side of the Quadrangle could be connected with the upper Hall of the University Museum by a suitable archway crossing West College Street, and it would involve least alteration of the University Building if the Eastern Gallery were appropriated to Natural History and the Western Gallery to the Industrial Museum.[53]

On 21 January 1857 the Royal Scottish Society of Arts again showed the 'deep interest taken by the Society in the establishment of the Industrial

Museum of Scotland and the relative Chair of Technology' by writing to the Lords of the Treasury:

> Your memorialists desire to bring before your Lordships the fact that the <u>old</u> buildings at present upon the ground cannot be made available for the exhibition of the industrial products which have been and are yet to be collected and that any expenditure of Money upon <u>them</u> would be virtually thrown away, and that the knowledge that their gifts cannot for an indefinite time be properly exhibited & then made available for the benefit of the Arts & Manufactures of Scotland, while they see no symptoms of the building of a Museum for their exhibition deter many persons engaged in the various branches of the useful arts from forwarding valuable specimens of their different products – the more valuable that many of them cannot be obtained for money.
>
> The object of this Memorial therefore is to solicit that a grant of money under the recommendation of your Lordships, be made during the approaching Session of Parliament, for carrying out the laudable intentions of Government in the Construction of a suitable Building for the Museum...[54]

They were glad to be informed by Sir Charles Trevelyan, in a letter written from Treasury Chambers on 27 January, that it was intended that a vote on account of the proposed building was to be placed before Parliament. A second letter, written by Lyon Playfair on the following day, confirmed that the Department of Science and Art had received instruction from the Treasury to include in the estimates of the year 1857-8 a certain sum on account for the erection of the museum building and that an officer of the Department would proceed to Edinburgh 'in the course of the next week to make the necessary enquiries on the subject'. That officer would probably then belong to a Department of Science and Art which was no longer a Department of the Board of Trade but, from 1857, answerable to the Privy Council Committee on Education.

Among other public bodies in Edinburgh which acted at this time was the Highland and Agricultural Society. A document in that Society's archives summarises the reasons for including a sum for the Industrial Museum in the estimates for 1857:

1. The importance of the Museum is conceded by Government.

2. The Highland Society, the University of Edinburgh, and the Town Council of the City have made gifts or concessions of property & privileges to the Museum.

3. All the influential Scientific Bodies and Societies of Edinburgh have moved in favour of it.

4. Several of the Peers and many of the Landed Gentlemen of the Country have earnestly recommended it.

5. The manufacturers of the three Kingdoms have willingly contributed to it.

6. The more educated Section of the public as represented by the Scientific Societies of Edinburgh, its Philosophical Institution, the Architectural Institute, the Educational Institute and the Mechanics Institutions of Scotland have voluntarily

expressed in the strongest terms, their satisfaction at the establishment of a Chair of Technology in connection with the Industrial Museum.

7. The less educated portions of the public have very largely availed themselves of the free admission conceded on certain days to the Natural History Galleries in the College which form an integral part of the New Museum; and they are impatient to be admitted to the Industrial Collections.

8. The buildings occupying the site of the proposed New Museum are totally unsuited for Exhibition Galleries, nor could they be rendered available for this purpose unless by an expenditure of money which would be be much more usefully and economically expended on a new Erection.

9. The knowledge that contributions to the New Museum cannot be exhibited to the public for an indefinate period keeps Manufacturers from Sending Specimens; yet many of these which would be of most value cannot be procured otherwise than as gifts, seeing that they are not in the market.

10 The Expectations of all parties was, that the New Museum would be built without delay; and only the occurrence of the Russian War was held to justify the postponement of their design.

11 Liberal grants have been recently made to the New Museums in Dublin and the Sum required is small, say £20,000 to begin with.[55]

Points from this document are included in communications to government by other bodies at this time, as for example that of the Royal Scottish Society of Arts quoted above. George Wilson probably circulated the summary himself to stimulate letters from these bodies in support of the Industrial Museum's inclusion in the estimates of 1857.

At a General Meeting of the Highland Society held on 13 January 1857, a communication praying H M Government to proceed with the establishment of the Scottish Industrial Museum was presented by Sir George Clerk and adopted. This motion went further than had that from the Royal Scottish Society of Arts, however, for with regard to the site it stated:

> The ground is itself too limited in extent for the accommodation which the development of the Institution will require, but it was understood to have been specially selected with view to the early acquisition of the adjoining buildings in Argyle Square.[56]

It was noted also that the buildings on the site could be used only as storehouses which militated against the efficiency of the technological chair. The distance between the stores and the lecture room prevented fragile specimens being carried to and fro, or of taking students in a body from the classroom to the storeroom. It was noted also that the Society's geological collection and agricultural models, which had been presented to government, were still with the Society because of the impracticability of exhibiting them in the Industrial Museum. (They were not registered in the National Collection until 1859.)

On a motion by Sir William Gibson-Craig, Lord Clerk Register and Keeper of the Signet, it was agreed that the memorial should be followed by a deputation. In preparing his brief for that deputation the Society's secretary, John Hall Maxwell, asked George Wilson a number of questions.[57] Wilson's reply of 9 February 1857 was a wonderful letter which clearly reveals his ambitions for the Industrial Museum of Scotland. Following his estimation made in July 1856 of the space required for the new Museum, Wilson appears to have had second thoughts. In preparing his figures for the Department of Science and Art he had been in correspondence with Trenham Reek of the Museum of Economic Geology, London and Robert Kane of the Museum of Irish Industry and he had become convinced that more space was needed. He wrote to Maxwell:

... The Reasons for which I ask for more space are that every industrial Art must be represented in the New Museum; that all the raw materials of all those Arts must be exhibited in full commercial detail, along with all the Stages through which the Materials pass before becoming finished products, besides the tools & often also the Machinery employed in working them; that the condition of those Arts must be illustrated historically, at least as practices in our own and other Civilised Countries within recent periods; and that their contemporary condition in the less Civilised Nations must also be illustrated (examples from Africa, India, China &c).

To render such collections useful, the Museum should contain at least two large Lecture Theatres, and two Smaller Lecture Rooms, for the accommodation at the same hour of separate Classes under distinct Professors or Lecturers. It must contain one or more Libraries, one large Laboratory with accessory furnace rooms, Balance Room, Apparatus Room and Consulting Room and Store Room, and corresponding Apartments mutatis mutandis must be supplied for the Natural History Side of the Museum. Apartments for Housekeeper, Porter, Clerks & other offices must likewise be included.

If moreover the Engineering Department of Technology is to be developed, space must be provided for Models such as do not come within the Scope of Technology as at present contemplated, and a large Area would be requisite for Mills, Steam-Engines, Agricultural Implements, and Naval Architecture Models such as most certainly the purchased area could not contain.

Further, it is desirable that either Models or drawings of Patent Machines and Copies of Specifications should be deposited in some portion of the Industrial Museum to be accessible to inventors and intending patentees.

It is not less desirable that the Geological Survey should have room to display in full their Maps. Their Officers, further desire, and have to some extent been promised by Government, apartments for conducting the Scientific part of the Survey in so far as Mapping, Calculating, arranging fossils & Classifying returns is concerned; and it is most important that the Geology of Scotland should have its head Quarters & local Scientific habitation in the Museum.

Once more it would render the important Palaeontological department of Geology much more instructive if a series of examples of Recent Comparative Anatomy especially as far as Skeletons are concerned, could be arranged in association with the Natural History and Industrial Museums. The Means of thus illustrating Palaeontology amply exist in the University, and it is understood that Specimens would be willingly furnished, if space were afforded for them.[58]

Wilson believed that the south and west sides of Argyle Square could be purchased by government for between £9,000 and £10,000.

Wilson's concern that accommodation should be provided in the new museum building for the Headquarters of the Geological Survey in Scotland reminds us that the geological surveying of the country and the establishment of the national museum were the twin objectives of the original memorials sent to Government by the public and scientific bodies of Scotland in 1851-2. When surveying began in 1854 the geologists were still based in London but they had a temporary store for maps and specimens in the Industrial Museum of Scotland (Wilson, 1977, 5 and 16).

There is no certainty in the affairs of state, however, and despite Playfair's assurance to the Royal Scottish Society of Arts, that Society, in April 1858, 'learned with regret that the intended grant for the purpose in question, although referred to, in the usual way, in the Parliamentary Notices of the House of Commons, was withdrawn, and that no vote was taken on it'.[59] Had the Highland Society's representations, with their talk of increased expenditure on enlarging the site, backfired and caused government to withdraw the estimate for the commencement of building?

The parallel institutions in Edinburgh and Dublin were interested in each other's development and it was a pleasure for George Wilson to visit Dublin in August 1857 'to study the arrangements of its Industrial Museum, and also attend meetings of the British Association' ([Wilson] 1866, 310). Sir Robert Kane FRS, Director of the Industrial Museum of Ireland and George Wilson, Director of the Industrial Museum of Scotland, had much in common. Both had come to chemistry through medicine, and they shared an enthusiasm for exhibition and exposition of applied science and the industrial arts. Both were convinced of the importance of their institutions in their respective countries. Both were now answerable to Lyon Playfair and the Department of Science and Art. Kane was nine years older than Wilson and his Institution was up and running, while Wilson's was still in its infancy. For Wilson it must have been an inspiration to see the completed galleries of the Irish Museum with its new lecture theatre which had been finished only three years before.

Alas, Wilson never saw the galleries of his own Industrial Museum, for the first phase of the new Museum in Edinburgh was not completed until 1865. Wilson's campaign of 1857 for the enlargement of the museum site in which, as we have seen, he had enlisted the support of Scottish public and scientific bodies, was an uphill task. He wrote to his brother:

No amount of business-writing seems to do otherwise than multiply letters, and the endless labour I have had to go through in reference to a better site for the Industrial Museum, makes me sorry for myself. If Argyle Square be purchased by Government, and a noble building erected there, whisper into your grandchildren's ears, after I have become historical, that Uncle George had a hand in that. ([Wilson] 1866, 315)

Wilson's efforts eventually bore fruit in The Industrial Museum (Scotland) Act 1860 which authorised the purchase by the government of properties in Argyle Square and Brown Square together with part of the City Wall and sundry other properties including a 'Range of Buildings comprehending a Barm Brewery, Stables, Coach House, Lofts, Dungstead and Cellar'.[60] His ambition that the headquarters of the Geological Survey in Scotland should be established in the new museum building, however, was not fulfilled.

In 1867 the Geological Survey of Scotland was formed with Archibald Geikie as its first Local Director. The Argyle Square buildings of the Industrial Museum were its first headquarters. When these houses were demolished to allow for the western extension of the museum building, the Survey removed to India Buildings in Victoria Street next to the Offices of the Highland and Agricultural Society. Despite a number of subsequent moves, the Survey headquarters never returned to the Museum.

1 *Evidence, Oral and Documentary, taken and received by the Commissioners ... for Visiting the Universities of Scotland, I, University of Edinburgh*, London 1837, 144.

2 *Report made to His Majesty by a Royal Commission of Inquiry into the State of the Universities of Scotland*, London 1831, 178.

3 William Hunter bequeathed his collection to the University of Glasgow in 1783, along with funds to construct a museum building. This was opened, on its original site on Glasgow's High Street, in 1807 and is claimed to be the oldest public museum in Scotland.

4 I am indebted to Davies (1995) for the Irish references in this section.

5 Glasgow University Archives 26700 p 327 entry for 16 April 1847. Search of Glasgow Corporation Minutes for the period reveals no reference to the Faculty's submission and it remains uncertain that this memorial was ever sent to the Treasury.

6 Adam White was educated at the High School of Edinburgh and served the Natural History Department of the British Museum from 1835. He published extensively on insects and crustacea and used the name of a spider as his pseudonym 'to signify patient perseverance'. He was pensioned from his post in 1863 through mental indisposition 'consequent upon the loss of his wife' (Woodward, 1900).

7 It was not until 1860 that the decision was taken to remove the Natural History collections from Bloomsbury. In 1863 the site of the International Exhibition at South Kensington of the previous year was purchased for the new British Museum (Natural History). Building of Alfred Waterhouse's museum commenced in 1873 and it was opened in 1880.

8 *Edinburgh Evening Courant*, 28 August 1847 and *Edinburgh Advertiser* 31 August 1847, reprinted in White (1850, 3-4).

9 There are various references to the exhibition in the Minutes of the Corporation of Glasgow (ref C1/1/64, indexed under Philosophical Society). The exhibition made a surplus of some £460 which was set aside for a purpose of a similar kind. To this may be traced the origin of the Kelvingrove Museum which was founded in 1870 (Murray, 1, 245).

10 White (1850) dedicated his reprinted letters to 'Gentlemen who have done much, and may yet do still more' to further the establishment of a national museum in Scotland. Among those listed was William Gourlie, a council member of the Philosophical Society of

Glasgow, and a member of the joint committee which organised the exhibition (see Glasgow University Library Special Collections, Minutes of the Philosophical Society of Glasgow for 23 March 1846 and *Proceedings of the Philosophical Society of Glasgow*, 6 (1845-1848), 28).

11 *Parliamentary Papers*, vol 4 (1845) (Bills: Public) 'A Bill to enable Town Councils to establish Museums of Art in Corporate Towns, as amended by Committee'. The 1845 Act was repealed in 1850 by a Bill introduced by Ewart and Brotherton which enabled town councils to levy a rate to found and maintain public libraries as well as museums of art and science.

12 Edinburgh City Archives, Town Council Record, vol 251, p 152 Minute of 16 January 1849.

13 *Edinburgh Evening Courant*, 18 January 1849, report of Town Council Proceedings.

14 John Fleming DD was professor of Natural History at The Free Church College to which he had been appointed in 1845 having come out with the disruption of the Church of Scotland in 1843 when professor of Natural History at King's College, Aberdeen. He had been elected FRSE in 1814 and wrote *The Philosophy of Zoology* (1822) and *A History of British Animals* (1828) while minister of Flisk. His personal collection of natural history was one of the finest in Scotland.

15 *The Witness*, 21 November 1849.

16 *The Witness*, 28 November 1849.

17 *The Witness*, 5 December 1849.

18 *The Scotsman*, 24 May 1851.

19 *The Scotsman*, 5 July 1851, 'The Heriot boys and the Excursion to the Exhibition'.

20 *Edinburgh Evening Courant*, September 11 1851 'Proposal for an Open Museum in Edinburgh'.

21 *Transactions of the Highland and Agricultural Society of Scotland*, New Series, July 1851-March 1853, p 5.

22 John Hall Maxwell of Dargavel was called to the Scottish bar in 1835 and was appointed secretary to the Highland and Agricultural Society in 1845.

23 Royal Highland & Agricultural Society (RH&AS) archive, Parcel 30/1, Ms 'Excerpt from Minute of a Meeting of persons interested in the development of the Geological Resources of Scotland, held within the Chambers of the Highland and Agricultural Society on the 25 of November 1851'. Also Minutes of Directors of 26 Nov 1851, Sederunt Book 33, pp 71-4.

24 RH&AS Sederunt Book 33, Minutes of Directors, 12 December 1851, pp 75-7, Minutes of General Meeting 13 January 1852, p 109, *The Scotsman*, 14 January 1852.

25 'Destructive Fire', *Edinburgh Evening Courant*, 22 November 1851.

26 NLS ACC 10000/19 Minute of Council of 28 November 1851 in consideration of a minute communicated by Mr Hall Maxwell of a private meeting held in the Highland Society's Hall.

27 The Committee was Robert Christison (Professor of Materia Medica, Edinburgh), John Fleming Professor of Natural Sciences, New College, Edinburgh), Thomas Anderson (Chemist), James Wilson (Naturalist and Curator of the Society's museum) and Professor J D Forbes (General Secretary) see NLS ACC 10000/19 Minutes of Council 12 December 1851, 30 January 1852, NLS ACC 10000/6 Minutes of Ordinary Meeting of 5 January 1852, NLS ACC 10000/257 Letter of Sir Thomas Makdougall Brisbane to James Wilson of Woodville of 6 February 1852, Letter of Cornswall Lewis, Treasury Chambers, to the President, Royal Society of Edinburgh of 13 February 1852.

28 See for example Royal Scottish Society of Arts Council Minute of 22 December 1851, NLS Dep 230/12.

29 NLS ACC 10000/357 Ms letter of Robert Jameson of 7 February 1852.

30 Edinburgh University Library, Senatus Minutes, 31 January 1852, pp 340-2

31 Edinburgh University Library, Senatus Minutes, 28 February 1852, p 348.

32 Edinburgh University Library, Senatus Minutes, 13 March 1852, pp 352-7.

33 Edinburgh City Archives, Town Council Record Vol 257, p 152 and pp 281-291.

34 Print in RH&AS archive, Parcel 30/2, 'National Museum for Scotland, Memorial of the Lord Provost, Magistrates and Council of Edinburgh to the Lords of Her Majesty's Treasury, 16th March 1852'.

35 *Edinburgh Evening Courant*, 12 January 1854, From Report of General Meeting of the Highland & Agricultural Society of 10 January 1854.

36 RH&AS Sederunt Book 33, Minutes of Directors 14 March 1852, p 145.

37 Edinburgh City Archives, Town Council Record, vol 259, pp 243-7.

38 RH&AS Sederunt Book 33, Minutes of Directors 4 March 1853, pp 246-7, Minutes of General Meeting of 13 July 1853, p 270, Edinburgh Evening Courant, 14 July 1853.

39 RH&AS Sederunt Book 33, Minutes of Directors 4 November 1853, p 274.

40 RH&AS Sederunt Book 33, Minutes of General Meeting of 10 January 1854, pp 311-12, *Edinburgh Evening Courant* 12 January 1854.

41 RH&AS Sederunt Book 33, Minutes of Directors, 10 February 1854.

42 RH&AS Sederunt Book 33, Minutes of Directors 3 March 1854, pp 334-7.

43 From what bodies or persons in Glasgow these strong representations had come remains unknown. Search of the minutes of the Corporation, the University and the Philosophical Society show no record of any memorial to Government having been made at this time by these bodies.

44 RH&AS Sederunt Book 33, Minutes of Directors 24 March 1854, p 339.

45 *Edinburgh Evening Courant*, 13 July 1854, From statement by Professor J H Balfour on the 'National Industrial and Scientific Museum' to the General Meeting of the Highland and Agricultural Society of 12 July 1854, and Ms briefing note in RH&AS archive Parcel 30/6.

46 Edinburgh University Library, Senatus Minutes of 4 April 1854, pp 467-472.

47 Edinburgh City Archive, Town Council Record, vol 263, pp 147-152.

48 RH&AS Sederunt Book 33, Minutes of Directors 3 May, and 10 November 1854, pp 354-5, 387.

49 NLS Dep 230/12, Royal Scottish Society of Arts Council Minutes, 4 January 1855. The other members of the committee were David Rhind FRSE (architect), Mr Smail (Vice-President) and Philip Kelland FRSE (Professor of Mathematics).

50 RH&AS Sederunt Book 33, Minutes of Directors 4 April 1855, p 438.

51 See for example Edinburgh City Archives, Town Council Record, vol 264, pp 11, 445, vol 265, p 63.

52 The Edinburgh Lands Act 18th &19th Vict Cap lxxx, 30 July 1855 Purchase of Ground for the Formation of a National Museum of Industry for Scotland by Commissioners of HM Works and Public Buildings.

53 RH&AS archive, Parcel 30/12 with plan 30/13, ms copy of memorandum from G Wilson and G J Allman to the Secretary of the Department of Science & Art dated 23 July 1856.

54 NLS Acc 4534/Dep 230.71 Envelope 3.

55 RH&AS archive, Parcel 30/17.

56 RH&AS archive, Parcel 30/24, ms copy of Memorial to the Commissioners of Her Majesty's Treasury and *The Scotsman*, 14 January 1857, part of Report of General Meeting of Highland and Agricultural Society of 13 January 1857.

57 RH&AS archive, Parcel 30/10, Parcel 30/18.

58 RH&AS archive, Parcel 30/11, ms Letter of G Wilson to J H Maxwell of 9 February 1857. The ideas expressed here were developed by Wilson in December 1857 in a lecture to the Merchant Company of Edinburgh entitled 'The Industrial Museum of Scotland in its relation to Commercial Enterprise', which was printed for private circulation through the liberality of the Master of the Merchant Company.

59 NLS Dep 230/12 Royal Scottish Society of Arts Council Minute for 21 April 1858.

60 The Industrial Museum (Scotland) Act 1860, An Act to confer Powers on the Commissioners of Her Majesty's Works and Public Buildings to acquire certain Property in Edinburgh, for the erection of an Industrial Museum for Scotland (28 August 1860).

CHAPTER FIVE

THE ROYAL SOCIETY MUSEUM IN DECLINE
1859-1910

Oui, cela était autrefois ainsi, mais nous avons changé tout cela ...

Molière

O'Shaughnessy's well known ode, lines from which headed the last chapter, contains the couplet 'For each age is a dream that is dying, Or one that is coming to birth'. The coming to birth of the dream of a national museum for Scotland was the concern of the last chapter. In the same age, the dream of the value of its museum to the Royal Society of Edinburgh was dying. The reasons for this were complex and are the concern of the present chapter.

On the death of James Wilson in 1856 the position of Curator of the Museum lapsed and the *status ante* was resumed when Dr Douglas Maclagan succeeded Traill as Curator of both Library and Museum. Maclagan was a popular figure and an experienced and decisive committee man (fig 16). Distinguished in the field of medicine, he was already President of the Royal College of Surgeons of Edinburgh and, as Sir Douglas Maclagan, was later to become President of the Royal College of Physicians of Edinburgh (1884-7) and of the Royal Society of Edinburgh (1890-95).

As early as 1851 the Society had requested the Board of Trustees to provide in the Royal Institution 'a room on the same floor and on the same side of the building with their present apartments in lieu of the Museum upstairs' and in April a committee was appointed to negotiate with the Board.' Eight years passed, however, before a letter was received from the Board of Manufactures agreeing to exchange the first floor room, which had housed the Society's collections since 1835, for an apartment of equal dimensions on the ground floor.² This was the West Gallery which adjoined the Society's Meeting Hall and lay to the south of it, immediately below the vacated Museum Room (plan p 55).

As soon as Council received the Board's letter, a committee was appointed 'with powers to effect the transfer of the Museum'.³ The collections had grown to such an extent that the Museum had become congested. In order to relieve the situation and permit better display of retained objects in the West Gallery, the committee cut the Gordian Knot by using their delegated powers to dispose of virtually everything in the Museum other than geological specimens. Seldom in the history of the Society can Council have received a more radical report than that given by the Curator at their meeting of 21 November 1859.[4] Maclagan had sought the cooperation of a group of influential Edinburgh men who were Fellows of the Society, J D Forbes (Secretary RSE, Professor of Natural Philosophy), John Hutton Balfour (Professor of Botany and Keeper of the Royal Botanic Garden), George J Allman (Professor of Natural History and Keeper of the Natural History Museum), George Wilson (first and last Professor of Technology in the University of Edinburgh, Director of the Industrial Museum of Scotland, Robert Chambers (Author and publisher) and J T Gibson Craig (Treasurer).

> After due inspection of the Society's collection these gentlemen were of opinion, that the attempt on the part of the Society to maintain a general Museum of Natural History, was inexpedient – that it would be much better to limit the Society's collections to the department of Geology & Mineralogy, of which it possesses a very valuable and useful series of specimens, and to deposit the Zoological, Botanical, Anatomical and Miscellaneous specimens in the other public Museums in Edinburgh, where they could not only be more accessible to persons interested in the subjects to which they refer, but would, from being placed beside other specimens, acquire a value which they could not possess in the isolated position in which they were in the Royal Society's Room.
>
> As the necessity of coming to some definite arrangement was urgent, and, from the Season of the year, there was no opportunity of getting a formal sanction from the Society, the Curator acted on that opinion, and, reserving the Geological & Mineralogical specimens to be placed in the new rooms, he provisionally distributed the other specimens...

There follow lists of specimens passed to the Royal Botanic Garden, the Natural History Museum, the Industrial Museum of Scotland, the Royal College of Surgeons and the Society of Antiquaries of Scotland.

In conclusion Maclagan stated that, with the active cooperation of Mr Carruthers, the former Assistant Librarian, and his successor Mr John S Livingston, the Geological and Mineralogical collections had been completely rearranged in the new accommodation. Council adopted the Curator's report and approved the distribution of the specimens. A number of bookcases had been installed around the walls of the new Museum and two dozen drawers were to be found below each of three of them, while open cases existed under some for the display of large specimens. Leslie's table case occupied the centre of the room as before.

THE MUSEUM IN ECLIPSE

During Skene's joint curatorship some pieces of fine art and ethnography had been passed to the Society of Antiquaries in 1828 (see p 54). During Maclagan's curatorship all the remaining collections of art and ethnography, technology, botany and zoology were given away and only certain geological specimens remained in the Society's museum. When we recall the importance which the Society had attached to its museum and the strong feelings which had motivated its wish for a Second Royal Charter to allow it to house its own collections it is remarkable that, less than fifty years after the granting of that Charter, its Council should have been able to dispose of the bulk of the Society's museum collections apparently without a murmur of objection. What had wrought such a change in the attitude of the Society's Fellows to the museum which they had recently prized so highly ?

The reasons were complex, some consequent upon local circumstances, others of more general significance. In the Royal Society of Edinburgh we see a microcosm in which this change is demonstrated. It is of particular interest because the academic Fellows of the Society were participants in those developments in science and teaching which necessitated change and were eventually influential in effecting it in Scotland. Their views foreshadowed the attitude of much of academia towards museums in Britain which still persists and, because of its continuing relevance, it would be helpful to understand the circumstances which brought it about. Evidence is given below which suggests that three main factors influenced the decision of 1859:

    a) the development of experimental science,
    b) consequent changes in university science teaching methods,
    c) the emergence of the national museum.

a) *Development of experimental science*

The development of experimental science during the first half of the nineteenth century meant that museum specimens alone could no longer answer many of the questions being posed, even in traditional museum subjects such as geology and biology. Increasingly these required to be answered in the laboratory rather than the museum. Wittlin wrote, 'With the gradual ascendancy of laboratory biology in universities, the descriptive botany and zoology dealing with entire organisms in museum collections took second place' (Wittlin, 1970, 134). How did these tendencies affect Scotland?

In this and the following section the important part played by Fellows of the Society in the development of experimental science and the changes in teaching methods which resulted, especially in Scotland, is outlined. Where those cited were Fellows the fact is indicated by (F) after the name. Dates of election are given in the Name Index.

As we have seen, it was concern at the fate of James Hutton's collection which was an immediate factor in the drawing up of the Second Charter of the Royal Society of Edinburgh (p 41-5). Although Hutton's scepticism of those 'who judge of the great operations of the mineral kingdom from having kindled a fire and looked into the bottom of a little crucible' is well known, his contemporaries knew Hutton to be an enthusiastic chemist (Hutton, 1795, I, 251). In the last quarter of the eighteenth century analytical mineralogy was emerging (Campbell Smith, 1978) and it is evident that Hutton used experimental methods, blowpipe, and microscope in his geological work.[5] Even during Hutton's lifetime, however, his young friend and disciple, Sir James Hall of Dunglass (F), began his experimental proofs of aspects of Hutton's theory which were published after his master's death. In a series of fusion experiments Hall demonstrated that the rate of cooling determined the crystalline character of igneous rocks. He also succeeded in converting powdered chalk into a substance resembling marble under great heat and pressure in his famous gun-barrel experiments.

During the nineteenth century many other techniques were developed in geology which were appropriate to the laboratory rather than the museum. For example the preparation of transparent thin sections of rock mounted on glass slides by William Nicol (F) opened the study of microscopic palaeontology and paved the way for the new study of microscopic petrology. The technique appears to have been developed in the late 1820s from one used by the Edinburgh lapidary George Sanderson and was discussed by Henry Witham (F) in 1830. By 1829 Nicol had perfected an efficient polariser which W H Fox Talbot (F) applied to the microscope. Nicol's instruments were inherited by Alexander Bryson (F) of Edinburgh who made many thin sections of minerals and rocks to show fluid cavities. These sections impressed H C Sorby when he visited Bryson in Edinburgh. From the mid eighteen fifties Sorby adopted the technique and has been acknowledged as the 'first scientist to make thin sections of rocks with the objectives of studying their mineralogy and textures under the microscope' (Morrison-Low, 1992; Dawson 1992). The thin section and the polarizing microscope revolutionized petrology and the study was developed by continental scientists such as Zirkel, Rosenbusch, Fouqué and Lévy. Microscopic petrology was introduced as a routine procedure to the Geological Survey in Ireland by the Local Director, Edward Hull, in 1871 (Davies, 1995, 72). Just as the museum mineral specimen required chemical analysis in the laboratory for its fuller understanding, so the museum hand-specimen could no longer illustrate the nature of the rock without physical examination in the laboratory.

The development of experimental biology also made the examination of the external aspects of plants and animals, as displayed by museum specimens, inadequate for their scientific description. The work of Antony Van Leeuwehoek in Holland and in England the publication of Robert Hooke's *Micrographia*, had shown the potentialities of the microscope as early as 1665. Potentialities which were realized, for example, in the field of plant microanatomy in Italy by Marcello Malpighi's *Anatome Plantarum Idea* 1671 and in England by Nehemiah Grew's *The Anatomy of Plants Begun* 1671. Considering the primitive instruments available to them these works were truly remarkable. 'The measure of the advance they jointly made is that for nearly a century and a half plant anatomy remained where they left it ...' (Morton,1981, 366). Among technical improvements which heralded the rapid advance of microscopy throughout the nineteenth century were the development of achromatic lenses and the use of the thin glass cover slip. The cover slip was adopted in the early part of the century and allowed tissues to be observed when immersed in fluids. New fields of discovery were opened up in microbiology, cytology and cellular pathology. Examples abound but in Germany Ehrenberg and Siebold laid the foundations of modern microbiology in their studies of Infusoria, while Mohl described vegetable micro-anatomy and cell reproduction. The discovery of the cell nucleus by Robert Brown (F) led to Schleiden's discovery of the nucleolus in embryonic plant tissue and Schwann's discovery that animals also contain cells with nuclei. Virchow was concerned with cells and disease and developed the discipline of cellular pathology.

Advance in chemical techniques had a profound influence also when applied to biology during the nineteenth century. Following the work of Scheele and Fourcroy, the Swedish chemist Berzelius (F) developed animal chemistry by analyzing organic substances associated with life. One of his students, Friedrich Wöhler, synthesised one such substance, urea, from inorganic elements.

In the same way the insights of physics were applied to living organisms in the nineteenth century. Of Brewster's (F) work on the micro-structure and optics of the lens of the eye Duncan has written 'I know of no better example of a publication that may be truly said to lay foundations for modern biophysics' (Duncan 1984,103). Abroad Helmholtz applied the principle of the conservation of energy to living organisms and Ludwig applied the understanding of electricity to the physiology of nerves.

Experimental biology advanced also in such fields as embryology and physiology. In embryology the work of Von Baer, Rathke and Pander fell within the first half of the nineteenth century as did many of the the advances in physiology through the work of such men as Johannes Müller.

A comprehensive review of the development of experimental geology and biology lies in the province of the history of science. The few examples given, however, suffice to show some of the ways in which, as science progressed in the first half of the nineteenth century, the laboratory increasingly supplied information concerning rocks, minerals, animals and plants which was inaccessible to the museum. While many of these advances were achieved abroad, they and the scientists working on them were familiar to the Edinburgh Fellows. Indeed many of these overseas scientists were elected Honorary Fellows of the Society.[6] It is in the nature of such honours that they are often bestowed many years after the work has been done which they recognize. There is no doubt, however, that when the decision on the future of the Society's museum was taken in 1859 members of Council were well aware of these and other advances in experimental science and how the scientific value of the museum hand-specimen had been reduced thereby.

b) Change in science teaching methods

Since the mid-eighteenth century or earlier science had been presented in Scottish universities by professors, many of international distinction. When the Royal Society of Edinburgh was founded the pedagogic system was at its height and distinguished professors were Fellows of the Society. Some in the physical sciences and anatomy illustrated their lectures by elaborate demonstration experiments. In the teaching of natural history the museum was the focus of practical study.

In the nineteenth century, however, with advances in experimental science such as those outlined in the last section, science teaching in Scottish Universities was revolutionized. The centre of practical studies moved away from the lecture theatre and the museum to newly established teaching laboratories where students could participate in practical work in order to gain skills in experimental techniques.

A comprehensive account of these changes as they affected the Scottish universities remains to be written; only chemistry, botany and anatomy have been well served in this respect A number of examples, chiefly from Edinburgh and taken from various disciplines, are described below, to illustrate the nature of the changes which were occurring and to give an indication of the timing of some of these events.

John Walker (F) was the first to establish geology as a classroom subject in a Scottish university. In paying tribute to him as the 'Father of Geological Education', H W Scott writes:

> Walker's classroom methods were essentially those used today: he lectured; distributed syllabuses; established a laboratory; and brought in rocks, minerals, and fossils, which were studied with a microscope. The laboratory work included the study of polished surfaces and a large suite of minerals and fossils (Scott, 1976).

Scott's summary of Walker's classroom methods, although interesting, may mislead because the laboratory elements in it, such as the study of polished surfaces of minerals and microscope work, were secondary to the emphasis which we know he placed on the importance of the museum in teaching. In this vital respect his teaching methods differed markedly from those of today. Walker here reflected the position of Hutton who, while doing experimental work, nevertheless regarded his collection of specimens, his 'Bibles', as of primary importance.

In his essay on the universities and the scientific revolution, Ashby notes that the first university laboratory to offer systematic training in chemical research was that established at Giessen in 1826 by Von Liebig (F),(Ashby, 1963). In the same year the University of London was founded and the educational needs of the emerging professional scientist in Britain were notably advocated by T H Huxley (F) and by organisations such as the newly-formed British Association in which David Brewster, the Society's indefatigable Secretary, played a seminal role.

The history of the teaching of Chemistry in the Scottish universities has been reviewed and details of the growth of practical laboratory teaching in that subject are available (Anderson 1978; Findlay 1935). The earliest practical chemistry instruction offered in Edinburgh was the extramural course given by Thomas Thomson (F) from 1807 (Anderson 1978, 38). The teaching laboratory which he then established is believed to have been the first in

Britain (Birse, 1994, 67). In 1818 he became Regius Professor of Chemistry at Glasgow where he set up another teaching laboratory. These laboratories were on a very small scale, and could accommodate only a few students but:

> Dr Thomson attaches so great importance to his class of Experimental Chemistry, that he continues it during ten months of the year. The object is to teach all who wish to become Practical Chemists... In the year 1827, the gentlemen of this class analysed sixty minerals, several of them quite new, and some exceedingly difficult and complicated; and they performed all the most difficult processes in Chemistry. Dr Thomson states, that he is not aware of any [similar teaching laboratory] in this country except his own. His Laboratory is not large enough to admit more than ten students into his Experimental class – and he is unwilling to admit more than six.[7]

Andrew Fyfe, later 'Mediciner' at King's College, Aberdeen, also offered extramural tuition in practical chemistry in Edinburgh from 1809 (Anderson, 1978, 38). These extramural courses were popular because the Professor, Thomas Charles Hope (F), never encouraged practical study and for many years none was provided in the university course. George Wilson tells us that, in the early years of the nineteenth century, a few of the better off and more energetic students, Robert Christison and James Syme among them, met in garrets or cellars to try experiments, which were often accompanied by 'conflagrations and unintentional explosions'.

Hope's assistants, John Wilson Anderson followed by David Boswell Reid (F), later gave practical instruction in the laboratory provided for the professor in the new College building which was first used in 1823. In 1831 the Commissioners reported:

> They who are to make further progress in the Science [Chemistry] must work themselves in the Laboratory, both in the University and out of it. Such opportunities in Practical Chemistry have for several years been offered. During the Session 1829-30, Dr Hope (T C Hope) has reported to Us, that the number who attended the Practical Courses of his Assistant Dr Reid have been 190: and during the ten months subsequent to the 1st November 1829, Dr Reid conducted ten distinct Practical Courses.[8]

Of Reid's practical classes, Wilson wrote

> Dr Hope gave little or no encouragement to the new movement ... Dr David B Reid, beyond the University walls, had commenced a system of instruction in Practical Chemistry which for the time was a great advance... The introducer of this system was a man of great energy, and by satisfying, to some degree, a strongly felt want of the time, laid the foundation of our educational system of practical chemistry (Wilson in Wilson and Geikie, 1861, 101).

In Brewster's evidence to the Commissioners he stated that a regular laboratory should be established as at all foreign universities, where young men can receive practical instruction in the analysis of minerals, which now forms one of the most important branches of chemistry.

Hope's successors in the Chair of Chemistry were William Gregory (F) followed by Lyon Playfair (F). Both had studied under Justus von Liebig at Giessen and were recognized as apostles of his chemistry in Britain and both were convinced of the need to build up schools of chemistry where provision for practical work and research was made. While 'Mediciner' at King's College, Aberdeen, Gregory revisited Giessen in 1841 and was impressed by the new laboratory which had been provided for von Liebig there by the State. On his return he urged government to provide funds to establish such practical schools in our universities (Gregory, 1842). During his tenure of the chair of Chemistry at Edinburgh, however, Gregory did little to improve laboratory facilities and when Playfair succeeded him he found the teaching laboratories inadequate. Playfair wrote:

> [Gregory] had not been able to found a teaching laboratory on a scale commensurate with the importance of the chair. This I determined to do, so far as the limited accommodation then in the University would permit. Before entering upon my duties as a professor, a considerable sum had to be spent in equipping the laboratories and chemical museum with the full appliances for teaching (Playfair in Reid, 1899, 179-80).

To do this Playfair 'used the whole of his professional income during his first year, and a large part of it for several years afterwards, to create a useful teaching laboratory' (Mackie, 1978, 18-20).

The provision of adequate teaching chemical laboratories in Edinburgh University, however, was long in coming. As late as 1870 Playfair's successor, Alexander Crum Brown (F), still complained that the chemistry laboratory could accommodate only twelve students at any one time and it was not until 1884 that proper provision was made in the new medical buildings for a practical laboratory with about 100 places (Birse 1994, 57 and 68). Birse has noted that, although the Edinburgh University Calendar stated that in 1869-70 laboratory courses were available in, for example, chemistry and natural philosophy, the evidence received by the Royal Commission of 1870 from the science professors painted a rather different picture. The urgent need for practical instruction was appreciated but laboratory accommodation still remained inadequate. Professor P G Tait (F) reported that the situation in Natural Philosophy was similar to that in Chemistry. Meanwhile, in Glasgow, Thomas Thomson had set up a laboratory to teach chemistry in 1818 but it was not until William Thomson, later Lord Kelvin (F) became Professor of Natural Philosophy in 1846 that the first teaching laboratory in that discipline was established there.

The establishment of classes in practical anatomy is of interest to our study because it represents an early example of formalized practical teaching on a large scale in Edinburgh and it has been well documented because of the public concern which was aroused in obtaining subjects for dissection.

As we have seen, the lecture demonstrations in anatomy of Alexander Monro *secundus* (F) were so popular that he had a purpose-built theatre erected in 1764 to accommodate the students. No class of practical anatomy then existed. The only dissection seen was that demonstrated by the professor although students could, no doubt, study the anatomical preparations which were exhibited in the Anatomical Museum. Students of the subject later felt that they required practical experience in dissection, however, and private schools of anatomy developed to meet their need. The position was formalized when the Royal College of Surgeons of Edinburgh required all their diploma candidates to have taken a class of practical anatomy. In 1824 Robert Knox (F) succeeded the popular anatomy teacher John Barclay (F) at the Royal College of Surgeons. Knox was an inspired teacher and his practical anatomy class did much to satisfy medical students who wished dissecting experience. Alexander Monro *tertius* (F) the Professor of Anatomy, was a poor teacher and when he introduced a practical anatomy class to the University curriculum, it proved no match for Knox's extramural opposition. At that time Scotland virtually monopolized medical teaching in Britain. It has been estimated that in the first half of the nineteenth century almost ninety-five per cent of doctors in Britain with medical degrees were educated in Scotland (Bell 1995, 140). The demand for subjects for dissection was therefore acute in Edinburgh; bodysnatching became more prevalent, and the need for regulation became urgent. In response to a request by the Home Secretary, Robert Peel, who had been approached on the matter by the President of the Royal College of Surgeons of Edinburgh, a report by a committee of the College was prepared in 1828 which estimated that the number of students studying medicine in Edinburgh was 900 and that 150 bodies had been dissected during the winter of 1827-8. The committee estimated that 300 subjects would be required if one body was to be supplied each year to each student attending practical anatomy classes (Cresswell 1926, 202-5). Even as the College committee was preparing its report, Burke and Hare were resorting to murder to obtain bodies for dissection. A regulating bill was first introduced in parliament in 1829 and two years later a revised version passed into law as the Anatomy Act.

As regards botany, practical botany had been taught in Edinburgh, supported by its physic garden, since the time of John Hope (F) and it is known that Hope demonstrated experiments to his classes. For example, 'he showed his students experiments demonstrating the interaction between light and gravity in the induction of curvature in stems and roots' (Morton 1986, 22).

The botany classes of Hope's successor, Robert Graham (F) were popular and especially so his botanical excursions. No instruction was given, however, 'in dissecting or examining plants, further than by pulling them to pieces with the fingers, and examining them with a pocket lens'.

But the science thus cherished had great advances to make. Impelled by the hidden law of its own progress; furnished day by day from every quarter of the globe with new materials to analyse and systematize; provided with new instruments of research, and beckoned to new discoveries by the illumination cast on its darker regions by the ever-brightening light of the advancing sister sciences, and the ever increasing demands of the progressive industrial arts, Botany was about to take a bound forward, which soon rendered new appliances for teaching it requisite on every side (Wilson in Wilson and Geikie 1861, 104).

Advances in microscopy revolutionized biological and medical teaching. A pioneer in this respect was Graham's successor, John Hutton Balfour (F). Balfour was born in the house at St John's Hill, Edinburgh, which had been built by his grandfather's cousin James Hutton. After graduating MD at Edinburgh he continued his medical education in Paris from 1832 to 1834. It is probable that Balfour, already inspired by Robert Graham's botanical lectures during his medical training, developed his interest in microscopy while in Paris. There, although formal teaching in medical microscopy had not yet been introduced, in the early 1830s 'Scientifically-minded Parisian physicians embraced the new technology, which was rapidly diffused among the Parisian medical elite' (Berge 1994, 298). Hutton Balfour was appointed Professor of Botany at Glasgow in 1841 and Professor of Botany and Regius Keeper of the Royal Botanic Garden, Edinburgh in 1845. While maintaining field botany as an important element in his course, he soon introduced demonstrations of microscopy and physiology in illustration of his lectures. He applied to the Commissioners of Woods and Forests for additional accommodation at Inverleith and a new classroom and 'microscopical room' were provided and occupied in 1851 (Fletcher and Brown 1970, 141-2).

> In the sphere of practical teaching this was a notable advance, and the more so when the technical difficulties are remembered – the days of cheap microscopes was but beginning, aniline dyes were not yet... (Balfour 1913, 296)

Hutton Balfour's successor, Alexander Dickson (F) had conducted microscopical studies when at Aberdeen and Glasgow and these were continued in Edinburgh but were cut short by his death. It remained for Hutton Balfour's distinguished son, Isaac Bayley Balfour (F) who succeeded Dickson in the Edinburgh chair of botany in 1888, to extend his father's initiatives. He had encouraged practical work in the laboratory when he taught in Glasgow and when he became professor in Edinburgh he introduced it as an essential part of his course and later had further teaching laboratories built at Inverleith (Morton and Noble 1983, 77). Thus, the nature of botanical teaching in Scotland was profoundly changed by the Balfours, father and son.

Similar changes eventually took place in natural history. The College Museum of Natural History was Professor Jameson's (F) great achievement and was regarded by him as an appendage of the lectureroom. In his teaching he was concerned largely with external characters.

> It was plain that such a state of matters could not last. Jameson begat a love of Natural History in his students which could not be fed upon dried skins and glass eyes... (Wilson in Wilson and Geikie, 1861, 114)

Jameson hardly changed with the times, although he apparently did not resent the initiatives of others to teach practical zoology. For example comparative anatomy was left to the like of Robert Knox in his human anatomy class. Knox had studied in Paris under Georges Cuvier (F), the father of comparative anatomy, and was himself brilliant in its practice. When natural history became an examinable subject in the medical faculty, students were no longer satisfied with skins and skeletons but sought instruction on what lay between; from the 1840s, this want was supplied by one of Jameson's own students, John Goodsir (F) a pioneer in the microscopic study of animal tissues, who became Professor of Anatomy in Edinburgh in 1846.

The untimely death of Edward Forbes, only months after he had succeeded Jameson in 1854, frustrated the reforms which would have been expected from such a man. His successor was the zoologist George James Allman (F). Space for practical teaching in natural history was provided only when the collections were removed from the College Museum to the Edinburgh Museum of Science and Art under Allman's supervision in 1865. A bridge connecting the university with the new museum building gave the professor and his students ready access to the natural history collections in their new location. Gradually the cases around the walls of the erstwhile college museum were filled by teaching collections and the room was converted into a teaching laboratory capable of accommodating eighty students. (Fraser 1989, 285)

Our last illustration is provided by the physician John Hughes Bennett (F) who became Professor of the Institutes of Medicine at Edinburgh University in 1848. He was not only a pioneer in Britain of the use of the microscope in medicine, but also revolutionized medical education to include instruction in microscopy. He graduated MD from Edinburgh University in 1837 and, like Hutton Balfour five years previously, went to France to continue his medical education and then to Germany before returning to Scotland. In Paris he was a student of Alfred Donné who offered the first public course in medical microscopy there in 1837 (Berge 1994, 299). Bennett was so impressed by the applications of the microscope in medical research that on his return to Edinburgh in 1841 he gave extramural lectures on histology in which he demonstrated the application of microscopy to anatomy, physiology, pathology and the diagnosis of disease. In 1842 he published a landmark paper in the Society's *Transactions* (Bennett 1842) in which the occurrence of microscopic fungi in human tissue was first described. In the following year he was elected to Fellowship. It was his use of the microscope which led, in 1845, to his famous discovery of the first-described disease of the blood which he called leucocythaemia, known today as leukaemia. Convinced of the importance of microscopy in the clinical investigation of disease, he became the first doctor in Britain to teach its use. Not only were his own students so taught but, through the influence of his textbooks, microscopy was soon part of medical degree courses throughout the world.

c) The emergence of the National Museum

The recognition that natural history museums had been marginalized in higher education by the growth of experimental science, and by the consequent changes in the teaching of practical science which that necessitated, must have influenced the decision to dispose of the Society's museum.

A third factor which surely altered the attitude of the Society towards its own museum were the new concepts concerning the *raison d'etre* of museums which were developing from the movement towards public national and municipal museums. As we have seen these were driven by a belief in the social benefits which free access to museum displays would have on the education of children and working people. Allman wrote in the Industrial Museum of Scotland Report for 1861

> The value of the Museum of Natural History as a source of rational amusement, and an instrument of instruction for the working and middle classes, seems now to be fully recognised; every year is affording fresh proof that there exists among the public a deep-seated love of the various forms of external nature – a love, too, which with the present facilities of gratification, is rapidly developing itself, and finds unmistakeable expression in the hosts which throng our museum on public days, led by the simple pleasure of seeing around them representatives of the natural objects...which exist upon our globe.

Jenni Calder has noted that, for public museums, the pre-eminent objective was to invite a public, eager for information and encouraged in ideas of self-education, to take a share of what the country's rapidly growing resources had to offer in the sciences, technology and the arts.[9] Such ideas, although retaining the enlightenment view of museums 'stimulating knowledge and enquiry', addressed a wider world than the university class or Society Fellow for whose scholastic and didactic needs the private museums of societies and universities had been formed.

With the development of public national and municipal museums, a new professionalism in museum curation and management was born. This brought with it a growing awareness in the Royal Society of Edinburgh that such curatorial skills, to say nothing of adequate accommodation, were not available in the Society. The expectancy that these would be provided in Scotland's emerging national museum was certainly a factor which influenced the Society in deciding the future of its museum.

THE MEN BEHIND THE 1859 DECISION

This chapter opened in 1859 with the recognition by Douglas Maclagan's committee 'that the attempt on the part of the Society to maintain a general Museum of Natural History was inexpedient' and the consequent decision that, in future, the Society's collections should be limited to geology and mineralogy. We saw this as a radical decision challenging the Society's view of its museum held since the granting of the Second

Charter. Did Maclagan's committee act irresponsibly in ringing the death-knell, so far as the Society was concerned, of so much of what they were in office to conserve? It is of interest that a comparable situation arose in the Royal College of Physicians of Edinburgh, where the laboratory, proposed in 1885 and started in 1887, 'came into being as College Museum activities ceased' (Craig 1976, 105).

Having reviewed the developments in experimental science, university teaching and public museums during the first half of the nineteenth century, we should look again at the position of Maclagan and his men. They could not be accused of lacking an appreciation of the value of museum collections. Maclagan himself was then President of the Royal College of Surgeons of Edinburgh which had its own extensive museum. We have already met George Wilson as the Director of the Industrial Museum of Scotland. George James Allman had succeeded Edward Forbes as the Regius Keeper of its natural history collections, and John Hutton Balfour was a pioneer of microscopic botany. We must note, however, that under Hutton Balfour's direction a Museum of Botany had been opened to the public in 1852 and since 1855 he had served the Highland and Agricultural Society as chairman of its Museum Standing Committee.[10] Robert Chambers, a prominent member of the Society of Antiquaries of Scotland, was a publisher and well-known also for his interest in geology. In the previous year his book on the relative level of land and sea *Ancient Sea-Margins* had been published. His anonymity remained as the author of the sensational *Vestiges of Creation*, which was first published in 1844 and which had already appeared in ten corrected and improved editions. It has been said that Charles Darwin regarded *Vestiges* as 'a valuable lightning rod in channelling off the initial thunders of orthodoxy' from his own seminal work *On the Origin of Species*, the first edition of which went on sale to the trade in November 1859, the same month that the Maclagan Committee reported to Council (Gillispie 1951, 217; Desmond and Moore 1992, 477). Although J D Forbes was a member of the committee by virtue of being General Secretary of the Society, he had already donated to the Society's museum a number of collections illustrating the geology of various districts of interest which he had visited on his travels.

As we have seen the beneficiaries of the Maclagan Committee's recommendations were all represented on the Committee itself – the Royal College of Surgeons (Maclagan), the Industrial Museum (Wilson), the Natural History Museum (Allman), the Royal Botanic Garden (Balfour) and the Society of Antiquaries (Chambers). It would be unworthy of the memory of these distinguished men, however, to suggest that they had been influenced by self interest.

The Maclagan Committee drew from the Society men who, because of their experience of science and museums, were best able to read the signs of the times. Their expressed reasons for transferring the non-geological specimens were sound. In the face of Swinton's donations from India,

Thomas Allan had called for a more specialised collecting policy many years before. Maclagan's committee agreed that future acquisition should build on the existing strength of the geological and mineralogical collection. Specimens placed beside other specimens acquire a value which they could not possess in the isolated positions they occupied in the Royal Society's Room. In public museums the specimens would be more accessible to persons interested in the subjects to which they referred.

The decision to limit the society's collections to geology and mineralogy did not stimulate much activity in these subjects. Professor Charles Piazzi Smyth, Astronomer Royal for Scotland and Professor of Practical Astronomy at Edinburgh University, gave a number of collections to the Society's museum under the new arrangements (fig 11). He was a pioneer in mountain astronomy and established observatories on summits in Tenerife where he had collected geological specimens which he presented to the Society in 1859. His donations of 1863, 1865 and 1880, however, can hardly be regarded as strictly geological. On 4 February 1863 lightning struck Nelson's Monument on Calton Hill damaging its lower story. Smyth lost no time in obtaining those portions of the leaden covering affected by the strike which he described and presented to the Society's museum (Smyth, 1863). These are now in the National Museums of Scotland. Smyth's mystical interest in the cubit led him to a study of the Great Pyramid and his donation of 1865 consisted of geological specimens from that site together with sixteen fragments of the casingstones of the pyramid itself (Smyth 1867, II, 293-4). These are also preserved in the collections of the National Museums of Scotland. His last donation, given in 1880, was of samples of rock attached to the old rock thermometers at the Calton Hill Observatory.

THE DEPARTMENT OF SCIENCE AND ART
HAS SECOND THOUGHTS

Maclagan presented his committee's report to Council on 21 November 1859. At eleven on the following evening George Wilson died at the age of forty-one. For many years the brilliance of his vision and enthusiasm had contrasted sadly with the frailty of his health and he was already an ill man when appointed Professor of Technology and Director of the Industrial Museum.

Wilson's untimely death presented an unexpected opportunity for the Department of Science and Art to have early second thoughts on the Industrial Museum of Scotland. The Regius Chair of Technology, established only four years previously, was abolished forthwith and a Superintendent appointed to the Industrial Museum who had no connection with the University of Edinburgh. Five years later (1864) the Industrial Museum of Scotland, against the wishes of the Superintendent, was restyled the Edinburgh Museum of Science and Art (Anderson 1995, 222). To understand this volte-face in policy we must look behind the facade of the South Kensington office of the Department of Science and Art.

Sir Wemyss Reid observed that 'It was not without many a struggle and many a feud that the Science and Art Department at last took shape.'(Reid 1899, 143) An early inhibition was the outbreak of the Crimean War in the year following the Department's establishment which, in Playfair's words, 'heavily taxed the country'. As resources became more limited, so tension between the interests of Science and Art within the Department appears to have intensified.

Playfair recalled that 'The art section of the new Government department progressed more rapidly than that of science'.(Playfair in Reid 1899, 152) This is not surprising since art entered the Department with considerable momentum derived from Cole's Department of Practical Art which already administered thirty-six schools of design. Although, on the science side, the Museum of Practical Geology and the associated School of Mines, The Museum of Irish Industry and the Royal Dublin Society came under the new Department, no college of science, other than Owen's College in Manchester and the Andersonian College of Glasgow, came under Playfair's aegis.

Cole and Playfair were powerful personalities and, although Cole had at first hotly resented Playfair's involvement in preparations for the Great Exhibition, they had worked together to make a success of it. It has been acknowledged, however, that jealousies between the two men may have continued, although none were displayed (Norrish 1951, 541). Playfair wrote of Cole 'He was a man of remarkable energy and ability, and had no other regard in any work in which he was engaged than the best method of ensuring its success...The public good was always the uppermost – I might almost say the only – motive in his mind.' (Playfair in Reid 1899) The same judgement was deserved of Playfair himself. It is hard to believe, however, that a situation in which two men of such character and differing so widely in their philosophies, yoked within the same Department to pursue different objectives – the encouragement of science on the one hand and art on the other – can have been without tension. Playfair's interest in process was surely inherited from his Scottish education, being a major concern of the Scottish Enlightenment. For example, Playfair believed that raw materials were a less important factor in production than 'intellect, trained in the application of science and art' the sentiment so forcefully argued by the Scotsman's leader writer in the article of 1851 quoted in the last chapter (p 87). For Cole, on the other hand, the emphasis was on the quality of the finished product. At first there was no provision for the joint working of their two departments and in 1855 Cole was appointed Inspector-General of Art and Playfair became Secretary of the united Department.

Despite his successes, Playfair found the promotion of science an uphill task. 'I began a crusade in favour of technical education. It was wearing and dreary work. My voice sounded to myself as the voice of one preaching in the wilderness' (Playfair in Reid 1899, 152).

Playfair's first wife died in the year that he became Secretary of the Science and Art Department. In 1857 he married a wealthy lady and the financial independence which this gave him meant that he no longer needed to be so committed to 'the wearing and dreary work' of the Department. By giving up his secretaryship and undertaking the half-time position of Inspector of Schools of Science he was able to resume scientific research. In the following year William Gregory died and Playfair succeeded him in the Chair of Chemistry at Edinburgh University for which he had been an unsuccessful candidate in 1844. As we have seen, he at once set about preparing a chemical laboratory and found apparatus and equipment which, although no longer useful, was of historic interest. This he presented to George Wilson and in so doing laid the foundation for the Industrial Museum's collection of historic scientific instruments (Anderson 1978). Henry Cole became Secretary of the Department of Science and Art.

In 1856 site work had begun at South Kensington for the erection of the prefabricated building which the public christened the 'Brompton Boilers', designed to house the South Kensington Museum . In command of the sappers and miners working on the site was Lieutenant John Donnelly RE, newly returned from distinguished service in the Crimean War at Inkerman and Sebastopol. Henry Cole invited him to join his Department and on 1st October 1859 Donnelly was appointed Inspector for Science in Playfair's place (Vetch 1912). The Brompton Boilers housed both the art and the science collections of the South Kensington Museum. Cole worked tirelessly for the improvement and enlargement of the art collections at South Kensington and, as quoted by Anderson, the Royal Commission on Scientific Instruction reported in 1874

> Though, from special circumstances, the Art Collections of this Museum have been, up to the present time, most developed, it has contained, from its earliest days, several Collections of a Scientific Nature."

We are now in a position to understand the volte-face of 1859 in the policy of the Department of Science and Art towards the Industrial Museum of Scotland as an outward expression of the inner tensions of that Department. George Wilson had died; Lyon Playfair, who had shared his vision for the Industrial Museum of Scotland, had left his position of influence in the Department of Science and Art. Captain Donnelly, still a new boy in the Department, had been Inspector of Science for less than two months. Henry Cole, now Secretary of the Department, reigned supreme. As the son of an officer of the 1st Dragoon Guards, born at Bath and educated at Christ's Hospital, he is unlikely to have had much understanding of the philosophy of the Scottish Enlightenment in which both Wilson and Playfair had been nourished. For them 'improvement' involved the application of rational knowledge to the useful arts in which industry had an important role. With his long- standing enthusiasm for art Cole presided over what Anderson termed 'the gentrification' of Playfair's industrial museums (Anderson 1995, 222). The change of name from the Industrial Museum of Scotland to the Edinburgh Museum of Science and Art in 1864 was symptomatic of this changing emphasis. Even if the withdrawal of the esti-mate for the museum building in 1857 had nothing to do with Cole's acces-sion as Secretary, I believe the abolition of the Chair of Technology and the circumstances of the appointment of Thomas Croxon Archer as the Super-intendent of the Industrial Museum had. Archer was a Londoner and had served as an official of the Customs at Liverpool for twenty years.[12] He formed a small museum for Liverpool of its vegetable imports and came to public notice for his part in the formation of a collection of imports enter-ing the Mersey which was displayed at the Great Exhibition of 1851. His interest in botany led him to conduct evening lectures in that subject as well as taking an active part in the various scientific societies of the city. Archer would appear an unlikely candidate for the directorship of the Industrial Museum of Scotland, but he must have been known to Cole through his connection with the Great Exhibition – and so he was appointed. Cole's man, however, would not have been acceptable to the University of Edin-burgh as their Professor of Technology and, rather than split the posts, the Chair of Technology was abolished with the consent of the University. An important strand in the relationship between university teaching and the Museum's collections, so fundamental to Playfair's philosophy, had been abandoned.

In the event, Archer's superintendence, and from 1866, directorship of the Museum of Science and Art was effective. Plans for the Museum build-ing prepared by Captain F Fowke RE were approved by the Lords of the Privy Council and work began on site in February 1861. The foundation stone of the east wing of the Museum was laid by the Prince Consort in October 1861 and the natural history collections of the University moved into this, the first phase of the new building, under Professor George Allman's direction in 1865. The east wing and the eastern part of the main hall of the Museum were opened to the public as the Edinburgh Museum of Science and Art by the Duke of Edinburgh in 1866.

In the same year, on the motion of Professor Lyon Playfair, the Royal Society of Edinburgh memorialized Parliament for two Members for the Scottish Universities.[13] The Reform Bill was in prospect and Playfair had not lost the urge for public service. In the election which followed the Repre-sentation of the People Act reaching the Statute Book in 1868, Playfair stood in the liberal interest and was elected member for the universities of Edin-burgh and St Andrews. Although he again left Scotland his interest in Scot-tish education continued, as was shown two years later when he used his influence to establish the Murchison Chair of Geology at the University of Edinburgh.

The Museum building remained unfinished and on 31 March 1868 Lord Provost William Chambers had an interview with the Chancellor of the Exchequer requesting that an estimate be introduced for the Industrial Museum.[14] Still with no further work in prospect, the Royal Society of Edin-burgh sent a letter to Mr Gladstone, the Prime Minister, in 1869 asking that a sufficient sum be put in the estimates in order that Parliament might vote the requisite amount to complete the Museum 'in which the Society, as well as the General Public, take the liveliest interest'.

> That Museum in itself combined the features of several Museums formerly detached. It possesses large collections of Natural History and Geology, formerly the property of the University of Edinburgh, and associates these scientific collections with their applications to Industry. In consequence of the interesting connection between Science and Industrial Art, the Museum is frequented by crowds of persons at all periods of the year, and especially of the Artisan class. The collections are rapidly accumulating and Temporary rooms are filled with most valuable materials for display.[15]

This letter the Prime Minister passed to the Chancellor of the Exchequer and building of the west end of the Main Hall of the Museum commenced two years later and was completed in 1875. Thomas Croxon Archer died in January 1885 having just completed arrangements for building the final phase of the original building which was completed in 1889. It is greatly to Archer's credit that in his directorship he achieved the commencement and completion of the original museum building. On 2 May he was succeeded by Robert Murdoch Smith, a Royal Engineer who was Director of the Persian Telegraph Department and a pioneer scholar in Persian art studies.

> Murdoch Smith was of course intimately known to the authorities of the Science and Art Department, and in particular to Sir John Donnelly, who in 1884 had succeeded Sir Francis Sandford as secretary of the department. (Dickson 1901, 301)

Sir Henry Cole, who had spotted Lieutenant Donnelly RE on the building site of the Brompton Boilers in 1856, had retired in 1873. Sir John Donnelly retired from the Science and Art Department in 1887 with the rank of Major-General.

FINAL LINK WITH THE UNIVERSITY SEVERED

Before returning to the affairs of the Royal Society of Edinburgh we must consider the severance of the second and last remaining organic link between the university and the museum. The Regius Professor and Regius Keeper of Natural History, George Allman, retired in 1870 and was succeeded in these offices by the marine biologist Charles Wyville Thomson. Since Allman had been responsible for moving the natural history collections from the university to the museum and arranging the material in its new home, he had an interest in maintaining order in the collections and exhibits when using specimens for teaching. Even in Allman's time, however, the relationship between the Keeper of Natural History and the Museum Director became strained (G N Swinney, in preparation). Wyville Thomson's main interests were in teaching and field work and it was not long before he and Archer fell out over the way he used the museum collections, Thomson claiming independence in the Natural History Department. Matters came to a head in 1872 when, as scientific director of the *Challenger* Expedition, Thomson left Edinburgh to sail around the world for three and a half years 'to add the greatest single contribution to scientific knowledge of marine life since Aristotle had begun this over 2000 years previously'(Yonge 1972, 1). Museum squabbles (Hooker, Busk & Donnelly, 1872, 1873,1874) appear petty when compared with the magnitude of Thomson's achievement but the work of the museum had to go on. In 1873 Ramsay H Traquair was appointed Keeper of the Natural History Collections with no university connection. Traquair represented all that was best in the new full-time museum professional and set a magnificent example as a curator in enlarging, caring for and researching the collections in his charge. Any bitterness which may have been felt by Edinburgh University at Traquair's appointment was sweetened by his merit as a scientist. It is a pleasure to record that among the many honours which Traquair received was the honorary degree of LL D from that university.[16]

Finally it is unfortunate that the well-known history of the University of Edinburgh by Principal Sir Alexander Grant is so often cited in connection with the founding of Scotland's national museum. He summarizes these events thus:

> We may say here that from first to last the University has been to a considerable extent beguiled in the matter of the Museum. In 1852 the University possessed Natural History collections 'second only to those of the British Museum', and also a space of ground to the west expressly purchased with the object of securing free light to her buildings from that side. The collections were taken away, and the ground was built over for the Museum, so that the west side of the University quadrangle is rendered nearly useless. She was to administer the new Museum by means of her Professors of Technology and Natural History; but the Professor of Technology was promptly suppressed, and in course of time the official Director of the Museum succeeded in playing the cuckoo to the Professor of Natural History, and in ousting him from his function of Regius Keeper of the Natural History collections. At length it went so far that even the free use of specimens from the Museum for the teaching of the Natural History class was denied. And thus the physical connection of the 'Bridge of Sighs' which joins the two buildings of the University and the Museum now chiefly serves the purpose of being a record of broken pledges.
>
> If the Science and Art Department of Her Majesty's Government resolved to establish a Museum in Edinburgh – which it was doubtless very proper for them to do – they might have done so without reference to the University. (Grant 1884, I, 357 and 377)

Grant's history reflected continuing ill-feeling in the University regarding its relations with the Museum. In the year following publication of his history the matter was reopened in a memorandum by the Senatus.[17]

Because of the damage this has done to relationships between the University and the Museum in the past, it would be well to put the record straight. From the documents quoted above Grant is shown to be both partial and inaccurate. It was at the express desire of the University that Government included consideration of the natural history collections of the University in the establishment of the national museum. Before the intervention of the 1852 memorial from the City of Edinburgh, as Patrons of the University, Government had been memorialized by others to establish a museum of economic geology. The natural history collections were 'taken away' to fulfil the wishes of the University for a museum extension which it was unable to provide from its own resources. To obtain government accommodation for its museum the University had donated the natural history collection to the crown in 1854. It was never agreed that the University would administer the new museum by means of her Professors of Technology and Natural History. Playfair's letter to the Lord Provost makes clear (para 2) that the new Museum would be 'as entirely under the charge of the Board of Trade as the Museum of Economic Geology in London, or the Museum of Irish Industry in Dublin' and (para 3) 'the Patrons of the University would have no controlling power in the management of the new Museum'. The appointment of the Keeper of Technology had always been in the power of the Department of Science and Art. The director of the Museum could not be accused of playing cuckoo to the Professor of Natural History since Playfair's intentions regarding his relationship to the Keeper of Natural History were made very clear in his letter (para 5). 'The Office of Keepership of the Natural History part would be viewed as being directly responsible to the Government, and not in any way to the Patrons of the University who would be asked to concede to the Crown any rights that they may have to appoint a Keeper of the present collections, and it must not be considered as interfering with the due responsibility of any General Director of the Museum who may hereafter be appointed'. In the event a General Director was not appointed until 1866 and the relationship of the Regius Keepers of Natural History and the Director and then Superintendent of the Industrial Museum remained ambivalent until then (Swinney, in preparation). The free use of specimens for the teaching of the Natural History class was subject to the qualification in Playfair's letter (para 3) that specimens should be used for instruction when 'compatible with their security and preservation'. This had always been the case under Jameson and Allman and it was for the Director of the Museum to judge if it was still the case.

THE END OF THE SCIENTIFIC MUSEUM OF THE
ROYAL SOCIETY OF EDINBURGH

In 1862, just three years after the Society's museum was reduced to its geological collections, there came a suggestion that any form of museum was unnecessary.[18] Rather than give it up, however, Council decided to accept Archibald Geikie's offer to make up a collection of specimens for the Museum illustrating the geology and palaeontology of the country around Edinburgh. Geikie had been stationed in Scotland with the Geological Survey since 1855 and with H H Howell had surveyed his native Edinburgh and district. Their one inch to one mile geological map of Edinburgh was published in 1859 and the memoir followed in 1861. Whether Geikie intended to 'make up' the collection from Geological Survey specimens or to collect new material from localities familiar to him is not known but in either case he was well placed to provide the collection he offered.

Since 1859 the proximity of the Museum to the Society's Hall had made it a convenient place to serve tea during meetings and the importance which Fellows attached to that conviviality soon outweighed their concern for the collection. Gradually, but significantly, the West Gallery ceased being called the Museum and became known to Fellows as the Tea Room. In 1876 the Library Committee 'considered that application should be made to Professor (Archibald) Geikie authorizing him to take charge of some of the Geological Specimens in the Tea room in order that additional accommodation may be obtained for the Books'.[19] Geikie was now the first occupant of the Regius Chair of Geology at Edinburgh University, endowed by Sir Roderick Murchison and instituted in 1871. What geological material was removed to the University at this time, if any, is not known.

In 1877 the Library Committee[20] asked Archibald Geikie 'to frame a Report on the Geological Collection belonging to the Society with special reference to the determination of the specimens which illustrate and those which do not illustrate the publications of the Society'.[21] In only four weeks Geikie submitted his report which listed the contents of all the cases, cupboards and drawers in the 'Tea Room' and noted that slabs of Burdiehouse fossils were stored in a small ante-room.[22] These lists provide a most interesting catalogue of the Museum featuring many collections which had been listed in previous donations lists and many others which are known only from Geikie's record (see Catalogue at Appendix I). He reported as follows:

> The present condition of the Collection is in the highest degree unsatisfactory. No attention seems to have been paid to the specimens for many years. For the most part they have no reference labels, and as it may be difficult or impossible now to ascertain their localities, the value of the collection has been seriously lowered.

He recognized seven categories of specimens and recommended that only material referred to in papers read before the Society and collections of historical interest should be preserved. Otherwise, he concluded,

> The greater part of the collection has no special scientific interest or value, while much of it is really not worthy of room in the Society's apartments.

The Committee adopted the Report but at the next meeting of the Library Committee Dr R H Traquair, in his capacity as Regius Keeper of Natural History at the Museum of Science and Art, was requested to cooperate with Professor Geikie in disposing of the geological and mineralogical specimens from the Society's Museum.[23] As the year drew to a close the Committee had made up its mind and agreed that

> ... the attention of the Council be recalled to Professor Geikie's Report to the Committee on the Society's Museum:- that the Council be recommended to

adopt Professor Geikie's suggestion as to sections I and II of that Report:- that the remainder of the specimens be handed over to Professor Geikie for the use of the Student's Collection which he is now forming:- that the Agassiz Type Specimens of Fossils be presented by the Society to the Museum of Science and Art:- and that Professors Geikie and Maclagan be authorised to carry out these recommendations.

Council accepted the Committee's recommendations and the Agassiz types were presented to the Museum of Science and Art in 1878 while non-type material was passed to Professor Geikie's departmental museum at Edinburgh University. In 1879 the Library Committee was able to agree to the installation of book shelving in the tea room![24]

With the drying up of donations after 1878, interest in the Society's Museum withered. The end came with the termination of the Society's lease at the Royal Institution (Waterston, 1996, 96). Under the National Galleries of Scotland Act of December 1906, the Board of Manufactures, the Society's landlord, ceased to exist and was replaced by the Board of Trustees of the National Gallery of Scotland. The Royal Institution, with the other buildings which came under the management of the new Board, was vested in the Commissioners of Works and given over to the use of the Royal Scottish Academy and was renamed accordingly. The Society's last meeting was held there on 26 October 1908.

The 1906 Act did not forget the claims of the Royal Society of Edinburgh and steps were taken to find it a new home under the Commissioners of Works. After a winter during which meetings were held in University premises, the Society had its first meeting in its present house, 22-24 George Street, on 1 March 1909 (Waterston 1996). Were the Society's geological collections to be exhibited or stored in the new building, or had the time come for their disposal? The Curator at the time was Rev Dr John Sutherland Black who raised the matter with Council in February 1909. He had invited Dr John Horne, Dr Benjamin Peach and Professor James Geikie to examine what still remained of the collections and had received a further memorandum from Professor Geikie which Black submitted to Council. Under Black's convenership a committee consisting of James Geikie, Ramsay H Traquair, John Horne and Benjamin N Peach was formed 'to take steps for giving effect to Professor James Geikie's suggestions in the best practicable way, and to report to Council'.[25] Sixteen months later the committee had done its work and Black reported to Council

> that ... the Geological and Mineralogical specimens then existing in the Society's repositories, have now been distributed as follows:-
>
> 1) Sundry specimens selected by the Director of the Royal Scottish Museum.
>
> 2) The Ure, Webb-Seymour, and MacKenzie Collections and sundry miscellaneous specimens, to the University of Glasgow, an undertaking having been received from them that the said collections would be preserved as separate units in their Geological Museum.

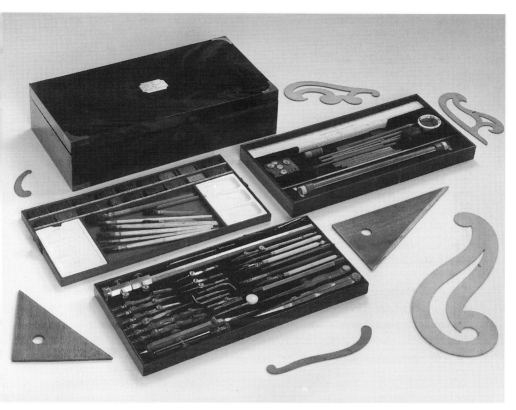

fig 21 Drawing Instruments by W Elliott, London given to the civil engineer Robert Stephenson (1803-59, FRS 1849, elected Hon FRSE 1855) by the mineral surveyor John Farey (1766-1826). Presented by Dr H Plenderleith in 1947. NMS T1989.3

3) Certain other specimens, selected by Professor James Geikie, to be preserved in the Geological Class Museum of the University of Edinburgh, or otherwise used for teaching purposes; and

4) The remaining specimens to Dr Horne to be distributed by him, amongst various qualified Educational Institutions.[26]

With this masterpiece of imprecision, Council ended any pretension to a scientific museum which the Society may have retained.

NEW HORIZONS

Accommodation was available in the back salon of the George Street building for the display of museum specimens and some objects of interest to Fellows continued to be given. One such donation was the contents of a drift bottle put in the sea from the Scottish National Antarctic Survey ship

Scotia at Burdwood Bank on 1 December 1903 and found on 7 September 1952 near the mouth of the Rangitikei River, North Island, New Zealand, 10,000 miles from the point of release.[27] That item speaks to us of the new enterprises which the Society was undertaking as its longstanding museum commitment was drawing to its conclusion. Support for the *Scotia* expedition, led by William S Bruce was one of these, the initiative for which was taken by the Royal Scottish Geographical Society. Others were the building and running of the Ben Nevis Observatory in association with the Scottish Meteorological Society and the Bathymetric Survey of Scottish Fresh-Water Lochs, also in association with the Royal Scottish Geographical Society. By discontinuing the longstanding commitment to its Museum, which the Society felt that others were then better fitted to fulfil, and by launching upon such new enterprises, the Royal Society of Edinburgh demonstrated the vitality which has assured its survival to pursue its chartered objectives in ever changing conditions.

Although the Society ceased to have a scientific museum of its own in 1910, its continuing interest and support for the wider museum movement has never been in doubt. Its concern was shown very soon. R H Traquair had retired from the keepership of the natural history Collections at the Royal Scottish Museum in 1906 and had been threatened with, and probably actually suffered, a reduced pension because Bumbledom considered that he 'had devoted much of the time to his private work' or, as we know to be the case, to scientific research which had brought international fame to the collections of the government museum which he served.[28] Following Traquair's death in 1912, the Society sought to avoid further injustice by writing to the Prime Minister, H H Asquith, seeking a pension from the Civil List for his widow, the well-known artist Phoebe Traquair.[29] More recently the Society's concern for the safekeeping of natural science collections was shown in 1981 by its support for the work of the Scottish Museums Council in listing the botany, geology and zoology collections known to exist in Scotland. This resulted in publication, by the National Museums of Scotland, of the first of a number of collection catalogues for which the Scottish Museums Council has been responsible (Stace, Pettitt and Waterston 1987).

ENFIN

One hundred and twenty seven years had passed since the Society first collected material to be housed in the College Museum and the Museum of the Faculty of Advocates, and ninety-nine since it had been permitted to retain its own collections under the Second Charter. Credit is due to the many men and women who freely gave collections and the many Fellows who, without payment, gave of their time and skill to care for them. In recording the history of the Museum of the Royal Society of Edinburgh this work seeks to do them honour.

1 Bishop Terrot, Dr Robert Christison, Mr John Russell (Treasurer), Mr David Milne and Professor J D Forbes (Secretary), (NLS ACC 10000/19 Council Minute of 4 April 1851).

2 NLS ACC 10000/20 Council Minute of 15 April 1859.

3 The committee comprised James T Gibson Craig (Treasurer), John Russell, Dr Robert Christison, Dr Douglas Maclagan (Curator) and J D Forbes (Secretary).

4 NLS ACC 10000/20.

5 I am grateful to Jean Jones for citing the following as examples of Hutton's experiments in geology; 1) his discovery that zeolite contains potash by treating it with muriatic (hydrochloric) acid and boiling it (B G Niebhur's Notes on T C Hope's Chemistry Lectures 1798 in the Bodleian Library and Playfair, 1805, 47; 2) his use of the microscope in his study of 'Brazilian Stone' (Hutton 1794, 89-90) and in his examination of the fibres in chalcedony (Niebuhr); 3) his use of the blowpipe to analyse rocks and minerals, for example with Black in examining an earth from Shetland (Edinburgh University Library, Special Collections, ms Gen 873, III, folio 198-9); 4) with Black, his heating of animal and vegetable substances in a Papin digester to prove that under pressure they can survive temperatures of 400-500F (Letter of Black to Menish, July 1792, Edinburgh University Library, Special Collections ms Gen 873, III, folio 228-31).

6 Of the overseas scientists mentioned, the following were elected Honorary Fellows of the Royal Society of Edinburgh: Baron Jons Jacob Berzelius (1827, previously elected to ordinary fellowship in 1820), Friedrich Wöhler (1867), Hermann Ludwig Ferdinand Helmholtz (1864), Carl Ludwig (1876), Christian Gottfried Ehrenberg (1845), Karl Theodor Ernst von Siebold (1864), Hugo von Mohl (1870), Rudolph Ludwig Carl Virchow (1868), Johannes Müller (1838).

7 *Report made to His Majesty by a Royal Commission of Inquiry into the State of the Universities of Scotland*, London 1831, Glasgow, p 47.

8 *Ibid* 1831, Edinburgh, p 56.

9 J Calder, 'A Source of Rational Amusement', unpublished article.

10 Hutton Balfour served as chairman of the Highland Society's Museum Committee until 1866 when it ceased to exist on the transfer of the collection of vegetable products of Scotland to Government. The museum was then converted into office accommodation for the Highland Society.

11 Royal Commission on Scientific Instruction, *Fourth Report*, 1874 (R G W Anderson 1995, 214).

12 'The Late Professor Archer', *The Scotsman*, 20 February 1885.

13 NLS ACC 10000/19 Minute of Council of 25 May 1866.

14 City of Edinburgh Archives, McLeod Bundle 25A item 33, vol xxi, p 121.

15 NLS ACC 10000/21 Minute of Council of 29 January 1869.

16 Traquair was a Fellow of the Royal Society of London. He was awarded the Neill and Makdougall-Brisbane Medals by the Royal Society of Edinburgh, the Lyell Medal by the Geological Society of London and a Royal Medal by the Royal Society of London.

17 Muir W Memorandum by the Senatus Academicus of the University of Edinburgh on the Relations of the University to the Museum of Science and Art March 1885.

18 NLS ACC 10000/20 Minute of Council of 16 January 1863.

19 NLS ACC 10000/230 Minute of Library Committee of 27 November 1876.

20 Members of the Library Committee were then Professor Douglas Maclagan (Convener), John Hutton Balfour (General Secretary, Professor of Botany and Keeper of the Royal Botanic Garden, Edinburgh), Dr Alexander Buchan (Meteorologist), Rev Philip Kelland (Professor of Mathematics, Edinburgh), Peter Guthrie Tait (Professor of Natural Philosophy, Edinburgh), and William Turner (Professor of Anatomy, Edinburgh).

21 NLS ACC 10000/230 Minute of Library Committee of 8 February 1877.

22 NLS ACC 10000/230 Minute of Library Committee of 8 March 1877 and NLS ACC 10000/396 ms report dated 7 March 1877.

23 NLS ACC 10000/230 Minute of Library Committee of 12 March 1877.

24 NLS ACC 10000/230 Library Committee Minute of 22 October 1879.

25 NLS ACC 10000/25, Minute of Council of 19 February 1909.

26 NLS ACC 10000/25, Minute of Council of 20 June 1910.

27 Council Minute of 8 December 1952.

28 I am grateful to Dr Paton for drawing my attention to a letter from Professor W C McIntosh of the Chair of Natural History at St Andrew's University – a friend of R H Traquair – to his nephew dated 4 October 1911 in which he wrote 'I think I told you that when Dr Traquair's retiring allowance had to be considered, the Government reduced it on the plea that T had devoted much of the time to his private work.' From the W C McIntosh Correspondence, St Andrews University Library.

29 NLS ACC 10000/25, Council Minute of 3 March 1913.

CHAPTER SIX

MUSEUMS
IN
CONTEXT

*...the specimens, the lilies of ambition still spring in their
climate, still unpicked...*

Keith Douglas

The present study has shown, within the microcosm of the Royal Society of
Edinburgh and its museum, what happened to collections when the context
of their use changed from that in which they were formed. These contextual shifts were sometimes misunderstood and often took place unknowingly,
but they profoundly influenced the way in which collections were regarded
and their ultimate fate.

To summarize: the context in which the Society's collections were used
suffered a threefold change during the museum's history.

Firstly, in the days of the First Charter, the pedagogic system of teaching
in Scottish universities was at its height and the Society's collections, along
with others in the College Museum, were used as a centre for research, and
the focus of practical study; the counterpart of the lecture demonstration in
the physical sciences. Transmission to the College Museum of natural productions donated to the Society meant that the Society had a role in assisting both research and education.

Secondly, under the Second Charter the role of the Society's museum
changed to a resource for research material and a repository of worked collections, many illustrative of scientific papers published by the Society. Its
educational role became minimal.

Thirdly, the final dispersals of 1859 and 1878 were triggered by the
advance of experimental science and the consequent changes in the teaching of university science. Much of the material was passed to the national
museum where ideas of egalitarian education and social improvement were
current.

That such changes can be detrimental was shown in describing how
Jameson's handling of the Huttonian Collection succeeded only in destroy-
ing it. Jameson was unable to see beyond his own viewpoint – representative, neptunist and catastrophist – to that of its collector – illustrative,
plutonist and gradualist.

It is ironic that another collection presented in 1843, a series of specimens
collected by J D Forbes from under the ice of La Brenva in Piedmont, and
others from the Grimsel and the Jura showing glacial polish and striation

together with a model, providing proofs and illustrations of glacier flow in the context of glacial theory, has been lost. There is no doubt that in this case Jameson would have valued the collection as supporting and illustrating his view of the former extension of land ice. On the other hand influential Fellows of the Society, such as David Milne, would regard the Forbes collection as worthless, again because of their inability to see it in any other context than their own belief in the floating iceberg theory.

It is not only when a collection falls into the hands of a curator who is antipathetic to the purposes of the collector, however, that danger arises. We have seen also that changing paradigms can, in time, endanger collections. The scientific and educational context in which academic Fellows found themselves changed radically, albeit passively, in the first half of the nineteenth century. While this changed viewpoint led to marginalization, neglect and eventual disposal of the Society's museum, it is important to remember that the purposes for which the collections were made remained valid.

Thus objective curation of a collection requires the purpose of its formation to be respected. The integrity of a collection will be lost if only those parts of it are preserved which can be fitted in to a context of use other than that for which it was made. This does not mean that all collections should be left in their original state so that their social context is preserved. It does mean, however, that records should be kept so that, if specimens from the collection are used for other purposes, it will always be possible to restore the collection to its original purpose when necessary. The value of a collection must be judged in its own context.

FROM MICROCOSM TO THE WIDER WORLD

The fate of the Royal Society Museum was in no way unique. Throughout Britain major and minor collections have suffered because their use has changed and nobody has been interested in their original context. As we noted at the outset, Enlightenment thought required the educated man to reflect on the basis of knowledge and to agree with others on its foundations (Shapin 1981, 319). Such an approach to learning was characteristic of Scottish scholarship in general and it remains crucial for the scholar curator in particular. It is a tradition of scholarship which understands and respects the intellectual context of collections and so ensures their safety and is far removed from short-termism, the quick fix and the soundbite. Where it has been neglected collections have suffered.

Academic collections

Nowhere does the intellectual climate change more rapidly than in a university department. Teaching reflects changing paradigms. Research is influenced by the questions and opportunities of the moment, not to mention the interests of changing personnel, especially heads of department. Even fine collections made in furtherance of today's research interest may be found worthless for tomorrow's. With honourable exceptions, many influential academics lost touch with the context of formation of the collections in their care, causing widespread disinterest in departmental or even university museums. This blindness persisted from the mid-nineteenth to the mid-twentieth centuries in the course of which unused or little-used collections in universities were neglected or even discarded and the museum heritage suffered great loss. Even during the period following the Second World War, when the financial floodgates opened for university expansion, money was often used to convert museum accommodation into staffrooms or laboratories with scant regard for the displaced collections. Too often the curation of university collections was not recognized as an official duty and, when done, was undertaken as a labour of love. These problems were the subject of reports by the Museums and Galleries Commission,[1] which have resulted in renewed public interest in the intrinsic value of university collections, when considered in their proper context.

Local collections

Museums of local history were formed, often in the nineteenth century by local societies, with the scholastic purpose of illustrating the social and environmental history of a locality. A curator who takes the trouble to understand the context of their formation acquires a unique understanding of the collections and their relationship to the locality; a scholarship which is unlikely to be undertaken by others who lack the curator's intimacy with collections. In so far as the many other activities of a local museum may remove it from its scholastic context, that museum's value is diminished. It may well be that the local curator must act as teacher, popularizer, tourist promoter and administrator but, if time is no longer available to respect and understand the context of the collections, the scholastic link may be weakened or even broken and the integrity of the collections jeopardized. It is unfortunately true that in the past objects from local museums have not been given the conservation priority which they deserve, or have even been disposed of, because their local significance has not been understood. Fortunately the advent of local museum councils, such as the Scottish Museums Council, have encouraged national action, underpinned by government grant, to support local museums in their curatorial reponsibilities.

National collections

The men who disposed of the Repository of the Royal Society of London and the collections of the Royal Society of Edinburgh recognized that reference collections for research purposes would be better placed in the national collection. The scientific community then expected that adequate accommodation and curatorial resources, which could no longer be provided by these societies, would be available for the curation of extensive national reference collections. The museum of which they dreamed, perhaps the utopian Baconian realisation, was defined in 1918 by Tate Regan, a past Director of the British Museum (Natural History):

> In an ideal museum every species would be represented by a series of examples illustrating its geographical range, variation, growth, seasonal changes, sexual characters etc, and all these specimens would be properly preserved, correctly named, labelled, catalogued, and arranged in systematic order according to their natural relationships. (Regan 1919, 65)

Regan recognized, however, that 'No such museum exists or ever will exist'.

MUSEUMS AND SYSTEMATICS

Tate Regan defined the purposes of a museum as the preservation of material for education and research. In 1918 he spoke for all museums, academic, municipal and national, when he expressed his view that

> At the present day the educational value of museums is appreciated to a much greater extent than the fact that museums are – or ought to be – centres of research.

Since Regan's time much good work has been done to develop the unique and important role which museums have in education. It is widely recognized that the actuality of a specimen invites an emotional and intellectual reaction in a museum visitor which is quite unlike that experienced by the portrayal of that object in any other medium. It is instructive to note, however, that what spurred Tate Regan to make his apologia of 1918 was the omission of the British Museum (Natural History) from a list of national institutions engaged in scientific research in a recently published report of the Advisory Council to the Committee of the Privy Council for Scientific and Industrial Research. On the personal level the reduction of Traquair's retiral allowance, to which reference was made in the last chapter, showed that contemporary officials had not begun to understand the importance to the extension and value to the national collection of systematic research. If today's custodians of the nation's reference collections overemphasise their role in education and entertainment, history will repeat itself and the essential place of museums and their scholar curators in the community of scientific research will again be forgotten.

When the Royal Society of Edinburgh passed its museum collections to the national and other museums in 1859, 1878, and 1910, it took the view that in doing so 'they could not only be more accessible to persons interested in the subjects to which they refer, but would, from being placed beside other specimens, acquire a value they could not possess in the isolated position in which they were in the Royal Society's Rooms'. Among the important scientific purposes for which these extensive national reference collections were formed is systematics, an important branch of research concerned with the description and classification of species. The study has developed since its principles were first outlined by Carl Linnaeus in his *Systema Naturae* (1735-1766). Sound description, nomenclature and classification lie at the root of biological communication. Without them data storage and retrieval in biology would be virtually impossible.

Systematics, like other branches of biology, has its own developing frontiers of research, as for example in the genetic field; work which is yielding exciting results and which is appropriately done in the laboratories of research institutes and universities. A second, and larger, function of systematics, however, remains the basis of a most important service – to answer, with scientific precision, the question 'What is it?' The success of this study relies on the availablility of large reference collections and is therefore appropriately done in museums or herbaria. Although the service thus provided is fundamental and ongoing, its popularity in relation to other more glamorous and 'frontier' branches of botany and zoology has diminished and its importance is not understood by the public and is imperfectly understood by many biologists. This is curious because few would question the scientific value of diagnostic services in medicine or of the service provided by chemical analyses in answering the question 'What is it?'

The value of determinative systematics is twofold, utilitarian and philosophical. All economic biology and mineralogy is based on a knowledge of species and their distribution. Upon that study depends the recognition of the world's resources and the provision of mineral wealth and essential natural products. Secondly, systematics is basic to the philosophic study of nature – those who study anatomy, physiology, evolution, ecology or mineral genesis must know exactly what species they are dealing with.

Not only do such collections serve for reference in identification, they also form an essential part of the nation's scientific heritage. In Tate Regan's words:

> The collections remain as a permanent record of the work done, and are suitable for reference and study. It is, I believe, necessary for the intellectual development and the material prosperity of the nation that this work should be carried on.

Today we are familiar with Popper's view that no statement can be regarded as scientific unless it is made in such a way as to render it falsifiable.

> I shall not require of a scientific system that it shall be capable of being singled out, once and for all, in a positive sense; but I shall require that its logical form shall be such that it can be singled out, by means of empirical tests, in a negative sense: it must be possible for an empirical scientific system to be refuted by experience. (Popper 1980,41)

We have seen that Hutton offered, not only descriptions of the field relationships of rocks and strata, but a collection of geological specimens as proofs and illustrations of his Theory of the Earth. His geological collection was part of the logic of his scientific theory which could be experienced and tested and thus was open to refutation in the Popperian sense. We have seen also that, with remarkable prescience, the Society's first curator, Thomas Allan, understood the importance of specimens in scientific method and urged that geological papers published by the Royal Society of Edinburgh should be accompanied by specimens placed in the Society's museum (Allan, 1812, 1815). They remained there as material evidence against which the scientific views of the authors could be tested or even developed. It was as a result of Allan's policy, for example, that it was possible for Sir George Mackenzie's collection of the rocks of Iceland, made in 1810, to be re-examined one hundred and fifteen years later, using techniques unavailable to Mackenzie, and so to be re-described in modern petrographic terms (Peacock 1925).

The importance of the provision of reference collections, and thus the place of museums and herbaria, to establish the scientific status of published papers in natural science is still inadequately understood. Can we regard lists of species published in palaeontological or natural history papers, if unsupported by the evidence of voucher specimens, truly scientific, or are they, as irrefutable statements, mere expressions of opinion? For example a species so listed may strike a reader as unusual in a certain ecological or geographical setting, but without voucher material it is impossible to determine whether the author has made an interesting observation or has made a misidentification. In the same way a cited species may subsequently have been recognised to consist of two or more subspecies but without voucher material it will not be possible to determine its true taxonomic position. The exploratory botanist may learn of the medicinal uses of certain plants from native tribesmen, and he may indeed note his identification of the plants concerned, but reference specimens must be collected as a record of his work and to vouch for the accuracy of his field identifications. It may be argued that these questions could be answered by collecting new material from the described site. With the passage of time, however, this is often no longer possible.

An essential element in establishing the scientific basis of systematics in natural science, in the Popperian sense, is the type concept in the designation of 'type specimens' as reference material against which any description of a species may be tested. The type concept has been established by international agreement in the procedures of taxonomy for recent and fossil species in botany and zoology, and lately in the recognition of new species in mineralogy.[2] The characters displayed by type specimens define the characters of species whether or not these have been accurately described by the original or subsequent authors. Thus type material is constantly re-examined and re-appraised by taxonomists and its curation is a special responsibility of museums and herbaria. Type collections provide a particular and permanent record of work done and represent the ultimate reference for natural science in answering the question 'What is it?'

Although botany, zoology and geology collections, through systematics, have a special relevance to natural science as a record of work done, Tate Regan's reference to the importance of reference and study collections as necessary for the intellectual development and the material prosperity of the nation has a far wider application. Collections of art, ethnography, technology, scientific instruments and local history also bring together a priceless record of human achievement which is essential to scholarship and the understanding of our civilisation.

Today the pressures upon the national museums, as with other museums, to use resources in contexts other than the scholastic one in which the collections were formed, is even greater than in Tate Regan's day and, in so far as these activities usurp the museum's scholastic curatorial base, the collections are jeopardized. The scholarly curatorial relationship with the collections, however, is a function within society which is unique to curators. The writer has sought to challenge museum authorities with this fact:

> Is it too much to hope that Ministers of the Crown and Boards of Trustees may yet learn...that their first charge, so far as museums are concerned, is to maintain our collections for the advancement of learning and useful knowledge and enhance them by wise additions using current opportunities which may never recur? By this stewardship they will be judged. Others may entertain, educate and do research, all activities appropriate also to the museum, but the authorities must recognise that only trained curators are equipped to maintain collections and must be given the means to do so. Only by facilitating their curators can these authorities discharge their responsibility to hand on to future generations the collections which they inherited in a better state than they found them.[3]

A museum director of our own day, reflecting on the threat to the evolution of collections posed by the pressures to which scholar curators are now subjected, has written:

> Museums must know about what they own and want to collect. Committees can't do this. Administrators can't do this. Educators can't do this. Registrars can't do this. These people have neither the time nor the full authority to do so.
> It is the work of curators. (Miller, 1992)

Failure in contextual awareness in museums has already resulted in serious loss to the museum heritage in Britain. Furthermore, at no time in the history of our museums has pressure for altered use, powered by politically determined changes in funding and management, been more pressing than now. The present study may be helpful, in the wider context, in pointing to dangers which it would be well to avoid.

1 See *Report on University Museums*, Standing Commission on Museums and Galleries, London, HMSO, 1977.

2 Taxonomy is the study of the laws of classification as applied to natural history. Informal references to type material had been made in the description of plant and animal species

for many years. In botany it became mandatory to designate a type specimen from 1 January 1958 (Greuter et al 1994, Article 37.1) and from 1 January 1990 a valid description of a new taxon required to include the words 'typus' or 'holotypus' (Greuter et al 1994, Article 37.4) and the herbarium, or institution in which the type is conserved required to be indicated. The history of the regulation of animal nomenclature has been given by Melville (Melville, 1995). The ninth International Zoological Congress suggested that formal provision should be made regarding type specimens in the animal kingdom. At the Paris Zoological Congress of 1948 proposals were made to embody what by then had become general practice regarding type material in the *Règles*. A draft was prepared (Bradley, 1957) for the 1958 International Zoological Congress which led to The International Code of Zoological Nomenclature, second edition 1961 which governs present practice. The many thousands of species of plants and animals described under the binomial system prior to these dates are now subject to the process of lectotypification whereby later authors designate type specimens for previously described species. The Commission on New Minerals and Mineral Names of the International Mineral Association was established in 1959. Its rules require that when a new mineral is described, or an existing one redefined, the author should exercise care in defining its type designation and should ensure that a type specimen is held as permanent reference material by at least one major museum or a nationally recognized mineral collection (Nickel and Mandarino, 1987).

3   C D Waterston, to the Geological Curators' Group, Scunthorpe, 3 December 1992, reported in *Geological Curator* 6, No 1, 1994, p 45. See also Waterston (1972, 1977, 1979).

RECONSTRUCTED CATALOGUE OF THE MUSEUM OF THE ROYAL SOCIETY OF EDINBURGH

Donations are listed in the first 22 volumes of the *Transactions of the Royal Society of Edinburgh* (here referred to as *Transactions*) which cover the period 1783 to 1859. The *Transactions* lists are fairly complete in the earlier volumes but become very inadequate later. From 1832 donations were given in the *Proceedings of the Royal Society of Edinburgh* (here referred to as *Proceedings*) but were never comprehensive. The printed *Billets* giving notice of Society meetings sometimes intimated donations. The *Billet* for 6 February 1843 gave a 'List of the principal Donations of the Royal Society, and which may be seen in the Museum' to which a number of references are made below. Other published sources giving information about donations are reports of the Society's meetings in journals, such as Brewster's *Edinburgh Journal of Science* and Jameson's *Edinburgh Philosophical Journal,* and references to donations by authors of published papers. Manuscript sources include Society minute books, reports to council and letters.

The National Museums of Scotland is abbreviated below to NMS.

DONATIONS UNDER THE FIRST CHARTER 1783–1811

The following donations are listed in *Transactions* 1, 1783–85, pp 77-80. The numbers refer to the order in which the articles were deposited in the Museum of the University of Edinburgh.

HIS GRACE THE DUKE OF BUCCLEUCH

[Henry Scott, third Duke of Buccleuch, fifth of Queensberry, first president of the Society]

The Head, Horns and Bones of the Bison Scoticus, found in a peat-moss upon the Duke's estate in Roxburghshire. 1-4.

DR ALEXANDER MONRO

[Professor of Anatomy, University of Edinburgh (1754-1808)]

Thirty-eight coloured Drawings of Birds, of the southern hemisphere. 5-42.

These drawings are now bound in a volume entitled *Original Drawings of Birds from Captain Cook's 2nd Voyage* in the NMS Archive Library, MS598.2.

The Head and Horns of the Arnee, from Bengal. 43.

According to Kerr (1792, 336) there was a specimen of the Arnee in the Edinburgh College Museum. 'No 43 The Head and Horns of an unknown quadruped brought from Bengal' is also recorded in Robert Jameson's list of the museum contents in his register of 1812. It is probable that this is one of the two arnees of unknown provenance now in NMS. See also Sweet (1972, footnote 18, p 400).

THE HONOURABLE LORD DUNSINNAN
[Sir William Nairne, Lord Dunsinnan]

A painting in oil, of the Head and Horns of an Elk, found in a marl-pit in Forfarshire. 44.

The painting was exhibited in The British Gallery of the Natural History Museum of Edinburgh University by Professor Jameson. J B Davies of the Museum of Science and Art confirmed that the painting had been transferred to the nation and was stored in the Museum of Science and Art. It was exhibited to the Society of Antiquaries of Scotland by J A Smith in 1871 who figured and described the skull as *Cervus alces* (Smith, 1873). It has not been traced in the collections of NMS.

THE HONOURABLE LORD HAILES
[Sir David Dalrymple, Lord Hailes]

A Large Mass of the Rock of Gibralter, containing Bones. 45.

The Ear of a Whale, from Greenland. 46.

The Head of a Fish, petrified. 47.

The Vertebrae of three different species of animals, petrified. 48, 49, 50.

Glossopetrae, belonging to two different species of Shark. 51, 52.

Two crustaceous animals petrified. 53, 54.

Three different species of Echinus petrified. 55, 56,57.

Four different species of Nautilus petrified. 58-62.

Six different species of turbinated Shells petrified. 63-8.

Ten species of turbinated Shells petrified 69-78.

Three species of Shells. 79-81.

Four species of Madrepore. 82-5.

Red Coral from the Mediterranean. 86.

Six species of Gorgonia. 87-92.

Spongia Aculeata Lin. 93.

Ostrea Folium Lin. 94.

Two Indian Arrows poisoned. 95.

CAPTAIN FAIRFAX OF THE NAVY
[Sir William George Fairfax, vice-admiral, died in Edinburgh. He was the father of Mary Somerville.]

Five species of Fishes from the Spanish main. 96-100.

REVEREND DR BOWMAKER, MINISTER OF DUNSE

[Robert Bowmaker]

Two species of Serpents from Florida. 101, 102.

THE RIGHT HONOURABLE LORD DAER

[Basil William Douglas, Lord Daer]

A collection of Indian Arms, Apparel and Utensils, from the South Seas; made during Captain Cook's last voyage. 103-77.

The following items in the ethnography collections of the Department of History and Applied Art in NMS have been identified by Dale Idiens as possibly Cook material. In most cases the identification is supported by the objects having Professor John Walker's original manuscript 'ME' or Musaeum Edinensis labels associated. They are as follows:

MEI10 (UC340) 1 & 2 Arrows, cedar shafts, painted, notched and feathered, one with a flint point.

MEI24 (UC789) Barkcloth, striped black and red. Label in Walker's hand 'Otaheite cloth striped. MEI24'.

MEI25 (UC442) Barkcloth, white painted ornament. Label in Walker's hand 'Otaheite Cloth. MEI25'

MEI28 (UC446) Piece of barkcloth, painted black design. Label in Walker's hand 'Otaheite Cloth. MEI28' (fig 3)

MEI30 (UC430) Barkcloth, white. Label in Walker's hand 'Otaheite Cloth. MEI30'

MEI32 (UC516) Barkcloth, white. Label in Walker's hand 'Otaheite Cloth. This is the finest cloth made in the Island and seems to have received the white colour from bleaching. MEI32'

MEI33 (UC470) Mat, hibiscus fibre. Tonga. Label in Walker's hand 'Friendly Is. MEI33' ...'Graminaceous'

MEI34 (UC466) Piece of mat, woven pandanus. Tonga.

MEI35 (UC475) Bag, plaited pandanus. Label in Walker's hand 'A bag of straw and very neatly and firmly made. Friendly Is. MEI35' (fig 4).

MEI36 (UC830) Cloak, flax with 'taniko' border. New Zealand. This specimen does not now have a Walker label, the information being taken from the UC register.

MEI75 (UC422,A & B) Fishhooks (2), bone and pearlshell with flax lines. Label in Walker's hand 'Fishhooks from New Zealand: MEI75'.

(MR WILLIAM ANDERSON)

A collection of Indian Arms, Apparel and Utensils, and of Natural Productions, made in the South Sea islands, and on the west coast of America, by MR ANDERSON, Surgeon to Captain Cook. 178-274.

Sir George Mackenzie's annotated catalogue of 1812, NLS ACC 10000/386 states 'There are two large trunks full of South Sea Cloth & Matting, besides a number of articles which are hung up in the museum'.

The following items in the ethnography collections of the Department of History and Applied Art in NMS have been identified by Dale Idiens as possibly Cook material. In most cases the identification is supported by the objects having Professor John Walker's original manuscript 'ME' or Musaeum Edinensis labels associated. They are as follows:

ME199 (UC833) Mat, palm leaf. Label in Walker's hand 'An Indian Straw Matt. South Sea. ME199'

ME200 (UC489) Mat. Samoa. Label in Walker's hand 'An Indian Mat of very fine Fabrick ME200'

ME201 (UC412) Barkcloth, Tahitian. Label in Walker's hand 'Straw coloured Otaheite Cloth, with circular spots of red. It consists of three Folds, glued and beat together. ME207'. (Another small parchment label = 'No.18')

ME202 (UC811) Barkcloth, dark brown. Label in Walker's hand 'Otaheite cloth. ME202'

ME203 (UC753) Barkcloth, brown. Label in Walker's hand 'South Sea Cloth. ME203'

ME204 (UC813) Barkcloth, painted red and black triangles. Label in Walker's hand 'South Sea Cloth. ME204'

ME208 (UC493) Flax Cloak. New Zealand. Label in Walker's hand 'A Matt of New Zealand hemp. ME208'

ME241 (UC834) Bag, plaited palm leaf, sinnet ties. Label in Walker's hand 'A Bag made of Leaves of a Reed. South Sea Islands. ME241'.

THE EARL OF HOPETOUN
[James Hope, 3rd Earl of Hopetoun]

A cabinet of Fossils, containing the following articles: Fifty-five species and varieties of antique Marbles. 275-338.

Probably from 'A Box with 100 different kinds of Marble' purchased by Lord John Hope, later 2nd Earl of Hopetoun, during his stay in Italy while on the Grand Tour (1725–27). Fifty marble specimens are preserved in the Geology Department of NMS as G1993.34.2-51, named by Professor John Walker, have his original manuscript 'ME' Musaeum Edinensis labels and numbers attached as follows:

ME275. *Psadurium Lucelleum* (Antique Black Marble)

ME276. *Psadurium Orientale* (Ner'e Bianco Anticho)

ME280. *Marmor Carrarense* (Carrara Marble)

ME281. *Marmor Lacteum*

ME282. *Marmor Palumbinum* (a. nebulosum)

ME283. *Marmor Palumbinum* (b. fasciatum)

ME285. *Marmor Carneum* (Antique Carnation)

ME287. *Marmor Verdello* (a. florentinum)

ME289. *Marmor Verdello* (b. thalafecnum)

ME290. *Marmor Luteo-virens*

ME292. *Marmor Ione*

ME293. *Marmor Cipolino*

ME294-295. *Marmor Undulatum*

ME297. *Marmor Dorata*

ME298. *Marmor Nivarium*

ME299. *Marmor Corallinum*

ME300. *Marmor Oculatum*

ME301-302. *Marmor Gragnialia*

ME303. *Marmor Sicilio* (a. vulgare)

ME304. *Marmor Sicilio* (b. rivulosum)

ME305. *Marmor Sicilio* (v. viridescens) (fig 1)

ME306. *Marmor Persechino*

ME307. *Marmor Coronella*

ME308. *Marmor Flammigerum*

ME309. *Marmor Myrmeiophoros*

ME311. *Marmor Sienno* (a. contortum)

ME312. *Marmor Sienno* (b. undatum)

ME313. *Marmor Veronese*

ME315. *Marmor Piombino* (fig 1)

ME317. *Marmor Pavonazzo*

ME318. *Marmor Floridum*

ME319. *Marmor Africanum*

ME320-321. *Marmor Porcellana*

ME322. *Marmor Semesanto*

ME322 bis. *Marmor Seme Santo*

ME324. *Marmor Brocatello*

ME327-328. *Marmor Brocatello*

ME329. *Marmor Interpolarum*

ME330. *Marmor Marginatum*

ME331. *Marmor Marmor Amygdaloides*

ME332. *Marmor Achatinum*

ME333. *Marmor Glomeratum*

ME335. *Marmor Pannosum*

ME336. *Marmor Circumscriptum*

ME337. *Marmor Obscurum*

ME338. *Marmor Castracana*

Six species of Florentine Marbles and other Landscape Stones. 339-344.

One of these specimens is preserved in NMS as G1993.34.52 named by Professor John Walker as follows:

ME344. Graphida Piniformis

Seventeen species and varieties of the Phengites, or antique Oriental Alabaster. 345-411.

Fifty-five of these specimens are preserved in NMS as G1993.34.1, G1993.34.55-104 and G1993.34.111-12 named by Professor John Walker as follows:

ME345-346. *Phengites Nebulosus* (a. matutinus)

ME348. *Phengites Nebulosus* (b. meridianus)

ME350. *Phengites Nebulosus* (v. vespertinus)

ME351-353. *Phengites Nebulosus* (i. turbidus)

ME355. *Phengites Nebulosus* (i. turbidus)

ME356-357. *Phengites Floridus* (a. albus)

ME358? *Phengites Floridus* (G1993.34.111)

ME359-363. *Phengites Floridus* (b. carneus)

ME364-366. *Phengites Floridus* (v. brocatello)

ME367-368. *Phengites Floridus* (i. puruchina)

ME370. *Phengites Floridus* (i. puruchina)

ME371-375. *Phengites Floridus* (e. ranciato)

ME376-378. *Phengites Onychites* (a. albus)

ME379. *Phengites Onychites* (b. griseus)

ME381. *Phengites Onychites* (v. rubidus)

ME383-384. *Phengites Onychites* (v. rubidus)

ME386-390. *Phengites Onychites* (i. luteus)

ME392. *Phengites Onychites* (e. coerulescens)

ME397-403. *Phengites Oculatus* (fig 1)

ME404. *Phengites Onychites*

ME405. *Phengites Onychites* (a. albus)

ME406. *Phengites Onychites*

ME407? *Phengites Onychites* (G1993.34.112)

ME408-410. *Phengites Onychites* (n. purpureus)

Thirty-five species and varieties of those antique Stones which are called by the Italians Pietre dure. They all belong to the siliceous class, and to the following genera: Jasper, Heliotrope, Petrosilex, Sinople, Lazuli, Chalcedony, Agate, Mocho, Jasper Agate, Egyptian Pebble, Onyx, Sardonyx, and Camea. 412-538.

Nine species of antique Porphyry, Serpentine, and Granite. 539-554.

Sir George Sinclair found that 'Three of these are wanting in 1812 (NLS ACC 10000/386). Five specimens are preserved in NMS as G1993.34.105-109 and named by Professor John Walker as follows:

ME544. Saurites Orientalis (a. albus)

ME545-546. Saurites Orientalis (b. luteus)

ME551. Leucostictos Ophiticum (Antique Serpentine)

ME552. Syenites Antiquorum

Earths, three species. 555-7.

Crystallized Shorls, two species. 558-65.

Garnets, three species. 566-9.

Semipellucid Gems, five species. 570-4.

Steatitical Stones, six species and varieties. 575-83.

Two of these specimens were found 'wanting' by Sir George Sinclair in 1812 (NLS ACC 10000/386). Two specimens are preserved in NMS, one Serpentine (G1993.34.113) whose original number and name have been obliterated and G1993.34.110 named by Professor John Walker as:

ME576. Catochites Ophiticus from Aberdeenshire

Amiantus, two species. 584-5.

Zeolitical Stones, four species. 586-98.

Verd d'Ecosse, Davila, cat 2, p 125, n4, 599.

Nickel and Cobalt, two species. 600-605.

Cubical Marcasite. 606.

Ferrum Haematites. beta nigrum, Lin. 607.

Grey, black and yellow Ores of Copper. 608-16.

Eight species and varieties of Lead Ores. 617-36.

Varieties of Copper Ore. 637-43.

Varieties of Silver Ores. 644-60.

A large mass of green antique Jasper polished. 661.

An Axe of black Whinstone, supposed to have been used by the Druids in their sacrifices. 662.

Petrified Corals from West Lothian. 663, 664, 665.

An ancient Amulet, called by the vulgar an Adder Stone. 666.

Three species of Indian Nuts. 667, 668, 669.

Two Goa Stones. 670, 671.

JOHN MACGOWAN ESQ, EDINBURGH
[Assistant Solicitor, Board of Excise]

Gorgonia Norvegica, the great Norway Sea Shrub. 672.

Crotalus Dryinas Lin. 673.

Two specimens of a large Snake from America. 674, 675.

The Roots of an Oak-tree inosculated. 676.

DR WILLIAM CULLEN
[Professor of the Institutes of Medicine,
University of Edinburgh]

Lacerta Bullaris Lin. 677.

Four species of West India Insects. 678-81.

Five species of West India Serpents. 682-7.

MR JAMES BRUCE, EDINBURGH

Two species of Scots Birds preserved. 688, 689.

688-689 'Decayed & thrown out' Sir George Mackenzie's annotated catalogue of 1812, NLS ACC 10000/386.

JAMES BOSWELL ESQ OF AUCHINLECK

A collection of West India Animals:

Insects, nine species. 690-8.

Lizards, eight species. 699-707.

Serpents, twelve species. 708-21.

MR JAMES DICKSON, BOOKSELLER, EDINBURGH
[Baillie of the City of Edinburgh]

Fourteen Coins of Silver and five of Copper, chiefly Scottish.

A list found among the papers now in NMS relating to the former coin collection of the Faculty is an inventory drawn up by Alexander Fraser Tytler, Secretary of the Royal Society, of some nineteen Roman, medieval and modern coins passed on in June 1786 (Brown, 1989, 175).

The following donations are listed in *Transactions* vol 2, 1785–89, pp 77-9:

JOHN MACGOWAN ESQ, EDINBURGH

Anacardium Occidentale Lin. The Fruit of the Cashen Tree. 722

Castor Fiber Lin. The Beaver, from Hudson's Bay. 723.

Felis Lynx Lin. The Hudson's Bay Lynx. 724.

Canis Lagopus Lin. The Arctic Fox, from Hudson's Bay. 725.

Crotalus Miliarius Lin. The small Rattlesnake. 726.

Coluber Alternus. 727.

723 'Decayed & thrown out', 724 'Head remains', 725 'Decayed & thrown out', Sir George Mackenzie's annotated catalogue of 1812, NLS ACC 10000/386.

THE RIGHT HONOURABLE LORD DAER

A number of articles, collected in the South Seas by Captain Bligh.

Two parcels of fine New Zealand Hemp. 728.

A Musical Instrument made of Reeds. 729.

An Arrow-head, formed of a hard black Schistus. 730.

730 'Wanting' Sir George Mackenzie's annotated catalogue of 1812, NLS ACC 10000/386

Fish-hooks of Mother of Pearl, and Lines, from the Friendly Islands. 731-3.

Fish-hooks and Lines, formed of the Sinews of an Animal from the coast of America, in Lat. 49'N. 734-6.

Capnias Australis from the South Sea Islands. 737.

Smectis Australis from the South Sea Islands. 738.

Catochites Australis from the South Sea Islands. 739.

737-9 'Wanting' Sir George Mackenzie's annotated catalogue of 1812, NLS ACC 10000/386.

JOHN DAVIDSON ESQ OF RAVELRIG
[Deputy Keeper of the Signet]

A Lion's Skin, with the Head, Teeth and Claws, from the Cape of Good Hope. 740.

Two Sea-weeds, taken out of the Atlantic, at a great distance from any land. 741, 742.

Six Arrows from Bengal. 743.

A Malay Poinard. 744.

Lapis Judaicus, from the East Indies. 745.

745 'Wanting' Sir George Mackenzie's annotated catalogue of 1812, NLS ACC 10000/386.

JOHN LEARMONTH ESQ, MERCHANT IN EDINBURGH

Scolopendra Gigantea Lin. above fourteen inches long, from the West Indies, preserved in spirits. 746.

PROFESSOR DALZEL

[Andrew Dalzel, Professor of Greek,
Edinburgh University]

A Sceptre of Ivory, mounted with silver, given by the King of Dachomy, in Africa, to Archibald Dalzel Esq; formerly Governor of Whydah, as a testimony of friendship. 747.

The Horn of an Antelope, from Africa. 748.

JAMES BOSWELL ESQ OF AUCHINLECK

Some large Nodules of Flint from Italy; each having crystallisations in a large central cavity, sent from Leghorn by Sir John Dick. 749.

CAPTAIN (ROBERT) LIDDEL(L)

A white Greenland Bear. 750.

In Edinburgh University Library DC 1.57, Andrew Graham, late Factor to the Hudson's Bay Company, wrote in January 1787 '...I advised my Aquaintance Captain Robert Liddell of Leith to present his Stuffed polar bear to the Edinburgh Royal Society'. According to Sir George Mackenzie's annotated catalogue of 1812, NLS ACC 10000/386, item 750 was then 'Decayed'.

FRANCIS KINLOCH ESQ OF GILMERTON

[Succeeded as Sir Francis Kinloch of Gilmerton in 1795
and was killed by a maniac a few months thereafter]

Colymbus Arcticus Lin. shot on the shore of East Lothian. 751.

751 'Decayed & thrown out' Sir George Mackenzie's annotated catalogue of 1812, NLS ACC 10000/386.

THE HONOURABLE LORD HAILES

Trichechus Rosmarus Lin. The Morse or Sea Horse; the Skeleton of the Head entire, with the Tusks. 752.

MR JOHN MACAULAY, TOWN-CLERK OF DUMBARTON

The Horn of a Stag, of a singular form, dug out of a stratum of Clay in Dumbartonshire. 753.

THE RIGHT HON THE LORD CHIEF BARON MONTGOMERY
[Sir James William Montgomery, Lord Chief-Baron of
the Court of Exchequer in Scotland]

An Indian Canoe, of fine workmanship, from the Island of St John. 754.

DR GREGORY
[James Gregory, Professor of the Institutes of
Medicine at Edinburgh University]

A large Lizard, from the West Indies, preserved in spirits. 755.

WILLIAM HENRY CHARTERS ESQ OF BURNTISLAND

Lava Garnets, found in the Lava which overwhelmed Pompeii. 756.

756 'Wanting' Sir George Mackenzie's annotated catalogue of 1812, NLS ACC 10000/386.

Two Copper Coins. 757, 758.

A Silver Coin of Henry VI, struck at Calais, and found in the river Jed. 759.

757-9, although allotted numbers, may have been lodged with the Faculty of Advocates. That they were not in the Natural History Museum is shown by Sir George Mackenzie's note against these numbers 'No coins in the Museum' made during his inspection of 1812 (see Mackenzie's annotated catalogue and his letter to John Playfair of 13th May 1812 both in NLS ACC 10000/386. See also note under donation by James Dickson 1783–85 above).

DR ROXBURGH AT MADRAS
[William Roxburgh]

A Chest of Plants from Bengal and the Peninsula of India, containing several hundred Plants, in fine condition, and arranged according to the Linnean system.

Collection now incorporated into the Herbarium of the Royal Botanic Garden, Edinburgh. It is accompanied by an ms catalogue by Dr William Wright dated 1794 (RBG Library Acc.No.725 at Folio 88) which states that the collection consists of dried specimens of 230 Genera and of about 565 Species. The specimens are mounted on papers embossed 'Edinburgh University Herbarium' with written provenance to Roxburgh (fig 2).

ANDREW GRAHAM
[Late Factor to the] Hudson's Bay Company]

DC 1.57-9 are three volumes of 'Essays, transcripts etc' in the John Walker manuscripts in Edinburgh University Library. A transcription of one document in DC 1.57 follows:

'The following curiosities presented to the Edinburgh Royal Society with a true Account of them by Andrew Graham late Factor to the Honble

Hudson's Bay Company. January AD 1787.

Indian Manitaw – Copper Bracelet – Esquimaux Bow and Arrows – A Beaver stuffed – Indian Garters – A Specimen of a Fishing Net made of the bark of the pine tree – A pair of Snow Shoes – A Leather Toga – A Tooth of the Sea Horse so called – A Sample of Talc – An Esquimaux knive made of the Tusk of the Sea Horse – A Breast Ornament of bone made from the Sea Horse Tusk Esqx – A pair of Snow Eyes Esqx – A Seal Skin Frock Esqx – A Canoe Esqx – A Canoe Indian – A Lancet Esqx – A Cradle or Back-board Indian – Two Shot pouches Indian – Two Snakes – A Stone Kettle or Lamp Esqx – Two Garments Esqx – Dishes of Birch-rind Indian – A Large Shell from the Lakes inland – A Straw Cap from New Zealand – A Stone Adze from Friendly Isles – A Sample of Hempen Rope from New Zealand – A Wooden Comb from Nutka Sound in America – A Fowling Dart Esqx – Seven Red berries/ like unto/.... from Capt. Cook's last Voyage – A Cloke pin from Capt. Cook's last Voyage – A Long Bow & two Arrows either Carribees Indians or from East Indies – A pair of Shoes leather Indian – Three Wood-peckers Hudson's Bay – Four Summer Birds Hudson's Bay – Two Cocks and one Hen Gros-beaks H. Bay – Three Black-Birds Hudson's Bay – A Snipe Hudson's Bay – An American Field Fare Hudson's Bay – A Bohemi-an Chatterer Hudson's Bay – Two Shore Larks Hudson's Bay – Great Northern Diver Hudson's Bay – Six Ptarmigans Hudson's Bay – Two Swedish Plover Hudson's Bay – The Eared Grebe Hudson's Bay – A Duck Hudson's Bay – Human Hair from Otaheite Isles – Metal Hudson's Bay – Crystals Hudson's Bay – A Round Stone like a Cheese Vide Cook's Voyage – Pyrites and other Stones Hudson's Bay.'

There follows a lengthy description of these objects by Andrew Graham to which are added two items not mentioned in the above list, Harpoon Darts and a Pelican. In the descriptions it is stated that the fishing net 'belonged to the Woman found by Mr Hearne on his Journey to Copper River/Vide/Introduction to Cook's Voyage'; The Copper Bracelet 'I received from Metanobee the Indian Leader who conducted Mr Samuel Hearne to Copper River'; the Bohemian Chatterer was 'sent to me by Mr Falconer, Factor at Severn, Anno Dom. 1785'; the lump of Talc was sent by Mr Thomas Hutchins from Albany Fort.

In the Ethnography Collections of the Department of History and Applied Art of NMS is preserved a piece of Hempen Rope from New Zealand (UC504) bearing an original 'ME'(Musaeum Edinensis) label. This appears to correspond to the specimen listed by Graham as having been obtained from Cook's last voyage which strongly suggests that Graham material is preserved in the NMS collections. I am grateful to Dale Idiens for identifying a number of other items in the collection which, although lacking contempo-rary labels, she believes are stylistically compatible with the period and region of Graham's collecting and, with differing levels of confidence, might be regarded as pro-viding circumstantial evidence for having formed part of the Graham collection. Of greater certainty among the Hudson's Bay Indian material are four birch-bark dishes (UC303.1-4, fig 5), a pair of garters decorated with porcupine quills (UC294 & A) two shot pouches decorated with porcupine quills (UC297-8) and a cradle backboard (UC302). Of three leather togas decorated with porcupine quills in the collection one (UC277, fig 6) is clearly the oldest in style and the most likely to be that presented by Graham. Although it is probable that the pair of shoes from the Graham Collection is present among the six pairs in the Museum's collection, they cannot be distinguished.

The following donations are listed in *Transactions* 3, 1789-93:

LORD DAER

An Esquimaux Dress. 1 March 1790.

JAMES BYRES OF TONLEY
[Antiquary and Architect, for long resident in Rome]

A Series of ancient Roman Weights of Basaltes or Porphyry 19 December 1791.

'Wanting' Sir George Mackenzie's annotated catalogue of 1812, NLS ACC 10000/386 but as antiquities these may have been lodged with the Faculty of Advocates.

The following Donations are listed in *Transactions* 4, 1793-7:

REVEREND ANDREW BROWN
[Minister of St Giles, Edinburgh, and Professor of Rhetoric in Edinburgh University]

A Model of an Indian Canoe, with the Belt and Pouch of an Indian Hunter, 1794.

ANONYMOUS

Three views of Geyser in Iceland.

'Wanting' Sir George Mackenzie's annotated catalogue of 1812, NLS ACC 10000/386.

The following Donation is listed in *Transactions* 5, 1799-1803:

DR JOSEPH BLACK
[Professor of Chemistry, University of Edinburgh]

The Collection of Fossils of the late Dr James Hutton FRSE May 1798.

The Huttonian Collection of Minerals arranged & marked in proper division. 'Ready for Inspection by the trustees' Sir George Mackenzie's annotated catalogue of 1812, NLS ACC 10000/386).

The following collections are listed in *Transactions* 6, 1804-11 as donations founding the Society's Museum following the New Charter which was sealed in 1811:

THOMAS ALLAN ESQ
[Banker and mineralogist]

Collection of 81 specimens illustrating the mineralogy of the country round Edinburgh (listed Allan, 1812). Of these Nos 77 and 78 are stated to have been specimens presented to Allan by Sir George S Mackenzie and marked in the handwriting of Dr Kennedy as the substances analysed by him (Kennedy 1803).

Listed in Billet of 1843 and by A Geikie in 1877 as being in drawers 19-20 below Book Case E, NLS ACC 10000/396.

LT COL NINIAN IMRIE
[Served in the Royal Scots until 1799, thereafter on half-pay. Mineralogist, collector]

Collection of Specimens illustrating the Section of the Grampians, with descriptive catalogue (Imrie, 1812).

'Rocks of the Grampians; with Printed List and Section' listed in Billet of 1843. Listed by A Geikie in 1877 as being in drawers 21-23 below Book Case E, NLS ACC 10000/396. Angus District Museum Service, Montrose, have 12 rock specimens collected by Lt Col Imrie from Dalradian, Highland Border Series and Old Red Sandstone of Kincardineshire donated by W C Orkney in 1916 (Stace, Pettitt and Waterston, 1987, p 180). It is probable that Imrie made up a number of sets from his collection to illustrate his paper.

SIR JAMES HALL BART
[4th Baronet of Dunglass, second President]

Model in Relief, representing the Granite Veins at the Windy Shoulder in Galloway. (Hall, 1815a, 99-101, 'I have also presented one of these models to the Geological Society of London').

Listed by A Geikie in 1877 as model 6, NLS ACC 10000/396.

THOMAS ALLAN ESQ

Rock specimens from Cornwall

Allan, 1815a, 133-8, Appendix listing 70 specimens presented to the Society.

SIR GEORGE MACKENZIE BART
[Sir George Steuart Mackenzie of Coul]

Collection of specimens, illustrating the Mineralogy of Iceland.

'Catalogue of Icelandic Minerals, being chiefly Geological Specimens. Presented to the Royal Society of Edinburgh, and deposited in their Cabinet' (Mackenzie, 1811, 435-456

Appendix III) lists some 300 specimens (fig 8). 'Collection of the Rocks and Minerals of Iceland...with Printed List' listed in printed billet 1843 and by A Geikie in 1877 as being in drawers 11-14 and 37-40 of the East Side, with printed catalogue, and drawer 79 of the West Side of the Table Case, NLS ACC 10000/396. By resolution of Council the collection was presented to the University of Glasgow, see NLS ACC10000/25 Minutes of Council of 7th May 1909 and 20th June 1910. The 217 specimens then received by the Hunterian Museum are registered as HM.R 200-389 and HM.R 401-427. Most of the specimens retain the original printed numbers corresponding to Mackenzie's published catalogue, eg [A 15] or [D 40]. The collection has since been described in detail (Peacock 1925a, 1925b).

- 1813 -

THOMAS ALLAN ESQ

Rock specimens from Faroe, with list.

Allan went to the Faroes with Sir George Mackenzie (Allan 1815b and Mackenzie 1815). Listed by A Geikie in 1877 as being in drawer 18 below Book Case C, NLS ACC 10000/396. Donated to the Hunterian Museum, Glasgow in 1909.

DR JOHN KIDD MD FRS MWS, OXFORD
[Professor of Chemistry and Physics at Oxford]

Collection of specimens of Flints. *Transactions* 9, Donations 19 April, which is accredited to THOMAS ALLAN through whom it probably came to the Society.

It is likely that this collection sent by DR KIDD is that which appears in the Billet of 1843 as 'Flint Fossils from England. Presented by Dr Kidd'. In a letter from Oxford, dated 21 December 1812 (NLS ACC 10000/389), which lacks the name of the addressee or sender but is probably from Kidd to Allan, the Society is informed that a box of flints has been sent - 'Our friend Lord Webb Seymour probably informed you it was my intention to send these specimens'. There follows a general description of them:

No 1 to No 6 are varieties of a species of sponge which seems to have attached itself to the surface of rocks etc. by means of a root consisting of horizontally branching fibres which converge irregularly to a common centre and unite to form a stem which rises in the form of an inverted cone.

No 7 to No 13 are varieties of sponge consisting of a cylindrical stem terminating in a cup.

No 14 to No 25 are varieties of branching sponge.

No 26 to No 27 are uncommon forms.

No 28 to No 37 are fragments of fossil sponges the substance of which is in the nature of Calcedony (sic).

No 38 to No 46 are miscellaneous specimens not belonging to any variety of sponge.

Listed in printed billet of 1843.

R WATSON OF DUNSE

The Head and Horns of a Large Animal of the Ox kind, found in a moss near Dunse. *Transactions* 9, Donations 31 May.

- 1815 -

CAPTAIN BASIL HALL RN
[Writer and explorer]

A Collection of Minerals, *Transactions* 9, Donations 6 November.

Specimens 1 to 10 were from Table Mountain (Playfair 1815). In a letter to John Playfair from Bombay of 1 January 1815, Hall lists the following specimens as having been sent to the Society (NLS ACC 10000/389):

1 (Marked 50+1) From Top of Table Mountain
2 (50+1) Pebbles found in water worn holes on top of the Mountain.
3 (50+2) From the sandstone strata – about 1/3rd of the way from the top of the Mountain.
4 (50+3) From the lower part of the sandstone: not in contact with the granite.
5 (50+4) Sandstone in contact with granite.
6 (50+5) Granite near the contact with the sandstone.
7 (50+6) Granite remote from the contact with the sandstone.
8 (50+9) Shows the granite veins streaming into the schistus.
9 (50+12) Stratified rock at some distance from the junction of the granite rib. It is here nearly vertical.
10 (50+14) loose crystal of hornblende from the Lion's Head; many similar ones were observed in the rock.

'Specimens of Rocks from Cape of Good Hope' listed in Billet 1843. 'Rock chips - Cape of Good Hope' are listed by A Geikie 1877 in drawer 23 under Book Case C, NLS ACC 10000/396

The following specimens were collected without any plan but represent the rocks of the stated localities:

11 (60+3) Trincomalee, Ceylon - the most prevalent rock there.
12 (61+2) Pt. de Galle, Ceylon.
13 (61+8) From a large mass of what is called the Cinnamon Rock at (?)Nilligam, near Pt de Galle, Ceylon.
14 (62+2) Colombo, Ceylon.
15 (70+5) Calicut on the Malabar Coast, India.
16 (80+1) Bombay.
17 (80+5) Elephanta Island near Bombay - this specimen is sacreligiously broken from the celebrated Elephant.
18 (80+8) From the Canara Caves on Salsette Island near Bombay.
19 (90+10) The Rock on which the Fort of Seringapatam Stands.
20 (90+11) Whin dyke passing through 90+10.
21 (90+12) Another kind of dyke passing through 90+10.
22 (90+12) Porphyry dyke passing through the gneiss rock near Seringapatam.
23 (90+21) Near Seringapatam.
24 A specimen, not numbered, from Bangalore.

THE BARONS OF EXCHEQUER

Two gold coins, one of King James the First, and the other of King James the Second. *Transactions* 9, Donations 17 February.

Listed as having been passed to the Society of Antiquaries (NLS AccIoooo/20 Council Minute of 21st November 1859.

MR GEORGE BULLOCK
[Furniture maker, Liverpool]

An Ink-stand, composed of a variety of British woods. *Transactions* 9, Donations 17 November.

- 1818 -

ALEXANDER KENNEDY ESQ
[Physician of the East India Company]

A specimen of the Worm found in the Eye of Horses in the East Indies. *Transactions* 9, Donations 10 November.

The specimen (Kennedy 1823), *Ascaris pellucidus*, was donated to the Natural History Museum of the University of Edinburgh in 1859, see Minute of Council of 21 November 1859, Acc 10000/20.

- 1819 -

DR SAMUEL HIBBERT
[later Hibbert-Ware]

Specimens of Native Hydrate of Magnesia , found in Shetland *Transactions* 9, Donations 6 December.

These samples of Hydromagnesite (Heddle 1901, I, 147) were found by Hibbert in 1817 at Swinaness, Unst (Brewster 1823).

FRANCIS SIMPSON ESQ
[Colonel Francis Simpson of Plean]

Sculptures of Indian Idols *Transactions* 9, Donations 6 December.

Described and figured by W A Cadell (1823) these four sculptures were probably passed to the museum of the Society of Antiquaries under the agreement of 1828. For some time they were on loan from the National Museum of Antiquities to the Royal Scottish Museum to which they were formally transferred in 1956. They are preserved in the Department of History and Applied Art of NMS and identified as follows: A1956.564-565 Avalokitesvara, from the Bengal/Bihar region, Pala Period, 11th-12th century AD (fig 9); A1956.566 Buddha, from the Bengal/Bihar region, Pala Period, 11th-12th century AD; A1956.574 Camunda, from the Bengal/Bihar region, Pala Period, 10th century AD.

Geological specimens brought from the East, collected during the voyage of HM sloops *Alceste* and *Lyra* under Captain Murray Maxwell CB 1816-17 (Hall, 1818).

These are mentioned as having been sent to the Society in a manuscript note from Hall (NLS ACC 10000/389). An appendix (Hall 1818, cxxii-cxxx) describes the specimens collected by the expedition which came from the following localities:

From China:
  2 from Macao
  1 from Hong-Kong
  1 from Great Lemma (Lamma Island)

From Southern Shore of the Yellow Sea:
  5 from 'Che-A-Tow'
  3 from 'Cung-Cung-Cheen' Islands
  1 from 'Oei-Hai-Oei'
  1 from 'Lung-Cung-Tao' Islands

From West Coast of Korea:
  6 from an island 37 45'N.
  5 from 'Hutton's Island' 36 10'N, 126 13'E.
  1 from Mainland of Korea
  1 from an Island 34 23'N,126E.
  1 from another island near the above

From Great Loo-Choo Island (Okinawa):
  2 specimens

It is not clear from the Hall ms (NLS ACC 10000/389) whether all 30 specimens were lodged with the Society or only a selection but specimens from, Korea, Hutton's Island and Great Loo Choo are mentioned.

- 1820 -

THOMAS ALLAN ESQ

A specimen of sandstone from Craigleith Quarry, near Edinburgh, exhibiting a vegetable impression of the Palm tribe with rudiments of buds or flowers. *Transactions* 9, Donations 5 June.

Described and figured by Allan (1823a), the specimen is a ulodendroid stem of *Lepidodendron veltheimi* (=*Megaphytpon allani Jongmans*). For some time it was numbered GS4997 in the collection of the Geological Survey (Anderson 1936, 32) but, through the courtesy of the Survey's Director, Dr Peter J Cook, it was restored to the NMS in 1995 where it is now registered as GI1995.3.1. (fig 10).

- 1821 -

THE MARCHIONESS OF HUNTLY
[Elizabeth Brodie, Marchioness of Huntly, in 1827 her husband succeeded as fifth and last Duke of Gordon]

A large specimen of Madrepore from Bermuda. *Transactions* 9, Donations 2 April.

According to a contemporary report in the *Edinburgh Philosophical Journal* 5, 386 'This specimen was of unusual magnitude, and is supposed to be the finest in the kingdom'.

MR ANDREW FLINT
[Civil Engineer]

Specimen of fossil shells bent and contorted. *Transactions* 9, Donations 2 April.

The specimens, which retained the marks of their having been in a soft pliant condition, were from a hill adjoining the east end of the city of Cincinnati in North America. Report of Proceedings of the Royal Society of Edinburgh for 8 January 1821 in *Edinburgh. Philosophical Journal* 4, 424.

MR JOHN RAMAGE OF ABERDEEN

A stickleback and a leech which was found in its intestines.

Report of Proceedings of the Royal Society of Edinburgh for 7 May, *Edinburgh Philosophical Journal* 5, 386.

THOMAS ALLAN ESQ

Rock specimens from the North of Ireland

Collection listed in Billet of 1843 but no date of acquisition has been found. Allan was in Northern Ireland with Lord Compton in 1820 (Allan 1823b). 11 belemnites from Larne are figured together with one sent to Allan from Dr Fitton (Pls XXV & XXVI) but there is no reference to a rock collection having been made. Since it is known that such a collection was presented by Allan, it is here assumed that he made it during the 1820 visit and donated it when his paper was read, as he had done on other occasions. Listed by A Geikie in 1877 as being in drawers 16-18 below Book Case E, NLS ACC 10000/396.

- 1823 -

LIEUTENANT MACNIVEN, 26th REGIMENT

Specimens of Osseous Breccia, found near Rosia in Gibralter. *Transactions*, Donations 6 May.

- 1822 -

EDWARD GRIMES ESQ RN

Series of Specimens of Flints from Warwickshire. *Transactions* 9, Donations 2 December.

The relevant paper (Grimes 1925) was read before the Royal Society, 2 December 1823. 'The specimens described in this paper are deposited in the Museum of the Society'. Six specimens are described.

JOHN ROBISON ESQ
[John Robison KH, General Secretary of the Society]

The Door of the Bookcase of Sir Isaac Newton. *Transactions* 10, p 479.

Removed by the donor's father, Professor John Robison, when he visited Woolsthorpe Manor in 1797, from 'the press at the side of the fire place of the room in which Sir Isaac was born' – see letter of Sir John Robison to J D Forbes dated 11 October 1834 now in the Royal Museum of Scotland NMS, History of Science Section: NPM Catalogues and Inventories, item H, at p 79, re No 2185. Presented by the Society to the National Trust in 1991 for reinstallation into the bookcase from whence it was taken. It may be seen at Woolsthorpe Manor, near Grantham, Lincolnshire, the birthplace of Sir Isaac Newton, now a National Trust property.

SIR GEORGE S MACKENZIE BART

The Vertebra of a Whale found in the Blue Clay near Dingwall. *Transactions* 10, Donations 17 March.

Found at Hilton, near Strathpeffer, Ross-shire (Mackenzie 1826).

JAMES SKENE ESQ
[James Skene of Rubislaw]

Fossil bones found in the Hyaena Cave of Kirkdale, in Yorkshire.

Report of Proceedings of the Royal Society of Edinburgh for 21 April in *Edinburgh Philosophical Journal* 9, 185.

SIR JAMES HALL BART

A Cast taken in Plaster of one of the Stones on Corstorphine Hill, supposed to bear traces of having been acted on by the attrition of stones carried along by a great current of water. *Transactions* 10, Donations 7 March. (*See Hall 1815b*)

THE MARCHIONESS OF HUNTLY

The Snout of a Saw-Fish. *Transactions* 10, Donations 7 March.

Four snouts of Sawfish are listed as having been passed to the Natural History Museum NLS ACC 10000/20 Council Minute of 21 November 1859.

GEORGE SWINTON ESQ, SECRETARY TO GOVERNMENT, CALCUTTA

A number of Burmese Idols dispatched per the ship 'Jane' which arrived in London in December 1825.

This was the subject of dispute between Professor Jameson, Keeper of the University Natural History Museum, and David Brewster, Secretary of the Society, to whom the case was addressed. It was recovered by Brewster in July 1827 and, according to Brewster NLS

ACC 10000/394, letter to T Allan 23 March 1828, the idols 'all went to the Royal Society, excepting two or three paltry images ...of these I took two and sent the rest to the Antiquarian Society'. In *Transactions of the Society of Antiquaries of Scotland* 3, 1831, 119, a donation is recorded as having been received from George Swinton on 25 October 1827 of 'Six Burmese Sacred Figures in the sitting posture of contemplation, each formed of a thin plate of metal, and filled with some resinous substance poured into them in a liquid state'.

UNDATED

The following are listed in the *Billet* of 1843 but their dates of acquisition are unrecorded.

LORD WEBB SEYMOUR (name not given in ms)

Rock specimens from Glen Tilt and adjacent country.

Included without donor's name in the Billet of 1843. 'Specimens from Glen Tilt - Playfair & Webb Seymour Trans VII' listed by A Geikie in 1877 as being in drawers 6-9 below Book Case E, NLS ACC 10000/396. Collection of 153 rocks (Seymour 1815) donated to the Hunterian Museum, Glasgow University, by resolution of Council, NLS ACC 10000/25, where it is now preserved.

THE ROYAL INSTITUTION, FIRST MUSEUM 1826–35

1826

THOMAS ALLAN ESQ

The scapula of a Whale found in sinking a Coal Pit in Ayrshire. *Transactions* 11, Donations 18 December.

LORD NAPIER

Specimens of Mineral Waters from St Michael's. *Transactions* 11, Donations 28 December.

- 1827 -

GEORGE SWINTON ESQ, CALCUTTA

The Snout of a Sword Fish. *Transactions* 11, Donations 5 February.

In Report of the Proceedings of the Royal Society of Edinburgh for 5 February 1827 in *Edinburgh Journal of Science* 6, 1827, 343 it is stated that 'this is one of the largest and finest specimens that has been seen.'

SIR THOMAS MAKDOUGALL BRISBANE KCB
[Fourth President]

Various Specimens of Natural History and Manufactures from New Zealand, New South Wales etc. *Transactions* 11, Donations 19 February.

In Report of the Proceedings of the Royal Society of Edinburgh for 19 February 1827 in *Edinburgh Journal of Science* 6, 1827, 343 it is stated 'There was presented by Sir Thomas Makdougall Brisbane KCB to the Museum of the Society various interesting objects of Natural History from New South Wales, and various specimens of the Cloth, Ropes etc of the Natives.' New Zealand Flax, Ropes made from New Zealand Flax and stem and bark of *Eucalyptus* sp. are listed as having been passed to the Royal Botanic Garden NLS ACC 10000/20 Council Minute of 21 November 1859.

THOMAS ALLAN ESQ

The Tusk of a Mastodon, with some other Bones, found in Woodhall Quarry near Kilmarnock. *Transactions* 11, Donations 5 March.

In Report of the Proceedings of the Royal Society of Edinburgh for 5 March 1827 in *Edinburgh Journal of Science* 6, 1827, 343 it is stated 'There was read a Paper by Thomas Allan Esq entitled "Notice respecting the Tusk of a Mastodon, with some Bones and Fossils, found in tirring Woodhill Quarry, near Kilmarnock"'. Mr Allan presented this Tusk and the other Fossils to the Museum of the Society. This tusk of *Elephas primigenius* is almost certainly the un-numbered specimen now exhibited in the Anatomical Museum of the University of Edinburgh. It is labelled 'On loan from the Geology Collection. Professor Geikie' and was probably one of the non-type specimens in the Society's collection which was passed to James Geikie for his Student's Collection in 1878.

GEORGE SWINTON ESQ, SECRETARY TO GOVERNMENT, CALCUTTA

Many Specimens and Objects of Natural History and the Fine Arts, collected in India. *Transactions* 11, Donations 3 December 1827.

In Report of the Proceedings of the Royal Society of Edinburgh for 3 December 1827 in the *Edinburgh Journal of Science* 8, 1828, 165 it is stated: 'The following, among many objects of natural history and the fine arts, were presented to the Society by George Swinton Esq. Secretary to the Government, Calcutta and FRSE'.

1 Three fine Marble Statues of Burmese gods

Transferred to the Society of Antiquaries of Scotland under the 1828 agreement. 'Burmese idols in marble and other articles came to the Antiquaries...' (Stevenson 1981, 69). Transferred to the Royal Scottish Museum in 1956 and now in Eastern Collections of NMS having the registered numbers A1956.585, A1956.586 and A1956.587).

2 Two models, as large as life, of a Dwarf now in Calcutta

See entry for Cases No 19 and 20 below. Listed as having been passed to the Royal College of Surgeons, Council Minute of 21 November 1859, NLS ACC 10000/20.

3 Head of a Dugong (fig 12)

See entry for Case No 6 below. The printed Billet for the Society meeting of 21 December 1829 stated that the following object, presented to the Society by Mr Swinton of Calcutta and prepared by Dr Knox, will be exhibited: 1. Cranium of the Dugong, and Cast from Ditto.

The skull was described in two papers (Knox,1829 and 1831). On p 390 of the latter Knox wrote: 'A considerable time ago, Mr Swinton, to whom this Society owes so many rare and valuable presents in anatomy and zoology, transmitted to this country the head of an apparently full grown dugong from the Indian Seas, clothed with all the soft parts, and seemingly in every respect, uninjured. Together with the head, which was preserved in strong spirits, and quite fresh when it reached this country, Mr Swinton had taken the trouble to forward in like manner to the Society the heart, stomach, and organs of generation, which appertain to the female, from which one may reasonably conjecture that these preparations belonged to the same individual, and, if so, that the cranium of the dugong, now in the possession of the Society, belonged to the female.'

The Skull of Dugong with a cast of the same and two drawings are listed as having been passed to the Royal College of Surgeons NLS ACC 10000/20 Council Minute of 21 November 1859. The specimen was listed as Knox Collection No 108 in the Anatomical Museum of Edinburgh University by Turner (1912, 147) and has now been presented to NMS where the bisected cranium and associated mandible are registered as Z1996.83.6.

Also listed by Turner (1912, 151) were dissections in spirit of Dugong heart, Knox Collection No 116, and Dugong Kidney, Knox Collection 121. Of these the Kidney has been presented to NMS where it is registered as Z1981.057.482).

4 Numerous Barrels and Bottles, containing Snakes etc from various parts of India (fig 13)

See entry for Case No 15 below. 'Collection of Indian Serpents by George Swinton Esq' listed as having been passed to the Natural History Museum NLS ACC 10000/20 Council Minute of 21 November 1859. 'A collection of Reptiles' from the Royal Society of Edinburgh was registered in the Natural History Museum as 1859.21. In the collections of the Department of Natural History of NMS are three Indian snakes, preserved in spirit and numbered Z1859.21. They are named *Bungarus fasciatus, Dryophis prasinus* and *Hypsirhyna enhydrus* and are almost certainly part of Swinton's original donation of snakes in spirit. A further eight spirit specimens, lacking registrations, are labelled as having been presented by Swinton. Three retain the original external label of the museum of the Royal Society of Edinburgh attached to the original glass jars. They are named as follows: *Bungarus fasciatus, Bungarus semifasciatus, Chrysopelea ornata = Dendrophis ornata var.* [having original label], *Dryophis Prasinia* [having original label], *Coronella colulla, Lycodon Hebe* [having original label], *Tropidonotus schistosus* [two specimens].

An Indian specimen of *Monitor Dracaena = Varanus bengalensis nebulosus* (NMS Unreg.63) is probably from this consignment and part of the collection Z1859.21.

5 An Armadillo

6 Ship Fish from Arracan

See entry for Case No 17h below. 'Fishes from India by George Swinton Esq.' passed to Natural History Museum, NLS ACC 10000/20 Minute of Council for 21 November 1859.

7 Head of a Horned Beetle

See entry for Case No 17h below.

8 Book of Natural History in the Talien language

See entry under Case No 17g below. An inscription by George Swinton in the ms reads 'This manuscript was procured at Rangoon by Mr Stewart, the medical officer attached to Mr Crawford's mission. It is said to be written in the old Talien (or Pegu) language of which Mr Stewart could offer no explanation. GS 14 March 1827'.

Dr Ginsborg of the British Library has identified this as a Divination Book and I am grateful to him for the following information. It is based on the Chinese 12-year system (year of the tiger, dog etc) which appears to have given rise to the idea that it was a book of natural history. It is written in Mon script and language (=Pegu or Talien) and dates from the late eighteenth century. The style of painting suggests that it was from Burma which would accord with it having been procured in Rangoon. The Royal Asiatic Society in London also has material sent by Mr Stewart.

Sold to the British Library (Acc No OR14532) 27 June 1989.

9 Two Dresses of Carian Women of Tavoy

Listed as having been passed to the Industrial Museum, NLS ACC 10000/20 Council Minute of 21 November 1859. They are in the collection of the Department of History and Applied Art in NMS with the registered numbers A1859.418 & A and A1859.419 & A.

10 Bamboo joints containing Tabasheer

See entry for Case No 17d below.

11 Specimen of Shola, in its natural state, and formed into sheets like paper

Stems of Shola, *Aschynomene aspera*, passed to Royal Botanic Garden NLS ACC 10000/20 Council Minute of 21 November 1859.

12 Corals and shells

13 Specimens of Oils, Varnishes, Bhela or marking Nuts, Gums, Minerals etc

In a letter from John Stark to John Robison dated 2 January 1830 NLS ACC 10000/391 he states that 'Dr Christison has kindly undertaken the analysis of, and to make experiments on, some of the varnishes, oils etc in the Museum, of which the results will be communicated to the Society.' The Billet for 7 February 1831 advertised a Report on various articles sent to the Society by Mr Swinton with analysis of the Petroleum of Rangoon (Christison 1836, Gregory 1836). In his paper Christison states that the following specimens were sent to him:

1 Specimen of black varnish used in different parts of Hindustan and the Burmese territories, with specimens of the juices of which these varnishes are said to be compounded.
2 Specimen of naphtha from Persia and of petroleum from Rangoon.
3 Specimen of wood oil, a variety of fluid turpentine.
4 Specimen of crude caoutchouc, and of solution of it in wood oil.

Fruit of *Semocarpus anacardium* (Marking Nuts) passed to Royal Botanic Garden NLS ACC 10000/20, Council Minute of 21 November 1859.

14 Stuffed Birds

15 Large Sponge, or Neptune's Cup, from Singapore

Spongia patera, Neptune's Cup, is listed as having been passed to the Royal College of Surgeons NLS ACC 10000/20, Council Minute of 21 November 1859.

16 The Leaf Insect from Sylhet

Listed as having been passed to the Royal College of Surgeons NLS ACC 10000/20, Council Minute of 21 November 1859.

17 Skeleton of Boa Constrictor

In Report of the Proceedings of the Royal Society of Edinburgh for February 5 1827 in *Edinburgh Journal of Science* 6, 1827, 353 (but in fact here referring to the present donation) it is stated:

'The same gentleman (Swinton) also presented to the Society, the skeleton of a Boa Constrictor, sixteen feet long, the mother of the young brood of Boa Constrictors described in this Journal ([Scott] 1826) accompanied by one of the brood preserved in spirits. Mr Swinton likewise presented various snakes from Arracan and Sumatra.' (See No 4 above)

Listed as having been passed to the Natural History Museum NLS ACC 10000/20, Council Minute of 21 November 1859.

18 Petrified Trunk of a Tree from the Irawaddy

19 Large *Chama gigas* from the South Seas

20 A pair of Elephant Tusks
Listed as having been passed to the Industrial Museum, NLS ACC 10000/20 Council Minute of 21 November 1859, and now in the NMS with the registered numbers 1859.415 and 415a.

21 Skeleton of the Iguana etc
Skeleton of Iguana listed as having been passed to the Natural History Museum, NLS ACC 10000/20, Council Minute of 21 November 1859.

The twenty-one items listed above refer, in part, to the shipment detailed in NLS ACC 10000/389 marked on the outside 'General list of things for Dr Brewster by Mr Lowson of Leith 19th March' (1827) and titled 'List of articles sent by *Louisa* addressed to Archd. Swinton - by whom they will be sent to Dr Brewster'. This list, which is itself incomplete, is as follows:

Case No 6 – contains Keg with the Head of a Dugong in spirits
(*Item 3 above*)

Case No 8 – 14 bottles of Sylhet varnish etc marked (Dr B) and apparently retained by Dr Brewster.
See Report of the Proceedings of the Society for Promoting the Useful Arts in Scotland for December 4th 1827 in *Edinburgh Journal of Science* 8, 1828, 360, 'A Notice by Dr Brewster on the Varnishes from the Varnish Trees of India was read, and specimens of articles varnished with them, and sent home by George Swinton Esq. of Calcutta, were exhibited.' Also in the Report of the Proceedings for 4 December 'An Account of the poisonous qualities of the Indian Varnishes' by Dr Brewster (See [Brewster] 1828a, 1828b)

One bottle of (Hyapootie?) oil, four bottles of (Snakes?) also pieces of the Shola (Iola?) or pith for making artificial flowers etc.

Case No 15 – 5 bottles and a small keg containing snakes etc.
(*see details under item 4 above*)
10 snakes are listed under their bengali names. It is noted that P Breton, Surgeon, had allowed the 'Boa' to bite a pigeon on the thigh on 4 March 1827 which had died in six and a half minutes. A second pigeon bitten by the same snake half an hour afterwards remained the whole day comatose but recovered on the following day. On 13 March 1827 P Breton allowed a variety of '*Boa fasciata*' to bite a pigeon in the thigh which had died in 12 minutes.

Case No 17 –
a) 2 cases of Nipaul paper
b) 2 lbs of ruby matrix brought from a mine 5 or 6 days journey to the NE of the capital of Ava by Burmese who trade with Calcutta
c) Burmese scales and weights
d) Box of Tabasheer from Sylhet (See Brewster 1828c, Turner 1828)
e) Orpiment and Vermilian with which the Burmese colour their lacquered work
f) Three lacquered Burmese drinking cups

g) Book of Natural History in the Talien language with plates *(Item 8 above)*

h) Head of a horned beetle *(Item 7 above)* & curious fish from Arakan called the Ship fish *(Item 6 above, listed in case No 15)*

Cases No 19 & 20 – 'The Clay figures in these cases are exact representations taken from the life of a Dwarf now in Calcutta aged 16 years made by a Bengallie artist called Kishnaghur' *(Item 2 above)*

- 1828 -

GEORGE SWINTON ESQ, SECRETARY TO GOVERNMENT, CALCUTTA

It is stated in the *Billet* calling the meeting of 7 January 1828, 'The following objects of Natural History will be presented to the Society by George Swinton Esq of Calcutta

1   Sixty-two specimens of Minerals, Fossil Shells, Fossil Wood and Fossil Bones, collected by the Mission to Ava in the journey from Rangoon to Ava in 1826-7.

See [Swinton] 1828a, 1828b). The latter was reprinted from the *Calcutta Government Gazette* of March 21, 1827 in which it is recorded that bones of Mastodon, fossil rhinoceros, Anthracotherium, horse-like and buffalo-like bones and Gavial, together with Turbo and Tellina shells and Fossil wood were found. On p 60 it is stated 'We have been promised a selection from these bones for the museum of the Royal Society of Edinburgh, ...'. Fossil wood from Irrawaddy is listed as having been passed to the Natural History Museum in NLS ACC 10000/20 Council Minute of 21 November 1859. The Billet of 1843 records 'Specimens of Ores, &c from Tavoy'.

2   Two Bottles, containing Heads of the Boa Constrictor from Cuttack.

THE RIGHT HON THE COUNTESS OF MORTON
[Susan Elizabeth, Countess of Morton]

Models and papers connected with the Erection of the Eddystone Lighthouse, which belonged to the late Mr Smeaton, Civil-Engineer. *Transactions* 11, Donations 7 January also *Billet* for 7 January.

Collection now in NMS having been donated by the Society to the Industrial Museum, see NLS ACC 10000/20 Council Minute of 21 November 1859. It consists of the following:

T1859.414. an engraved perspective view (published 1699) of the first lighthouse (1696-1703) built by Henry Winstanley of Littlebury.

T1859.B.1-7 objects relevant to the second lighthouse: (1709-1755) built by Rudyerd:

T1859.414.B.1-2 drawing and elevation of lighthouse T1859.414.B.3 model of lighthouse (fig 15), T1859.414.B.4 model of the interior stonework, T1859.414.B.5 model showing the lower courses of stone and timber work and the stepping of the rock, T1859.414.B.6 model showing fourteen courses of the stone work, T1859.414.B.7 a piece of lead taken from the stomach of a Keeper after the fire of 1755 (Spry, 1756).

T1859.C.1-25 objects relevant to the third lighthouse (1759-1882) built by John Smeaton: T1859.414.C.1-3 drawings of elevation, plan and section of lighthouse, T.414.C.4 drawing of plan and section of the lantern, T1859.414.C.5 drawings of different courses of stone,

T1859.414.C.6 model of the lighthouse, T1859.414.C.7-11 models showing aspects of the stonework and construction, T1859.414.C.12 vertical moulds, south, south-west and north-east of lighthouse, T1859.414.C.13-16 models of details, T1859.414.C.17 three of the lantern copper sash screws, T1859.4124.C.18 an iron screw-nail for fixing the angular cast iron pillars of the lantern, T1859.414.C.19 a copper socket for holding one of the pillars of the lantern, T1859.414.C.20 a sample of the gneiss forming the Eddystone Rock, T1859.414.C.21 a sample of the granite or moorstone of which the exterior is built, T1859.414.C.22 a sample of the Portland Stone of which the interior of the solid shaft is built, T1859.414.C.23-25 sample of Watchet limestone, cement and polished cement.

T1930.74 contemporary label removed from T1859.414.B.7 reading 'the lead found in the body of Wm. Hall, Edystone Lt. Keeper'.

MR WOODBINE PARISH, H M CONSUL-GENERAL AT BUENOS AYRES
[Sir Woodbine Parish, diplomat]

Transactions 11, Donations 4 February.

1 A Mass of Metallic Iron, supposed to be Meteoric
See Allan, 1828. In a note written by Parish from Buenos Ayres on 7 December 1825 (NLS ACC10000/391) he lists a further two specimens as having been sent to the Society:

2a small piece of the Iron flattened by the Indian who brought it to Salta, by beating it with a hard stone.

3a small bar of the same, forged.

WILLIAM BALD ESQ
[Civil engineer and surveyor]

Models of the Islands of Clare and Eigg, and Drawings illustrative of Topographical Modelling and Delineation. *Transactions* 11, Donations 1 December.
Among the models listed by A Geikie, 1877, are '1.Clare Island, Ireland, 2. Island of Eigg by Bald'. NLS ACC 10000/396).

- 1829 -

LIEUT SMART RN

Some Specimens of Minerals. *Transactions* 11, Donations 2 February.

GEORGE SWINTON ESQ

Various objects of Natural History, Calcutta. *Transactions* 11, Donations 16 February.

The *Billet* for 16 February states 'The following Articles, in addition to those lately presented, have been received from George Swinton Esq. Calcutta.

1 Specimens of the long-armed Gibbon (mother and son) from Assam
Knox (1829a) wrote 'Two specimens of Gibbons.... put in my hands by J Robison Esq, Secretary to the Royal Society (to which they were sent by George Swinton Esq) with a request to prepare them in whatever way I thought most beneficial to science'. See also

Billet for 21 December 1829 below. An unnumbered female adult skull of *Hylobates hoolock* is preserved in the Anatomical Museum of Edinburgh University and limb bones of the same species have been presented to the NMS by the Anatomical Museum. It is almost certain that these are from the now disarticulated mounted skeleton of the adult female presented to the Society by Swinton and described by Knox.

2   A stuffed animal from Assam

3   Sun-dried Bricks from the Ruins of Babylon, taken by Colonel Macdonald, Envoy to Persia

Transferred to the Museum of the Society of Antiquaries of Scotland 23 March 1829 see *Antiquaries' Society Transactions 3*, 1831, Appendix p 135, List of Donations.

4   Varieties of Corals

5   *Boa fasciata* from Assam

6   *Boa fasciata* from Arracan

7   Alligator from Salueen River.

Probably the small crocodile preserved in spirit now in NMS Z1859.21 collection labelled 'August 1859'.

8   Leaf Insect from Sylhet.

'Specimen of a Leaf Insect' is listed as having been passed to the Royal College of Surgeons, Council Minute of 21 November 1859, NLS ACC 10000/20.

9   Two specimens of *Ornithorhynchus platypus*

10   Skin of Cassowary of New Holland

11   A quantity of Indian Rubber from Assam.

India Rubber, concrete & Fluid juice is listed as having been passed to the Royal Botanic Garden, NLS ACC 10000/20, Council Minute of 21 November 1859.

12   Horn of a Rhinoceras.

Item 12 not mentioned in 'List of cases & parcels per *Louisa*' NLS ACC 10000/389.

Additional information about this consignment is given in a note from J Robison to J Skene NLS ACC 10000/ 391

'List of articles received from G Swinton Esq.

Case No 1 – 2 Jars with large & small long-armed Gibbon *(Item 1 above)* A Bamboo with a small stuffed animal *(Item 2 above)* some corals much broken.

Case No 4 – a quantity of branches of corals.

Case No 5 – 4 Bottles of specimens in spirits viz. *Boa fasciata* from Arakan *(Item 6 above)*

Alligator from Salueen River *(Item 7 above)* *Boa fasciata* from Assam *(Item 5 above)*

Leaf insect from Sylhet – 'a splendid specimen' Swinton *(Item 8 above)* large block of Amber from Mogaum (to the SE of Assam) Gum Copal from the Persian Gulf supposed to come from Zanzibar, E. coast of Africa.'

This list is correct but incomplete according to the 'List of cases & parcels per *Louisa*' and the following should be added to complete the published list above:

Case No 5 – Indian Rubber from Assam

Case No 7 – Two Stuffed Duck Bills (*Item 9 above*) Skin of Cassawary (*Item 10 above*)

Other items intended for the Royal Society Museum in 'List of cases & parcels per *Louisa*' but not mentioned in the printed list were as follows:

Case No 7 – clay models of the hand, foot, lower jaw & eye tooth of the Great Sumatran Monkey.

A note in Swinton's writing is preserved in NLS ACC 10000/391,'Model of the lower jaw of the Great Sumatran Oran Otang. This was made under my own eye – and may be depended on – If anything it is smaller than the original – owing to shrinkage of the clay – Every part was measured by the Compasses – The Native artist is a very clever workman.'

These probably were not kept since the ms has against this item 'Received JR decayed'.

Case No 9 – 'Clay model of my famous Monkey… it is a most accurate model in every respect and may be relied on'

An animal presented to Mr Swinton by W Montgomerie Esq, who brought it to Calcutta in July 1827 (Grant, 1828). 'Model of a Young Orang - Swinton' is listed as having been passed to the Natural History Museum in Council Minute for 21 November 1859, NLS ACC 10000/20.

The Billet for 21 December 1829 states that 'the following objects presented to the Society by Mr Swinton of Calcutta, and prepared by Dr Knox, will be exhibited':

7   27 Specimens of Ophidian Reptiles

(An ms in John Stark's writing, NLS ACC 10000/391 lists 30 specimens mounted on a board for this occasion, sent by Swinton in this and previous consignments, and named as follows:

No 1 & 18	Boa Constrictor Shaw
No 2	Cumberi Mukeen Russell pl 26 Contn
No 3	Coluber mycterrans Shaw - Russell pl 24 Suppt
No 4	Cacilia glutinasa Shaw?
No 5	Anguis
Nos 6 & 7	
No 8	Boa Johnii Russell Contn pl 16 Erutaley Nagam
No 9	Young Psedoboa?
No 10	Pseudoboa, Oppel – Bungaris annularis, Daudin – Boa fasciata Shaw – Bungarum Pamah, Russell pl 3
No 11	Coluber mortuarius Daudin?
No 12, 17, 29	Coluber ibiboboca Daudin – Kalla Jin, Russell Contn pl 2
No 13	Snake from Arracan, Green-coloured
No 14, 16, 20, 28	Bungarus caeruleus Daudin – Boa Lineata Shaw – Pseudoboa, Oppel – Gedi Paragoodoo & Pakta Poola, Russell, pl 1
No 15	Snake from Arracan – A longer specimen of No 9
No 19	Coluber Lachesis Shaw var.

No 21, 24, 25	Coluber Naja Lin – Naja Laurenti, Vipera Najii Daudin – Nagoo Russell var pl 5 & 6 & 1 Suppt The Cobra de Capello
No 22, 23	Coluber pictus Daudin – Patza Tutta Russell pl 29
No 26	Coluber pictus Daudin, a variety
No 27, 30	Vipera elegans Daudin – Katuka Rekula Poda, Russell pl 7

- 1830 -

GEORGE SWINTON ESQ, CALCUTTA

Transactions 11, Donations 6 December.

1   A cask containing the greater part of the body of a Dugong, preserved in spirits.

Dr Knox read a paper 'Additional observations on the Anatomy of the Dugong' to the Society on 6 February 1832 which remained unpublished and is preserved in ms in NLS ACC10000/292. It states:

> The materials for the present brief memoir are two portions of a dugong, seemingly adult, probably belonging to the same animal presented to the Royal Society by that distinguished Patron of Natural Science Mr Swinton. These portions, which have been preserved in spirit, include
>
> 1st   The Head, Throat and pectoral extremities,
>
> 2nd   The tail of the animal, but no part of the thorax & its viscera, nor of the abdomen & its contents, these had seemingly been lost in India.
>
> Scanty though these material be & unhappily in no very good state of preservation, I have thought it due to the Society & to the munificent donor to submit to it whatever observations occurred to me of any moment during the dissection, it being for the Society to judge how far they merit a place in their Transactions.

There follow descriptions under the following headings - Integuments, Muscular System, Sanguiferous System, the Brain and Nerves, Ears, Organs of Vision, Dentition (already described), Nostrils, Mouth & tongue & palate, Pharynx, Gullet, Trachea, Larynx & epiglottis.

This specimen may have been unsuitable for dissections to be preserved since none have been traced.

2   Specimens of Edible Nuts, from the Eastern Islands.

3   Specimens of Amber from Assam.

4   Specimens of different qualities of paper made from Vegetable Matter in Nepal.

5   A large case containing 150 pounds weight of Vegetable Matter in a preparatory state, for the purpose of being tried by Paper-makers in this country.

6   Specimens of Lackered Work referred to in the communication published in Gleanings of Science at Calcutta.

7   Specimens of Rocks etc. of the Diamond Mines in India.

The Billet of 1843 lists 'Specimens connected with the Diamond Mines of India' 'Rock chips- Diamond matrix with list' recorded in 1877 as being in drawer 20 below Book Case C by A Geikie, NLA ACC 10000/396.

MR HERMAN DE MEYER, FRANKFURT
[Hermann von Meyer, Palaeontologist]

Plaster Cast of a Fossil Animal. *Transactions* 11, Donations 6 December.

WILLIAM WHITELAW

Timekeeper with an escapement which requires no oil and a pendulum made of marble, made for the Society by Whitelaw in 1830.

See Robison (1831). This specimen is in the Reception Hall of the Society's House.

- 1831 -

ANDREW BERRY MD

Part of an Aerolite which fell in the territories of the Madras Government in 1810. *Transactions* 11, Donations 3 January.

GEORGE FAIRHOLME ESQ

Two specimens of the Black Salamander found very high on the Alps in the Canton Berne.

With a letter dated 17 January 1831, D Brewster sent 'two Lizards' presented by George Fairholme Esq to J Robison which Robison forwarded to J Stark on the following day. NLS ACC 10000/391. The Billet for 21 February 1831 advertises a notice regarding the Black Salamander of the Alps (Stark 1831) and records the two specimens presented by Fairholme.

- 1832 -

ROBERT ALLAN ESQ
[Mineralogist]

A collection of specimens from the Lipari Islands. *Transactions* 12, Donations 16 January, also in *Billet* for that date.

Allan (1834) contains a descriptive catalogue of the collection of 50 specimens. Listed in Billet of 1843. 'Specimens from Lipari etc.' are listed by A Geikie in 1877 as being in the open case under Book Case C, NLS ACC10000/396.

SIR WALTER SCOTT BART
[Third President]

A large Specimen from the New Volcanic Island in the Mediterranean (Graham's Island). *Transactions* 12, Donations 16 April.

Listed in Billet of 1843. 'Miscellaneous large specimens, one said to have been sent by Sir

Walter Scott' are listed as being in the open case under Book Case C in 1877 by A Geikie
NLS ACC 10000/396.

DR JOHN DAVY
[Inspector-General of Hospitals]

A selection of specimens from the New Volcanic Island in the Mediterranean (Graham's Island). *Transactions* 12, Donations 16 April.

Listed in printed billet of 1843, see also A Geikie's listing under Sir Walter Scott above.

ROBERT ALLAN ESQ

A Collection of Fishes from the neighbourhood of Nice, prepared in a pecu-
liar way. *Transactions* 12, Donations 16 April.

'Specimens of some Mediterranean Fishes' listed in Billet of 1843. Passed to the Natural
History Museum NLS ACC 10000/20 Council Minute of 21 November 1859.

MRS R COCKBURN

Two specimens of *Draco lineatus* from Ava. *Transactions* 12, Donations 3
December.

PROFESSOR F W JOHNSTON, DURHAM
[Lecturer in chemistry and mineralogy at Durham]

Twenty nine specimens of British Fishes. *Transactions* 12, Donations 3
December.

'Specimens of some British Fishes' listed in Billet of 1843. Passed to the Natural History
Museum NLS ACC 10000/20 Council Minute of 21 November 1859.

- 1833 -

DR SIBBALD

A variety of specimens of Minerals from the Coast and Interior of Ceylon.
Transactions 12, Donations 18 March

Listed by A Geikie in 1877 as being in drawer 16 below Book Case C, NLS ACC 10000/396.

PROFESSOR J D FORBES
[Professor of Natural Philosophy, University of Edinburgh,
General Secretary]

A small Collection of Specimens from the Volcanic District of the Rhine.
Transactions 12, Donations 1 April.

Listed in Billet of 1843 and by A Geikie 1877 as being with other Forbes rocks in drawers
1-5 below Book Case E, NLS ACC 10000/396.

COLLECTED FOR THE SOCIETY UNDER THE DIRECTION OF
THE GENERAL SECRETARY AND DR SAMUEL HIBBERT

Collection of Fossil Organic Remains from Burdiehouse made during the winter of 1833 and 1834, many described by L Agassiz (Agassiz, 1833-1843) and S Hibbert (Hibbert,1836).

Listed in Billet of 1843. In 1877 A Geikie listed the following drawers as containing specimens from Burdiehouse 6-12 under Book Case C, 22-23 and 36 on East side of Table Case. He also listed 'Slabs of Fish-remains from Burdiehouse' as being stored in the Small Ante-room, NLS ACC 10000/396. In 1878 type and figured specimens were donated to the National Museum when 21 Agassiz type and figured specimens were registered (NMS GI878.18.1-21), six of these had been donated by Lord Greenock in 1842 (qv) and the remainder had been collected by the Society. Other specimens, including many described and figured by Hibbert, were given to the National Museum at that time but were not then numbered and have since been registered. In 1885 six frames containing 24 specimens of fossil fish remains from Burdiehouse set in plaster were presented to the National Museum (NMS GI885.60). In 1878 unfigured Burdiehouse material was presented to the Museum of the Geology Department of the University of Edinburgh. The Council of the Society had previously donated specimens from the Burdiehouse Collection to the Institut de Géologie de l'Université de Neuchatel [IGUN].

NLS ACC 10000/353 contains a list of 112 specimens from Burdiehouse belonging to the Society and sent to Agassiz in London by Hibbert on 29 September 1834.

RS 1 to 26	Scales etc.
RS 27 to 29	Parts of one bony ray
RS 30 to 31	ditto
RS 32 to 36	ditto
RS 37 to 39	Smaller bony rays etc.
RS 40 to 49	Various bones of larger size
RS 50 to 53	Parts of one bone, the cranium
RS 54 to 55	Parts of one bone
RS 56 to 58	Larger bones
RS 59	Jaw of one of the ?? of the large animal with teeth
RS 60	Part of the head of a young animal
RS 61 to 64	Four specimens of young animals remarkable for the texture of the skin
RS 68 to 109	Various specimens of fish and scales
RS 110	The largest tooth found
RS 111	The one next in size (braded at the base)
RS 112 to 114	Sections of smaller teeth.
RS 65 to 67	Parts of an ironstone nodule from Craigleith Quarry containing a coprolite and fish scales

In her history of the discovery of fossil fishes in Scotland up to 1845 Dr Mahala Andrews has compiled checklists of the Burdiehouse material described and figured by Agassiz (Andrews, 1982, pp 38-41). In the course of that work she made a parallel list to the above, numbered 1-130, which she compiled from Joseph Dinkel's notes on the Royal Society of Edinburgh's Burdiehouse collection (from the Agassiz Archives, deposited by the Institut de Géologie de l'Université de Neuchatel at Archives de l'Etat de Neuchatel, Switzerland AEN 123/3.4.) Dinkel was Agassiz' illustrator and managed the collections sent to Agassiz in London for description (Andrews, 1982, 54-5). The specimens were numbered in 1833-4 in white paint thus – RS 25. Specimens which have been traced by Dr Andrews from this list, with her comments, are as follows:

RS 25   *Ctenoptychius denticulatus* Ag [*Callopristodus pectinatus* (Ag)] Figured Agassiz *Recherches Sur Les Poissons Fossiles* 1833-43, Tome III, Tab 19, fig 7, NMS G1878.18.16.

RS 58   *Rhizodus* sp., unfigured opercular bone, Department of Geology, University of Edinburgh (EUGeol.)

RS 69   *Elonichthys robisoni* (Hibbert) possibly counterpart of specimen figured by Hibbert 1836, pl 7, fig 3. EUGeol. numbered 189.

RS 71   *Eurynotus crenatus* Ag. NMS G unnumbered.

RS 74   *Eurynotus crenatus* Ag. Figured Agassiz 1833-43 Tome II, Tab 14a, fig 2. NMS GY1878.18.11.

RS 82   Stated to be *Palaeoniscus striolatus*: Agassiz 1833-43, Tome II, p 91 = *Elonichthys robisoni*, specimen he figured ibid Tab 10a, figs 3 & 4 (scales). NMS G1878.18.9.

RS 85   *Elonichthys striolatus* Ag. Unfigured? EU Geol.

RS 89   *Elonichthys robisoni* (Hibbert) Figured Hibbert 1836 pl 6, fig 7 TYPE (p 191). Figured Agassiz 1833-43, Tome II, Tab 10a, fig 1-2 (p 89) (fig 14). NMS G1878.18.8.

RS 93   *Elonichthys robisoni* (Hibbert) Unfigured, EUGeol.

RS 97   *Eurynotus crenatus* Ag Unfigured, EUGeol.

RS 102 *Elonichthys bucklandi* Unfigured, EUGeol.

RS 110 *Rhizodus hibberti* (Hibbert ex Ag) Figured Hibbert, 1836, pl 9, fig 2 (*Megalichthys*). NMS G1950.38.63.

RS 111 *Rhizodus hibberti* (Hibbert ex Ag) Figured Hibbert, 1836, pl 9, fig 10 (*Megalichthys*). NMS G1950.38.65.

RS 112 *Rhizodus hibberti* (Hibbert ex Ag) Figured Hibbert 1836, pl 9, fig 3 (*Megalichthys*). NMS G1973.61.1

RS 114 *Rhizodus hibberti* (Hibbert ex Ag) Figured Hibbert 1836, pl 9, fig 6B (*Megalichthys*) NMS G1973.61.2

RS 118 *Rhadinichthys ornatissimus* (Ag) Figured Agassiz 1833-43, Tome II, Tab 10a, fig 6. NMS G1878.18.7.

Additional specimens from this collection figured by Agassiz 1833-43 and traced by Dr Andrews are:

Tome II   Tab 10a, fig 5 *Palaeoniscus ornatissimus* Ag. NMS G1950.38.94

Tome II   Tab 14a, fig 1 *Eurynotus crenatus* Ag. NMS G1878.18.12 and counterpart.

Tome II   Tab 14a, fig 3 *Eurynotus crenatus* Ag. NMS G1878.18.13.

Tome II   Tab 14a, fig 4 *Eurynotus crenatus* Ag. NMS G1878.18.14.

Tome III   Tab 1, fig 11-13 *Sphenacanthus serrulatus* Ag.
             NMS G1878.18.15.

Tome III   Tab 19, fig 2 *Ctenoptychius pectinatus* Ag.
             [*Callopristodus pectinatus* (Ag)] IGUN 150.

Tome III   Tab 19, fig 4 *Ctenoptychius pectinatus* Ag.
             [*Callopristodus pectinatus*] IGUN 151.

Tome III   Tab 19, fig 5 *Ctenoptychius denticulatus* Ag.
             [*Callopristodus pectinatus*] IGUN 152.

Tome III   Tab 19, fig 6 *Ctenoptychius denticulatus* Ag.
             [*Callopristodus pectinatus*] IGUN 153.

Additional specimens from this collection figured by Hibbert 1836 and traced by Dr Andrews are:

Pl 7, fig 3   *Elonichthys robisoni* (Hibbert) = *Palaeoniscus* (p 190)
              NMS G1950.38.92.

Pl 9, fig 9   *Rhizodus hibberti* (Hibbert ex Ag) = *Megalichthys*
              NMS G1950.38.64.

Pl 11, figs 1A and 1B, Bony ray(s) of fish – p 194 *Gyracanthus (formosus)* p
              188. NMS G1950.38.7.

On 2nd October 1834 William Hutton, writing from Newcastle to John Robison, the Society's General Secretary, says that he has seen several vegetable fossils from Burdiehouse which, with Dr Lindley, he wishes to describe and asks permission to borrow them (NLS ACC 10000/353).

(Three specimens from the Society's collection were described and figured by J Lindley and W Hutton, in *Fossil Flora of Great Britain*...vol III, 1837, are now in the collection of the National Museum of Scotland, *Sphenopteris crassa* GY1959.15.251, *Lepidostrobus comosus* and *Sphenopteris hibberti*).

HOPE, SIR JOHN

[Sir John Hope of Pinkie, 11th baronet Craighall]

3 specimens from petrified trees found in the Coal Mines belonging to Sir John Hope.

NLS ACC 10000/353 contains a memorandum addressed from Pinkie House on 16 April 1834 regarding these specimens:

No 1 On top of the Clayknows Coal; at 14 fathoms deep, a vertical column of free stone, or sandstone, was found having the Tree appearance, and not composed of the same material which surrounded it; and on which it stood, these being coal or claystone. The section of this herewith sent is marked No 1.

No 2 The fragment of column marked No 2 was found on top of the Bar's Coal, in Pinkie Burn pit, at about 36 fathoms from the surface and in similar Claystone as No.1, it also stood upright from the top of the coal.

No 3 The fragment resembling the under section of an Oak Tree and marked No 3 was

178

found in sinking the Jewel Coal pit, at New Craighall Colliery under the Beefie Coal, in reddish sandstone, also in a vertical position at about 18 or 20 fathoms deep.

Note: The Strata in which No 3 was found is about 56 fathoms under the Coal in which No 1 stood, and No 2 was about 100 fathoms under the reddish sandstone which contains No 3.

MAXWELL, SIR PATRICK

Fossil remains from Cauldronlee Quarry, Ecclefechan.

NLS ACC 10000/353 contains a letter from J Shaw Stewart of Springhill, by Ecclefechan dated 1 October 1834 to John Robison stating that these were from a limestone quarry and were to be presented to the Society. 'My friend Mr David Milne who saw them and minutely examined the Rock in which they were imbedded has undertaken to furnish any particulars ...'

JOHN GORDON ESQ

A Camelon, a Fly Fish and a Lantern Fly, preserved in Spirits. *Transactions* 13, Donations 1 December and *Proceedings* 1, p 70 for 1 December 1833.

THOMAS ALLAN ESQ

Rock specimens of Transition Rocks from various localities.

Included in the Billet of 1843. In 1877 A Geikie listed 'Rock Chips from Lake District - Allan' as being in drawers 10-12 under Book Case E and 'Miscellaneous rocks - Allan' in drawer 24 under Book Case E, NLS ACC 10000/396.

- 1835 -

PROFESSOR J D FORBES

A Collection of Specimens from the Volcanic District of Auvergne. *Transactions* 13, Donations 21 December, *Proceedings* 1, p 105 for 21 December 1835.

See Forbes (1836). Listed in Billet of 1843 and by A Geikie in 1877 as being in drawers 1-5 below Book Case E with other Forbes rocks, NLS ACC 10000/396.

THE ROYAL INSTITUTION, SECOND MUSEUM 1835-59

- 1836 -

DR RICHARD PARNELL
[Agrostologist and Ichthyologist]

Prepared specimens of the following species of fish were presented by Dr Parnell:

Trigla Blochi, Aspidophorus cataphractus, Gasterosteus trachurus, Blennius Pholis, Zoarcus viviparus, Belone vulgaris, Clupea Harengus, C. sprattus, C. alba, Salmo eriox, S. fario – male, *S. fario* – female, *S. salmulus, Gadus luscus, Platessa vulgaris, P. fusus, P. pola, P. Limandoides, Microcephalus petrosus, Solea vulgaris, Raia radiata.* (*Parnell, 1845a, for surviving specimens see below under comprehensive list of fishes presented by Dr Parnell*).

- 1837 -

DR RICHARD PARNELL

Trigla lucerna, Monochirus minutus Parnell

Parnell (1845b), for surviving specimens see below under comprehensive list of fishes presented by Dr Parnell.

DR RICHARD PARNELL

'A large collection of Preserved Fishes was also presented by Dr Parnell'(Parnell 1845c, 164-5)

The following is a list of what have been presented by the same gentleman on this and on some prior occasions:

Perca fluviatilis, Labrax lupus, Trachinus draco, T.vipera (Trigla cuculus), Trigla lucerna, T.gurnardus, Cottus scorpius, C, bubalis, Gasterosteus leiurus, G.spinachia, Pagellus acarne, P.centrodontus, Scomber scomber, Caranx trachurus, Cantharus griseus, Zeus faber, Mugil chelo, Atherina presbyter, Blennius gattorugine, Muranoides guttata, Anarrhichas lupus, Gobius niger (in spirit), *G. minutus* (in spirit), *G.unipunctatus* (in spirit), *G. bipunctatus* (in spirit), *G.gracilis* (in spirit), *G.albus* (in spirit), *Callionymus lyra, C. dracunculus, Lophius piscatorius, Labreus masculatus, Crenilabrus tinca, C. cornubicus, Leuciscus rutilus, L. dobula, L. phoxinus, Cobitis barbatula, Salmo salar, S. caecifer, Osmerus eperlanus, Coregonus maraenula, Alosa finta, Gadus morrhua, G.aeglefinus, Merlangus vulgaris, M. pollachius, M. carbonarius, Merlucius vulgaris, Lota molva, Motella quinquecirrata, M. glauca* (in spirit), *Raniceps trifurcatus, Platessa limanda, Hippoglossus vulgaris, Rhombus maximus, Rhombus vulgaris, R. hirtus, R. megastoma, R. arnoglossus, Solea pergusa, Monochirus lungula, (M. Minutus), Cycloperus lumpus, Echeneis ramosa, Anguilla acutirostris, Ammodytes tobianus, A. lancea, Syngnathus typhle, Scyllius canicula, S. catulus, Mustelus laevis, Spinax acanthus, Squatina angelus, Raia batis, R. intermedia, R. clavata, Petromyzon marinus.*

(See Parnell 1840, 1844c.) The above list of Dr Parnell's fishes appeared in the Billet of 1843. The collection was passed to the Natural History Museum NLS ACC 10000/20 Council Minute of 21 November 1859, and registered as 1859.23. Three collections of Parnell's fishes are preserved in the Natural History collections of the NMS, the others are NMS NH1834.8 comprising several fishes from the Firth of Forth presented by Parnell to Professor Jameson in 1834, and by him to the Museum, and a collection of 119 skins of British Fishes bequeathed by Richard Parnell's widow in 1888 and registered as NMS NH1888.12.1-119. Most of the fish skins are preserved on their original mounts on which identifications and collecting data are given. Unlike specimens in the 1888 collection, those belonging to the 1834 and 1859 collections were not numbered individually. It is reasonable to suppose, however, that specimens which were collected after 1834 and do not have 1888.12 registrations belong to the collection received from the Royal Society of Edinburgh (Z1859.23) They are:

Cantharus griseus, Brixham, 1836
Cottus scorpius, Firth of Forth, July 1836
Crenilabrus cornubicus, Firth of Forth, July 1835
Crenilabrus rupestris, Brixham, September 1836 (fig 17)
Crenilabrus tinca, Firth of Forth, August 1835
Leuciscus autelus, Union Canal, Edinburgh, August 1836
Leuciscus rutilus, Lochmaben, August 1836
Merlangus vulgaris, Firth of Forth, March 1836
Monhua lusca, Firth of Forth, 1837
Monochirus minutus, Brixham, September 1836
Mugil chelo, Firth of Forth, September 1835
Mugil chelo, Firth of Forth, July 1835
Mustelus laevis, Firth of Forth, June 1836
Pagellus centrodontus, Firth of Forth, September 1835
Perca fluviatalis, Duddingston Loch, Edinburgh, 1837
Pleuronestis megastoma, Brixham, September 1836
Rhombus arnoglossus, Brixham, September 1836
Rhombus vulgaris, Firth of Forth, December 1837
Trachinus draco, Brixham, 1836
Trachinus vipera, Firth of Forth, June 1835
Trigla blochii, Firth of Forth, June 1836
Trigla blochii or *Trigla cuculus*, Firth of Forth, July 1835
Trigla cuculus, Firth of Forth, 1837
Trigla hirundo, Firth of Forth, August 1835
Trigla hirundo, Brixham 1836
Trigla lucerna, Brixham, September 1836
Unmounted fish skin, possibly *Salmo salar*

- 1839 -

MR JOHN SHAW OF DRUMLANRIG

Specimens illustrating the growth of the Salmon.

'I have transmitted a series of the specimens referred to, from the ovum to the smolt, and including the ordinary and transitionary state of the parr, to be exhibited when my paper is read' (Shaw 1840, footnote to p 556). Up to 13 specimens are mentioned (Shaw 1845).

Listed as having been passed to the Natural History Museum NLS ACC 10000/20 Council Minute of 21 November 1859.

- 1840 -

MR J H SANDERSON

Two fossils from Burdiehouse. Letter from Sanderson to John Stark, 30 January 1840 (NLS ACC 10000/389).

SIR THOMAS MAKDOUGALL BRISBANE BART.

A specimen of *Clavagella Balanorum* (Scacchi) from the shores of Naples, was presented by Sir Thomas Brisbane and laid on the table with remarks given by Dr Traill on 3 February 1840.

(See Traill, 1845a)

J O M'WILLIAM ESQ, RN

The following African Shells, collected by J O M'William Esq, Surgeon RN, were presented by that gentleman through Dr Traill, who, on 16 March 1840, made a few remarks on each, especially the rarest Nos 3, 4, 5, 7 and 11.

1 *Achatina Perdix* – Accra, Gold Coast
2 *Achatina Scabra* – Isle of Princes
3 *Achatina reversa Purpurea* – Isle of Princes, (fig 18)
4 *Helix Polyzonalis* – Madagascar ?
5 *Helix* ? allied to *H. Ungulina* and *H. Oculus*
6 *Lymnaea Columna* – Isle of Princes
7 *Ampullaria Corrugata* – Madagascar
8 *Trochus Turbinatus* – Isle of Princes
9 *Nerita Atrata* – Isle of Princes
10 *Nerita Puligera* – Isle of Princes
11 *Nerita Carona* – Mozambique
12 *Turbo Muricatus* – Isle of Princes
13 *Cypraea Moneta* – Africa
14 *Patella Lacustris* – Kafferland
15 *Patella Longicosta* – Simon's Bay, Cape of Good Hope
16 *Patella Monopis* – Simon's Bay, do.
17 *Patella Granatina* – Simon's Bay, do.
18 *Crepidula Porcellana* – Cape of Good Hope
19 *Voluta Volvacea* – Africa
20 A small *Echinus*

See Traill (1845b), 'A small series of named African Shells' passed to the Natural History Museum of Edinburgh University according to the Council Minute of 21 November 1859, Acc 10000/20, and were registered under the collection number 1859.24. The following are preserved in the collections of NMS: z1859.24.3 *Achatina reversa* having the ms label 'Achatina Reversa allied to A. Bicarinata Lam. Bulla Purpurea [Lam], Isle of Princes'; z1859.24.11 *Nerita carona* Linn = *Neritina longispina* Recluz with ms locality label 'Isle of Princes' which may be misplaced since this species was said to come from Mozambique; z1859.24.16 *Patella monopis* = *Patella oculatus* Born., Simon's Bay, Cape of Good Hope.

R S G KILBEE ESQ

There was also presented by Professor Forbes, on the part of R S G Kilbee Esq. a collection of Fossil Shells, from the great deposit near Uddevalla in

Sweden, of which deposit a description is given. *Proceedings* 1, 297-8, 16 March 1840.

SIR GEORGE S MACKENZIE

A Collection of Fossil Organic Remains from Touraine. *Transactions* 14, Donations 20 April 1840.

In a letter from to Sir John Robison of 28 March 1840 (NLS ACC 10000/389) Mackenzie states that two boxes of Fossils from Touraine, which he wishes to present to the Society, are at the Customs House, Leith. Listed in Billet of 1843 and by A Geikie in 1877 as being in drawers 2-4 below Book Case C, in drawer 8 on East side of Table Case and also some specimens exhibited in Table Case, NLS ACC 10000/396.

PROFESSOR LOUIS ALBERT NECKER OF GENEVA
[Professor of Mineralogy and Geology, Geneva]

Specimens of Fossil Vegetables and Shells from Shetland and Skye. *Transactions* 14, Donations 20 April.

In a letter dated 12 April 1840 (NLS ACC 10000/389) Necker writes that three specimens are vegetable imprints in sandstone from Bressay, Shetland and the rest are fossil shells from the east coast of Skye to the north of Portree. 'Fossil Organic Remains from the Isle of Skye' are listed in Billet of 1843.

CHEVALIER MICHELOTTI OF TURIN

A Collection of Specimens of Fossil Organic Remains. *Transactions* 15, Donations 20 April, *Proceedings* 1, 311, for 6 April 1840.

Ten species of *Solarium spp.* are figured by the donor (Michelotti 1844) and representative specimens of them may have been in the collection. In a letter from Mr Roberton of the Royal Society, London, to Sir John Robison of 19 March 1840 (NLS ACC 10000/389) it is stated that the box of fossils from Michelotti has been placed in the hands of Mr Cadell, Bookseller, The Strand, who has paid the charges and started to Edinburgh. Listed in Billet of 1843.

ROBERT BALD ESQ
[Mining Engineer]

Exhibited a collection of organic remains from the Airdrie Coal Measures on 6 April 1840, *Proceedings* 1, p 311.

It is not stated that this collection was donated but in 1877 A Geikie reported that drawer 13 below Book case C contained Fossils from Airdrie NLS ACC 10000/396.

DR THOMAS STEWART TRAILL
[Professor of Medical Jurisprudence, University of Edinburgh]

A Collection of Fossil Fishes from Orkney. *Transactions* 15, Donations 21 December, *Proceedings* 1, 1840, 316.

See Traill (1845c). Listed in Billet of 1843 and by A Geikie in 1877 as being in drawers 32-33 on east side of Table Case, NLS ACC 10000/396.

CHARLES MURRAY CATHCART, LORD GREENOCK

A number of Mineral and Fossil Organic Specimens, from various localities. *Transactions* 15, Donations 5 December, *Proceedings* 1, 1842, p 388.

In the Billet of 1843 the collection is described as comprising Fossil Organic Remains from various formations in England, viz., Tertiary, Chalk, Gault, Green Sand, Wealden, Oolite, Lias, and Coal.

JOHN STARK ESQ
[Printer and publisher]

Transactions 15, 5 December.

Specimens of Land and Fresh-water Shells, chiefly from the neighbourhood of Edinburgh.

Listed in Billet of 1843. This series of shells was passed to the Natural History Museum NLS ACC 10000/20 Council Minute of 21 November 1859.

Specimens of Marine Shells, chiefly from the Firth of Forth.

Listed in Billet of 1843. This series of shells was passed to the Natural History Museum NLS ACC 10000/20 Council Minute of 21 November 1859.

Specimens of Zoophytes, chiefly from the Firth of Forth.

Listed in Billet of 1843.

JOHN STARK ESQ

Specimens illustrative of Mr Stark's paper 'On the Food of the Herring and Salmon' *Transactions* 15, Donations 19 December.

See Stark (1845). This series of dried specimens on cards is listed as having been passed to the Natural History Museum NLS ACC 10000/20 Council Minute of 21 November 1859.

JAMES ANSTRUTHER ESQ

Specimens of Woods of Ceylon (fifty different kinds). *Transactions* 15, Donations 19 December.

Listed in Billet of 1843. Probably the 'Specimens of wood' passed to the Royal Botanic Garden NLS ACC 10000/20 Council Minute of 21 November 1859.

DR JOHN DAVY

Specimens of Minerals and Fossil Organic Remains from Malta, the Ionian Islands and Ceylon. *Transactions* 15, Donations 19 December.

Listed in Billet of 1843. A Geikie records that in 1877 'Fossils from Ionian Islands' were in drawers 14-15 under Book Case E and Tertiary Fossils from Malta in drawer 9 on the East side of the Table Case, NLS ACC 10000/396.

PROFESSOR J D FORBES

Geological Specimens from the Velay and Vivarais (Haute Loire and Ardèche). Transactions 15, Donations 19 December.

Listed in Billet of 1843.

- 1843 -

DAVID MILNE ESQ

[David Milne Home of Milne Graden, advocate and landowner]

Specimens illustrating the geology of Roxburgh

Milne (1844, 498-500) catalogues 95 specimens illustrating the foregoing memoir, and lodged in the Royal Society Museum. A list of a further 19 specimens collected by Rev Mr Barton of Castlelaw, being fragments from Liddesdale boulders, is appended p501. Listed by A Geikie in 1877 as being in drawers 43-46 of West Side of Table Case, also 'Chips of Sandstone etc partly Mr Milne Home's' in drawers 2-7 below Book Case B, NLS ACC 10000/396.

JOHN STARK ESQ

Specimens of Fossil Organic Remains from East Kilbride and neighbourhood, Lanarkshire. Collected by the late Rev. David Ure, AM; and a number of them figured in his *History of Rutherglen and East Kilbride*. Transactions 15, Donations 9 January.

Listed in Billet of 1843. 'Dr Ure's Rutherglen Fossils' are listed by A Geikie as having been on exhibition in 1877 in the Top West Side of the Table Case NLS ACC 10000/396. Collection donated to Glasgow University by resolution of Council NLS ACC 10000/25, Minutes of Council of 7 May 1909 and 20 June 1910. Collection of *c*2300 specimens donated to the Hunterian Museum in 1909 (Stace, Pettitt and Waterston, 1987, 347). Many specimens figured by Ure (1793, pls X-XX) remain in the collection. For example the following were refigured by Burns (1993) at Fig 2 and Plate 2:

Ure XV,1, *Spirifera striatus* Martin GLAHM L11905; Ure XV (fig 19), 2, *Carbonicola pseudorobusta?* GLAHM S35312; Ure XX,6, *Aulophyllum fungites* (Fleming) GLAHM C4366; Ure XVIII,13, ?*Parazeacrinites* sp. GLAHM E1593; Ure XIX,1, *Fish coprolite* GLAHM X1105; Ure XV,7, *Echinoconchus punctatus* (Sow.) GLAHM L11096; Ure XX,7, *Conularia quadrisulcata* Sow. GLAHM C122011. Among other specimens figured by Ure the following have been recognised, Ure XIV, 12 *Crurithyris urei* (Fleming) GLAHM L1790 in T N George, *Quart J.Geol.Soc Lond* LXXXVII, 1931, pl iv, figs 1a-d; ?Ure XIV, 9, *Euphemites urii (Fleming)* GLAHM S18790 R L Batten, *Monogr.Palaeontogr. Soc.* 1966, pl I, fig 4. Ure XX,1, *Cellepora urii* Fleming GLAHM D785-781 and D900-908).

ROBERT BRYSON ESQ

Tail of a Wild Elephant from Ceylon. *Transactions* 15, Donations 9 January.

This is a fly whisk made from an elephant's tail and was transferred to the Industrial Museum of Scotland, as 'An Indian Implement' NLS ACC 10000/20, Council Minute of 21 November 1859. Preserved in the Department of History and Applied Art of NMS with the registered number A1859.416.

DR JOHN DAVY

Specimens of Fossil Fishes from Syria. *Transactions* 15, Donations 9 January.

MR ANDREW YOUNG, INVERSHIN, SUTHERLANDSHIRE

Three specimens of Salmon, showing the rapid growth (on descending to the sea) of the Smolt to the state of Grilse, and of the latter to the adult condition. *Transactions* 15, Donations 23 January.

SIR THOMAS MAKDOUGALL BRISBANE BART

Specimens of Volcanic Rocks from Vesuvius, and Minerals from Derbyshire. *Transactions* 15, Donations 6 February.

A Geikie lists a 'Set of Vesuvius rocks - school series' as having been in drawer 17 under Book Case C and 'Chips from Derbyshire with list (poor)' in the top of the Table Case on the West Side in 1877, NLS ACC 10000/396.

JOHN STARK ESQ

Specimens of Fossil Shells from Grignon, collected by Dr (James) Stark in October 1833. *Transactions* 15, Donations 6 February.

D BALFOUR ESQ, YOUNGER OF TRENABY

A Specimen of a Vegetable Impression from Burdie House. *Transactions* 15, Donations 6 March.

PROFESSOR J D FORBES

Models illustrating glacier flow, see *Proceedings* 1, 414, for 20 March 1843.

Model showing the curve generated (experimentally) by the matrix of a viscous fluid and model showing the effect of two streams on the motion of a viscid fluid. 'Plaster model to illustrate Prof. J D Forbes on glacier motion' listed by A Geikie in 1877 as being in the open glass case below Book Case D, NLS ACC 10000/396.

LORD GREENOCK

Specimens of Hypersthene Rocks of the Cuillin Hills, and of the Limestone and Dykes traversing the Cuillin Hills at Kilbride, Isle of Skye. Collected by G Bellas Greenough Esq. *Proceedings* 1, 419, for 27 March 1843.

LORD GREENOCK

Specimens of the Calcareous Formation of the Bermudas and Bahama Islands. Collected by Lieut-Colonel Emmett RE. *Proceedings* 1, 419, for 27 March 1843.

'Rocks from Bahamas' listed by Geikie 1877 as in drawer 13 under Book Case E.

LORD GREENOCK

Series of Specimens of different Rock Formations (150 specimens). *Transactions* 15, Donations 3 April.

It is likely that many of Lord Greenock's figured specimens were included in this donation, since most of those whose whereabouts are known were in the collection of fossil fishes described by L Agassiz which was donated to the National Museum by the Society in 1878, Andrews (1982, note 41, p 59). Dr Andrews (Checklist 1, p 39) lists the following fossil fishes from Newhaven, Edinburgh, now in NMS, as having been presented by Lord Greenock to the Society and described by Agassiz in *Recherches Sur Les Poissons Fossiles* Tome II, p 106-9, Tab 4b, *Amblypterus striatus* Ag [*Cosmoptychius striatus*(Ag)] specimens G1878.18.1-3; Tab 4c *Palaeoniscus carinatus* Ag [*Rhadinichthys carinatus* (Ag)] G1878.18.5; and *Amblypterus punctatus* Ag [*Gonatodus punctatus* (Ag)] G1878.18.4 and 6.

MR JOHN SHAW OF DRUMLANRIG

Specimens connected with Mr Shaw's paper on the Development and Growth of the Sea Trout of the Solway. *Transactions* 15, Donations 3 April.

See Shaw (1844) where 11 specimens are described. These are listed as having been passed to the Natural History Museum NLS ACC 10000/20 Council Minute of 21 November 1859.

DR JOHN DAVY

Transactions 15, Donations 1 May.

A Head of Boodhoo in Dolomite from Ceylon.

Listed as having been passed to the Society of Antiquaries NLS ACC 10000/20 Council Minute of 21 November 1859.

Specimens of Coal from Penteraclea, the Ancient Heraclea, on the Black Sea.

JAMES MILLER ESQ

Specimens of Burn Trout or *Salmo Fario*, taken from the compensation Pond, weighing 6lb. *Transactions* 15, Donations 1 May.

SIR GEORGE S MACKENZIE

A Specimen of Chalcedony from Iceland. *Transactions* 15, Donations 1 May.

PROFESSOR J D FORBES

Transactions 15, Donations 1 May.

Six Specimens shewing the Actions of Glaciers on Rocks:

1 Limestone taken from under the Ice of the Glacier of La Brenva, in Piedmont, in July 1842.

2, 3, 4 Specimens of Granite from the Grimsel, supposed to shew Glacier Polish.

5, 6 Specimens of Limestone from the Jura, shewing (supposed) Glacier Polish.

'Series of stones striated by Ice - J D Forbes' listed as having been in the open case below Book Case E in 1877 by A Geikie NLS ACC 10000/396.

PROFESSOR J D FORBES

Specimens of Fossil Fish, from the Old Red Sandstone of Morayshire, named by M. Agassiz. *Transactions* 15, Donations 1 May.

- 1844 -

J SHEDDEN PATRICK

Series of fossil plants from a quarry of Carboniferous freestone on the estate of Mr Warner of Ardeer, in the parish of Stevenston and district of Cunninghame, Ayrshire.

Twenty-five plant taxa were represented in the collection (Patrick, 1845) including '*Dictyodendron patricii* Landsborough Type?'.

Also impure ironstone from a coal pit on the same estate containing *Unio Urii*.

THE HON MRS M CATHCART

14 Specimens of British Land and Fresh-water Shells. *Transactions* 15, Donations 15 January.

'A collection of British Shells' donated by the Royal Society of Edinburgh was registered as 1859.22 in the Natural History Museum.

8 specimens of *Theodoxus fluviatilis* from England, and bearing this number, are preserved in the shell collection of NMS and are recognised as belonging to Mrs Cathcart's collection.

CAPT P DALL RN

Block of Sandstone, with organic remains imbedded in it, found in one of the Dry Docks at Leith, when enlarging it; originally from Rosyth Quarry, Fifeshire. *Transactions* 15, Donations 15 January.

- 1847 -

SIR GEORGE S MACKENZIE BART

Specimen of Metamorphic Limestone, dislocated by the vicinity of Trap Rocks, near North Berwick. *Transactions* 16, Donations 1 February.

J W DAWSON ESQ

Proceedings, 3 May 1847

There was exhibited, in illustration of the following paper (Dawson 1851), a large collection of specimens, presented by the author to the Society.

- 1848 -

SIR GEORGE S MACKENZIE BART

A Collection of Fossil Plants from the Newcastle Coalfield.

Transactions 16, Donations 17 January and *Proceedings* 2, 160, 17 January 1848.

PROFESSOR J D FORBES

A series of specimens illustrating the geology of the volcanoes of Vivarius.

See Forbes (1851, 158) where it is stated 'A series of specimens illustrating the paper had formerly been presented to the Society'. See also Forbes (1853 ,21) where a cast of a vegetable stem in lava is described and it is stated 'The specimen illustrating this curious fact, and others referred to in this paper, are now placed in the Museum of the Royal Society of Edinburgh'.

- 1851 -

PROFESSOR J D FORBES

Collection of Specimens illustrating the Geology of the Eildon Hills. *Transactions* 20, Donations 7 April.

See Forbes (1857) where it is stated 'A collection of specimens, illustrating the paper, is deposited in the Museum of the Royal Society'. See also Forbes (1853b 216-7) where a catalogue of the thirty-eight specimens presented is given. 'Chips from Eildon Hills, J D Forbes Trans XX' listed by A Geikie in 1877 as being in drawer 34 on East Side of Table Case. NLS ACC 10000/396.

JOHN RUSKIN ESQ
[Art critic and teacher]

Specimens illustrating the geology of Chamouni.

See Ruskin (1862) where artifical sections are described and it is stated that 'Specimens of the more important rocks have been placed in the Museum of the Royal Society'. Perhaps 'Rock chips from Alps (J D Forbes)' listed as being in drawer 21 below Book Case C by A Geikie in 1877 NLS ACC 10000/396.

In the 'List of the principal Donations of the Royal Society, and which may now be seen in the Museum' printed with the *Billet* of 6th February 1843 the following donations are listed which were probably made in 1843 or earlier but do not appear in the dated gifts listed above:

RODERICK I MURCHISON ESQ
[Director General of the Geological Survey]

Fossil Organic Remains and Rocks of the Silurian System.

J R WRIGHT ESQ

Model of Arthur Seat and King's Park, Edinburgh

Listed as model 3 by A Geikie in 1877, NLS ACC 10000/396.

- 1859 -

PROFESSOR C PIAZZI SMYTH
[Astronomer Royal for Scotland]

Geological specimens from the Peak of Teneriffe. *Transactions* 22, Donations 7 March and *Proceedings* 4, 183 for 7 March 1859.

THE ROYAL INSTITUTION, THIRD MUSEUM 1859-1909

1863

EDINBURGH TOWN COUNCIL PER MR J D MARWICK, TOWN-CLERK

Lead from the roof of the lower storey of Nelson's Monument, injured by lightning. *Proceedings* of 6 April 1863.

See Smyth (1866, 106) where it is stated '...I lost no time in applying to Mr J D Marwick, town-clerk, for those portions of the leaden covering which contained the marks in question, with the view of presenting them to the Royal Society.' Donated to NMS in 1982 and registered as T1996.163.

- 1865 -

PROFESSOR C PIAZZI SMYTH

Examples of geological specimens, together with sixteen casing-stone fragments from the Great Pyramid.

See Smyth (1867, 2, 294) where it is stated 'Examples of all the geological specimens, together with sixteen of the casing-stone fragments, have been presented to the Royal Society, Edinburgh, and are deposited in their Museum.' In ibid pp 293-4 a catalogue of specimens brought home is given. Geological specimens listed by A Geikie in 1877 as being in drawer 19 below Book Case B, and 'parts of the Great Pyramid' almost certainly the casing-stones, as model 4, NLS ACC 10000/396. The casing stones were exhibited in the Society's museum on a wooden stand made to exhibit thirteen stones. 12 casing stones were donated to NMS in 1977 and are now registered as T1996.162. Another of the original sixteen casing stones may be that obtained by NMS from the Royal Observatory in 1986 which had been cut and polished in 1875.

PROFESSOR C PIAZZI SMYTH

Samples of rock found attached to the old rock thermometers at the Calton Hill Observatory.

See letter of Smyth to P G Tait of 19th January 1880

[J Jones Archive Catalogue 21.8.6. NLS ACC 10000/?] and Smyth 1880

The following identifiable collections were listed by A Geikie (NLS ACC 10000/396) in 1877 but have not been matched in the earlier donations lists:

SIR WYVILLE THOMSON
[Professor of Natural History at the
University of Edinburgh]

Fossil and recent Echinoderms

Listed by Geikie as in drawer 15 under Book Case B.

DONOR UNKNOWN

Bones from Lunel

Listed by Geikie as in drawer 1 under Book Case C, and drawers 80-81 under West Side of Table Case.

DONOR UNKNOWN

School set of 352 small mineral specimens from the Hartz

Listed by Geikie as being exhibited on the West Side of the Table Case.

DONOR UNKNOWN

Two large specimens of Crystalline Structure in Coal

Listed by Geikie along with the models.

DONOR UNKNOWN

Fish from Solenhofen

Listed by A Geikie as being in drawer 72 on west side of Table Case.

DONOR UNKNOWN

Footprints

Listed by Geikie as being in open glass case below Book Case D.

DONOR UNKNOWN

Rock chips from the Harz

Listed by Geikie as 'very poor' in drawer 50 on west side of Table Case.

THE LAST OF THE COLLECTIONS 1909-1990

- 1922 -

DR T W DEWAR, KINCAIRN, DUNBLANE
[Lecturer in Anatomy, Extra Mural School of
Medicine, Edinburgh]

Chemical case used by Professor J D Forbes on his European travels.

NLS ACC 10000/26 Council Minute 5 June.

- 1952 -

DR J B TAIT, MARINE LABORATORY, TORRY, ABERDEEN
[Deputy Director, Fishery Board of Scotland]

Contents of a Drift Bottle put in the sea from the Scottish National Antarctic Survey ship *Scotia* at Burdwood Bank on 1 December 1903 and found on 7 September 1952 by Mr P Larsen of Tang i moana, Palmerston North, New Zealand near the mouth of the Rangitikei River, North Island, New Zealand, 10,000 miles from the point of release. Received by Dr Tait from the Hydrographic Department of the Admiralty.

See Council Minute of 8 December 1952. The Bottle and its Contents are preserved in the Society's Rooms.

CATALOGUE OF SCIENTIFIC INSTRUMENTS, THE PROPERTY OF THE ROYAL SOCIETY OF EDINBURGH

A Standard Thermometer, constructed by Samuel Healy, Dublin. Presented by the Royal Irish Academy, see donations listed in *Transactions* 3, 1789–93.

The following were listed by Professor T S Traill as instruments belonging to the Society (NLS ACC 10000/18, Council Minute of 25 November 1839):

1   A Time piece by Whitelaw; Scapement & pendulum by Bryson.

Described by Sir John Robison (1831). Made by William Whitelaw in 1830, the instrument has an escapement which requires no oil and a pendulum made of marble. It is in the Reception Area of the Society's House. [Listed also in Appendix I].

2   Standard Barometer with level adjustments & attached thermometer.

Probably the instrument made for the Society by John Newman for £20.5.0 and for which a receipt is preserved in Sir John Robison's correspondence of 1832 (NLS ACC 10000/391). In 1834 J D Forbes stated 'that in consequence of some imperfection in the construction of the Standard Barometer made for the R. Society by Newman of London, it had become useless for the purpose of observation, & that it was necessary that it should be returned to the Maker to be rectified.' (NLS ACC 10000/17, Council Minute of 1 December 1834) Donated in May 1982 to NMS and is registered as T1982.91.

3   Large compound microscope by Adie (fig 7).

Large polarising microscope ordered by the Royal Society of Edinburgh from Alexander Adie at the request of David Brewster, the Society's General Secretary, and delivered in 1829. It is contained in a fitted box with accessories. I am grateful to Miss A Morrison-Low for these details. Donated in May 1982 to NMS and now registered as T1982.90.

4   Thermometer (inclosed in a Glass tube) by Crichton of Glasgow with ivory scale graduated from +10' to 115' Fahrenheit.

5   Thermometer (in leather case) by Adie Edinr. brass scale graduated from -13' to 237' Faht.

6   Thermometer (in a Mahogony box) by Troughton & Simms marked 'Standard', brass scale graduated from -12' to 325' Faht.

7   Thermometer (in Wallnutwood Case) by Collardeau of Paris, a glass scale graduated in Fahrenheit & Centigrade. NB this thermometer was carefully compared with the Standard thermt. in the Observatory of Paris and, when sent to Edinr, was accompanied by a report of the state on comparison.

8   Hansteed's Intensity Compass with two Needles No 1 cylindric, & No 2 flat – A Box with glass sides and top in a leather case.

9   Hansteed's tripod stand for the above in a box & Case (in charge of Prof Forbes).

10 Dipping Needles by Bate of London with two compound Needles A & B; a sole & Stand in a mahogany box & leather case.
Donated to NMS in 1982 and is registered as T1982.226.

11 Chronograph (in a red Morocco Case) by Henri Robert of Paris.

12 Standard Metre by Fortin of Paris, with a standard Yard laid down on the same bar by Troughton & Simms of London – in a mahogany box. NB this Standard was presented to the Society by Lt General Sir Th. Makdougal [sic] Brisbane Bart. president.

> 'It was intimated to the Meeting that it was the intention of the President to present to the Society a Standard French Metre made by Fortin of Paris' [NLS Acc 10000/17 Minute of Council of 21 January 1833]. Donated to NMS and is registered as T1982.213. [Listed also in Appendix I].

Osler's Anemometer
'Treasurer authorised to pay £40 for Osler's Anemometer ordered 7 June 1844 for Granton Pier Meteorological observations' (NLS Acc 10000/18, Minute of Council of 16 January 1846).

The following have been acquired from the Society by the National Museums of Scotland:

Magic lantern signed by J Duboscq of Paris, in brass and blackened metal on four brass legs with wooden slide carrier. Donated May 1982 and registered as T1982.92.

Percussion machine consisting in a row of balls suspended on strings. Donated May 1982 and registered as T1982.93.

Demonstration Gyroscope. Donated 1982 and registered as T1982.224.

Chondrometer by W Fraser and Son of London, c1830. Donated 1982 and registered as T1982.225.

Aitken's Thermometer screen. Acquired 1983 and registered as T1983.281.

Magazine case of drawing instruments by W Elliott of London about 1830 (fig 21). Given to Robert Stephenson by John Farey and presented to the Royal Society of Edinburgh in 1947 by Dr H J Plenderleith. With Dr Plenderleith's concurrence, sold to the National Museums of Scotland in 1989 where it is registered as T1989.3.

BIBLIOGRAPHY

AGASSIZ, J L R. *Recherches sur les Poissons Fossiles*. Text 5 volumes, Atlas 5 volumes, Neuchatel, 1833–43.

ALLAN, D A. The Royal Scottish Museum, General Survey in *The Royal Scottish Museum 1854–1954*. Edinburgh: The Royal Scottish Museum, 1954.

ALLAN, R. Abstract of a Paper accompanying a Suite of Volcanic Rocks from the Lipari Islands, presented to the Royal Society' [1833] *Transactions of the Royal Society of Edinburgh* 12, 1834, 531-7.

ALLAN, T. On the Rocks in the vicinity of Edinburgh [1811] *Transactions of the Royal Society of Edinburgh* 6, 1812, 405-33.

Remarks on the Transition Rocks of Werner [1812] *Transactions of the Royal Society of Edinburgh* 7, 1815, 109-38.

An Account of the Mineralogy of the Faroe Islands [1813] *Transactions of the Royal Society of Edinburgh* 7, 1815, 229-65.

Description of a Vegetable Impression found in the Quarry of Craigleith [1821] *Transactions of the Royal Society of Edinburgh* 9, 1823, 235-7, pl XIV.

Observations on the Formation of the Chalk Strata, and on the Structure of the Belemnite [1821] *Transactions of the Royal Society of Edinburgh* 9, 1823, 393-418.

On a Mass of Native Iron from the Desert of Atacama in Peru. *Edinburgh Journal of Science* 9, 1828, 259-62 with supplement, Examination of the Specimen of Native Iron from the Desert of Atacama in Peru by Edward Turner *ibid* 262-4, also *Transactions of the Royal Society of Edinburgh* 11, 1831, 223.

ALLEN, D E. James Edward Smith and the Natural History Society of Edinburgh. *Journal of the Society for the Bibliography of Natural History* 8, 1978, 483-93.

ANDERSON, E M. *Catalogue of Types and Figured Specimens of Fossils in the Geological Survey Collections now exhibited in The Royal Scottish Museum*. London: HMSO, 1936.

ANDERSON, R G W. *The Playfair Collection and the Teaching of Chemistry at the University of Edinburgh 1713-1858*. Edinburgh: The Royal Scottish Museum, 1978.

Joseph Black: An Outline Biography in A D C Simpson *Joseph Black 1728-1799 A Commemorative Symposium*. Edinburgh: The Royal Scottish Museum, 1982.

Connoisseurship, Pedagogy or Antiquarianism? *Journal of the History of Collections* 7, 1995, 211-25.

ANDREWS, S M. *The Discovery of Fossil Fishes in Scotland up to 1845*. Edinburgh: The Royal Scottish Museum, 1982.

ANON. Literary Intelligencer in *The Bee or Literary Weekly Intelligencer* 10, 1792, 262.

ANON. *Laws of the Society Instituted at Edinburgh MDCCLXXXII for the Investigation of Natural History*. Edinburgh, 1803.

ANON. Proceedings of the Royal Society of Edinburgh. *Edinburgh Philosophical Journal* 5, 1821, 386.

ANON. *Catalogue of the Museum of the Highland and Agricultural Society of Scotland*. Edinburgh, 1841.

ANON. Sir Henry Cole (1808-1882) in *Dictionary of National Biography* 11, 1887, 268-70.

ASHBY, E. *Technology and the Academics; An Essay on Universities and the Scientific Revolution*. reprinted London, 1963.

BALFOUR, I B. A Sketch of the Professors of Botany in Edinburgh from 1670 until 1887 in F W Oliver *Makers of British Botany*. Cambridge, 1913.

BELL M. Edinburgh and Empire. Geographical Science and Citizenship for a 'New' Age, ca 1900. *Scottish Geographical Magazine*, 111, 1995, 139-49.

BENNETT, J HUGHES. On Parasitic Vegetable Structures found growing in Living Animals [1842] *Transactions of the Royal Society of Edinburgh* 15, 1844, 277-94.

BERGE, A LA. Medical Microscopy in Paris, 1830-1855. French Medical Culture in the Nineteenth Century. *Clio Medica*, 1994, 296-326.

BIRSE, R M. *Science at the University of Edinburgh 1583-1993*. Edinburgh, 1994.

BOUD, R C. Institutional and Individual Influences on Scottish Geological Maps, 1804-1847: A Cornucopia of Publication or a Mere Trickle? *The Cartographic Journal* 25, 1988, 5-19.

The Highland and Agricultural Society of Scotland and the Ordnance Survey of Scotland, 1837-1875. *The Cartographic Journal* 23, 1986, 3-26.

Episodes in Cartographic Patronage / The Scottish Agricultural Society and the Coal District Maps 1834-1847. *Cartographica* 26, 1989, 59-88.

Cartographic patronage and the Highland and Agricultural Society: The County geological premium competitions 1835-1847. *The Cartographic Journal* 30, 1993, 13-29.

BRADLEY, J C. Professor J Chester Bradley's Draft of the English Text of the *Règles International de la Nomenclature Zoologique* as revised by the Paris (1948) and Copenhagen (1953) Congresses. *Bulletin of Zoological Nomenclature* 14, 1957.

BREWSTER, D. Account of the Native Hydrate of Magnesia, discovered by Dr Hibbert in Shetland [1821] *Transactions of the Royal Society of Edinburgh* 9, 1823, 239-42.

[BREWSTER, D] Notice respecting the Varnish and Varnish Trees of India. *Edinburgh Journal of Science* 8, 1828, 96-100.

[BREWSTER, D] Account of the Poisonous Qualities of the Vegetable Varnishes from India and America. *Edinburgh Journal of Science* 8, 1828, 100-4.

BREWSTER, D. On the Natural History and Properties of Tabasheer, the Siliceous concretion in the Bamboo. *Edinburgh Journal of Science* 8, 1828, 285-94.

On the Anatomical and Optical Structure of the Crystalline Lenses of Animals, particularly the Cod. *Philosophical Transactions of the Royal Society of London* 123, 1833, 323-32, *ibid* 126, 1836, 35-48.

Address [1864] *Proceedings of the Royal Society of Edinburgh* 5, 1866, 321-6.

BROWN, I G. Chapter 8, This Old Magazine of Antiquities, The Advocates Library as National Museum in P Cadell and A Matheson *For the Encouragement of Learning Scotland's National Library 1689–1989*, Edinburgh: HMSO, 1989.

BROWN, S. William Smellie and the Early Days of the Society *Newsletter, Society of Antiquaries of Scotland* 1994, 4-5.

BROWN, T. *Biographical Sketches and Authentic Anecdotes of Horses; with a Historical Introduction, and an Appendix on the Diseases and Medical Treatment of Horses*, Edinburgh, 1830.

BUCKLE, H T. *History of civilization in England*, 2 vols London, 1857–61.

BURNS, J H. David Ure (1749–98) Breadth of Mind and Accuracy of Observation. *Glasgow Naturalist* 22, 1993, 259-75.

CADELL, W A. Description of some Indian Idols in the Museum of the Society [1820] *Transactions of the Royal Society of Edinburgh* 9, 1823, 381-92, pl XXIV.

CAMPBELL, N and R M S SMELLIE. *The Royal Society of Edinburgh (1783–1983)*. Edinburgh: The Royal Society of Edinburgh, 1983.

CAMPBELL SMITH, W. Early mineralogy in Great Britain and Ireland. *Bulletin of the British Museum (Natural History), History Series*, 6, 1978, 49-74.

CANT, R G. David Steuart Erskine, 11th Earl of Buchan: Founder of the Society of Antiquaries of Scotland in A S Bell *The Scottish Antiquarian Tradition*. Edinburgh, 1981.

CHITNIS, A C. The University of Edinburgh's Natural History Museum and the Huttonian-Wernerian Debate. *Annals of Science* 26, 1970, 85-94.

The Scottish Enlightenment: A social history. London 1976.

CRAIG, W S. *History of the Royal College of Physicians of Edinburgh* Edinburgh, 1976.

CHRISTISON, R. Chemical Examination of the Petroleum of Rangoon [1831] *Transactions of the Royal Society of Edinburgh* 13, 1836, 118-23.

Address [1868] *Proceedings of the Royal Society of Edinburgh* 6, 1869, 392-428.

The Life of Sir Robert Christison, Bart. edited by his sons, Edinburgh and London, 1885.

COCKBURN, H. *Memorials of His Time* Edinburgh, 1872.

COOK, E T & A WEDDERBURN. *The Works of John Ruskin, Letters* 36, London, 1909.

CRESWELL, C H. *The Royal College of Surgeons of Edinburgh, Historical Notes from, 1505 to 1905*. Edinburgh, 1926.

CUNNINGHAM, F. *James David Forbes: Pioneer Scottish Glaciologist*. Edinburgh, 1990.

DAICHES, D. The Scottish Enlightenment in D Daiches, P Jones and J Jones. *A Hotbed of Genius* Edinburgh, 1986.

DAVIE, G E. *The Democratic Intellect*. Edinburgh, 1961.

DAVIES, G L HERRIES. *North from the Hook*. Dublin, 1995.

DAWSON, J B. First Thin Sections of Experimentally Melted Igneous Rocks: Sorby's Observations on Magma Crystallization. *Journal of Geology* 100, 1992, 251-7.

DAWSON, J W. 1851 On the Boulder Formation and Superficial Deposits of Nova Scotia [1847] *Proceedings of the Royal Society of Edinburgh*, 2, 1851, 140-1.

D.E. Directions for collecting and preserving natural curiosities. *The Bee or Literary Weekly Intelligencer*, 14, 1793, 146-151.

DENDY, A. *Animal Life and Human Progress*. London, 1919.

DESMOND, A and J MOORE. *Darwin*. London: Penguin, 1992.

DESMOND, R. *Dictionary of British and Irish Botanists and Horticulturalists*. London: Natural History Museum, 1994.

DICKSON, W K. *The Life of Major-General Sir Robert Murdoch Smith KCMG, Royal Engineers*. Edinburgh, 1901.

DUNCAN, G. Brewster's Contribution to the Study of the Lens of the Eye: An Experimental Foundation for Modern Biophysics in A D Morrison-Low & J R R Christie *'Martyr of Science' Sir David Brewster 1781-1868*. Edinburgh, Royal Scottish Museum Studies, 1984.

DURANT, G P and W D I ROLFE. William Hunter (1718-1783) as natural historian: his 'Geological interests'. *Earth Science History* 3 (1) 1984, 9-24.

EMERSON, R L. Science and the Origins and Concerns of the Scottish Enlightenment. *History of Science* 26, 1988, 333-66.

Sir Robert Sibbald, Kt, the Royal Society of Scotland and the origins of the Scottish enlightenment. *Annals of Science* 45, 1988, 41-72.

The Scottish Enlightenment and the end of the Philosophical Society of Edinburgh. *The British Journal for the History of Science* 21, 1988, 33-66.

EYLES, V A. Introduction. G W White, *James Hutton's System of the Earth 1785*. Connecticut, 1970.

FARRAR, W V and K R FARRAR. Thomas Allan, Mineralogist: An Autobiographical Fragment. *Annals of Science* 24, 1968, 115-120.

FAUJAS-SAINT-FOND, B. *Voyage en angleterre en écosse et aux Iles Hébrides*. 2 vols. Paris, 1797.

FERGUSON, J de L. *The letters of Robert Burns.* 2 vols. Oxford, 1931.

FINDLAY, A. *The Teaching of Chemistry in the Universities of Aberdeen.* Aberdeen, 1935.

FLETCHER, H R and W H BROWN. *The Royal Botanic Garden Edinburgh 1670-1970.* Edinburgh: HMSO, 1970.

FORBES, G. *Theory of the Glaciers of Savoy by M le Chanoine Rendu, translated by Alfred Wills, to which are added the original memoir; and supplementary articles by P G Tait and John Ruskin.* London, 1874.

FORBES, J D. On the Geology of Auvergne, particularly in connexion with the Origin of Trap Rocks and the Elevation Theory. *Edinburgh New Philosophical Journal* 21, 1836, 1-21.

Travels through the Alps of Savoy and other parts of the Pennine Chain with observations on the phenomena of Glaciers. Edinburgh, 1843.

Account of a Geological Examination of the Volcanoes of the Vivarius [1848] *Proceedings of the Royal Society of Edinburgh* 2, 1851, 158.

On the Volcanic Geology of the Vivarius (Ardèche) [1848] *Transactions of the Royal Society of Edinburgh* 20, 1853, 1-38.

Notes on the Geology of the Eildon Hills, in Roxburghshire [1851] *Transactions of the Royal Society of Edinburgh* 20, 1853, 211-7.

On the Geology of the Eildon Hills [1851] *Proceedings of the Royal Society of Edinburgh* 3, 1857, 53-4.

Address [1862] *Proceedings of the Royal Society of Edinburgh* 5, 1866, 2-24.

FORMAN, L L. On the Typification of Names of William Roxburgh's Species of Phanerogams. *Kew Bulletin* In press.

FRASER, A G. *The Building of Old College: Adam, Playfair & The University of Edinburgh.* Edinburgh, 1989.

GEDDIE, W. *Chambers's Twentieth Century Dictionary.* Edinburgh, 1959.

GEIKIE, A. *The Founders of Geology.* London, 1897.

GILBERT, J T. Kane, Sir Robert John (1809–90). *Dictionary of National Biography* 13, 1892, 238-9.

GILLISPIE, C C. *Genesis and Geology* Harvard, 1951.

GORDON, M M. *The Home Life of Sir David Brewster.* Edinburgh, 1869.

GRANT, A. *Story of the University of Edinburgh during its first three hundred years.* 2 vols. Edinburgh, 1884.

GRANT, E. *Memoirs of a Highland Lady.* ed Strachey, London, 1898.

GRANT, J. 'Account of the Structure, Manners, and Habits of an Orang-Outang from Borneo' in a letter to Dr Brewster from Calcutta 30th November 1827. *Edinburgh Journal of Science* 9, 1828, 1-24.

GRAY, J. *Biographical Notice of the Rev. David Ure; with an Examination, critical and detailed of his History of Rutherglen and East Kilbride.* Glasgow, 1865.

GRAY, J M. *Lord Selkirk of Red River.* Toronto, 1964.

GREENOCK, LORD. A General View of the Phenomena displayed in the neighbourhood of Edinburgh by the Igneous Rocks, in their relations with the Secondary Strata; with reference to a more particular description of the Section which has been exposed to view on the south side of the Castle Hill [1833] *Transactions of the Royal Society of Edinburgh* 13, 1836, 39-45.

General Remarks on the Coal Formation of the Great Valley of the Scottish Lowlands [1834] *Transactions of the Royal Society of Edinburgh* 13, 1836, 107-17.

GREGORY, W. On the Composition of the Petroleum of Rangoon and Remarks on Petroleum and Naphtha in general [1834] *Transactions of the Royal Society of Edinburgh* 13, 1836, 124-30.

Letter to the Right Honourable George, Earl of Aberdeen, Kt ...on the State of the Schools of Chemistry in the United Kingdom. London, 1842.

GREUTER, W ET AL. *International Code of Botanical Nomenclature*. (Tokyo Code) Koningstein, 1994.

GRIMES, E. Observations on the Flints of Warwickshire (communicated by Thomas Allan). *Edinburgh Journal of Science* 3, 1825, 77-80.

HAHN, R. *The Anatomy of a Scientific Institution - The Paris Academy of Sciences 1666-1803*. Berkeley, 1971.

HALL, B. *A Voyage of Discovery to the West Coast of Corea and the great Loo-Choo Island in the Japan Sea...* London, 1818.

HALL, J. On the Vertical Position and Convolutions of certain Strata, and their relation with Granite [1812] *Transactions of the Royal Society of Edinburgh* 7, 1815, 79-108.

On the Revolutions of the Earth's Surface [1812] *Transactions of the Royal Society of Edinburgh* 7, 1815, 139-212.

HEDDLE, M F. *The Mineralogy of Scotland*. 2 vols. Edinburgh, 1901.

HEDGE, I C and J M LAMOND. *Index of Collectors in the Edinburgh Herbarium*. Edinburgh: HMSO, 1980.

HERMAN, J S. *Cetacean Specimens in the National Museums of Scotland*. Edinburgh: National Museums of Scotland Information Series 13, 1992.

HIBBERT, S. On the fresh-water limestone of Burdiehouse in the neighbourhood of Edinburgh, belonging to the Carboniferous Group of rocks. With supplementary notes on other fresh-water limestones [1833, 1834] *Transactions of the Royal Society of Edinburgh*, 13, 1836, 169-282.

HOOKER, J D, BUSK, G & DONNELLY J F D. *Confidential Reports on the Natural History Collections of the Edinburgh Museum of Science and Art*, 12 August 1872, 10 March 1873 and 8 May 1874. HMSO.

HOPPEN, K T. The Nature of the Early Royal Society. *British Journal of the History of Science* 9, 1976, 1-24, 243-73.

HUNTER, M. *Science and Society in Restoration England*. Cambridge, 1981.

HUNTER, W. Account of some bones found in the Rock of Gibraltar. *Philosophical Transactions of the Royal Society of London* 60, 1771, 414-6

HUNTER, W. *Biggar and the House of Fleming, An Account of the Biggar district, archaeological, historical and biographical.* 2nd ed. Biggar, 1867.

HUTTON, J. On the Flexibility of the Brazilian Stone [1791] *Transactions of the Royal Society of Edinburgh* 3, 1794, 86-94.

Theory of the Earth with Proofs and Illustrations. London and Edinburgh, 1795.

IMRIE, N. A short mineralogical description of the Mountain of Gibraltar [1797] *Transactions of the Royal Society of Edinburgh* 4, 1798, 191-202.

A Description of the Strata which occur in ascending from the Plains of Kincardineshire to the Summit of Mount Battoc [1804] *Transactions of the Royal Society of Edinburgh* 6, 1812, 3-19.

JACKSON, J W. Biography of Captain Thomas Brown (1785-1862), A former Curator of the Manchester Museum [1945] *Memoirs and Proceedings of the Manchester Literary and Philosophical Society* 86, 1943–5, 1-28.

JARDINE, W. Memoir of John Walker DD in *The Birds of Great Britain and Ireland* III, London, 1842, 3-50.

JONES, J. The Geological Collection of James Hutton. *Annals of Science* 41, 1984, 224-8.

JONES, J, H S TORRENS and E ROBINSON. The Correspondence between James Hutton (1726-1797) and James Watt (1736-1819) with Two Letters from Hutton to George Clerk-Maxwell (1715-1784): Part I *Annals of Science* 51, 1994, 637-53.

KARK, R M and D T MOORE. The life, work and geological collections of Richard Bright, MD (1789-1858); with a note on the collections of other members of the family ... *Archives of Natural History* 10, 1981, 119-51.

KEESING, R G W. letter 'Gravity Loss'. *Country Life*, January 31, 1991.

KELLY, T. *George Birkbeck: Pioneer of Adult Education.* Liverpool, 1957.

KENNEDY, A. Account of a non-descript Worm (the Ascaris pellucidus) found in the Eyes of Horses in India. In letters from Alexander Kennedy MD FRS Edin. to Professor Russell and Dr Hope. With a Description of the Animal by Captain Thomas Brown FRSE & FLS [1816, 1819] *Transactions of the Royal Society of Edinburgh* 9, 1823, 107-11.

KENNEDY, R. A Chemical Analysis of Three Species of Whinstone, and Two of Lava. *Transactions of the Royal Society of Edinburgh* 5, 1803, 76-98.

KERR, R. Translation with additions of J G Gmelin, *The Animal Kingdom, or Zoological System, of the celebrated Sir Carl Linnaeus* ... London, 1792.

Memoirs of the Life, Writings and Correspondence of William Smellie. 2 vols. Edinburgh, 1811.

KNOX, F J. *Anatomists' Instructor and Museum Companion being Practical Directions for the formation and subsequent management of Anatomical Museums.* Edinburgh, 1836.

KNOX, R. Remarks on the structure of the Gibbons, a subgenus of the Orangs or Pitheci. *Edinburgh Journal of Science* NS 1, 1829, 155-7.

Notice regarding the Osteology and Dentition of the Dugong. *Edinburgh Journal of Science*, NS 1, 1829, 157-8.

Observations to determine the Dentition of the Dugong ... [1830] *Transactions of the Royal Society of Edinburgh* 11, 1831, 389-416.

Observations on the Natural History of the Salmon, Herring, and Vendace [1833] *Transactions of the Royal Society of Edinburgh* 12, 1834, 462-502.

LASKEY, J. *A general Account of the Hunterian Museum*. Glasgow, 1813.

LEVESON, D J. What was James Hutton's Methodology? *Archives of Natural History* 23, 1996, 61-77.

LIDDELL, A. Statistical Account of the Philosophical Society's Exhibition during the Christmas Holidays. [1848] *Proceedings of the Philosophical Society of Glasgow* 2, (1844–8), 145-53.

LONSDALE, H. *A Sketch of the Life and Writings of Robert Knox, the Anatomist*. London, 1870.

LYSAGHT, A. Some eighteenth century bird paintings in the library of Sir Joseph Banks. *Bulletin of the British Museum (Natural History), History Series*, 1 (6), 1959, 251-371.

McKAY, M M. *The Rev Dr John Walker's Report on the Hebrides of 1764 and 1771*. Edinburgh, 1980.

MACKENZIE, G S. *Travels in the Island of Iceland during the summer of 1810*. Edinburgh, 1811.

An Account of some Geological Facts observed in the Faroe Islands [1812] *Transactions of the Royal Society of Edinburgh* 7, 1815, 213-27.

Notice respecting the Vertebra of a Whale, found in a Bed of bluish Clay, near Dingwall [1823] *Transactions of the Royal Society of Edinburgh* 10, 1826, 105-6.

MACKIE, A. William Cullen and the Edinburgh School of Chemistry. *Royal Society of Edinburgh Year Book 1978*.

MACLAURIN, C. *An Account of Sir Isaac Newton's philosophical Discoveries ...* London, 1748.

MAITLAND, W. *The History of Edinburgh from its Foundation to the Present Time*. Edinburgh, 1753.

MEIKLE, H W. The Chair of Rhetoric and Belles-Lettres in the University of Edinburgh. *University of Edinburgh Journal* 13, 1945, 95-7

MELVILLE, R V. *Towards Stability in the Names of Animals: A History of the International Commission on Zoological Nomenclature 1895-1995*. London: ICZN, 1995.

MICHELOTTI, J. 'De Solariis in supracretaceis Italiae stratis repertis' (Monograph of the fossil species of the genus Solarium of Lamarck found in the upper Chalk formation of Italy) [1841] *Transactions of the Royal Society of Edinburgh* 15, 1844, 211-8.

MILLER, S. Endangered Specimens. *Museums Journal* October 1992, 32.

MILNE, D. Geological Account of Roxburghshire [1842 and 1843] *Transactions of the Royal Society of Edinburgh* 15, 1844, 433-502.

MINIHAN, J. *The Nationalisation of Culture. The Great Development of State Sub-sidies to the Arts in Great Britain.* London, 1977.

MONCREIFF, J. Address [1884] *Proceedings of the Royal Society of Edinburgh* 12, 1884, 451-75.

MORRISON-LOW, A D. Edinburgh Portraits 'William Nicol FRSE c1771-1851 Lecturer, Scientist and Collector'. *Book of the Old Edinburgh Club* New Series 2, 1992, 123-31.

MORTON, A G. *History of Botanical Science.* London, 1981.

John Hope 1725-1786, Scottish Botanist. Edinburgh, 1986.

MORTON, A G and M NOBLE. Botany and Mycology in W W Fletcher. Two Hundred Years of the Biological Sciences in Scotland. *Proceedings of the Royal Society of Edinburgh* 84B, 1983, 65-83.

MURRAY, D. 1904 *Museums, their history and their use.* 3 vols. Glasgow, 1904.

NEAVES, C. Obituary of Lord Greenock [1859] *Proceedings of the Royal Society of Edinburgh* 4, 1862, 222-4.

NICKEL, A H and J A MANDARINO. Procedures involving the IMA Commission on New Minerals and Mineral Names and guidelines on mineral nomencla-ture. *American Mineralogist* 72, 1987, 1031-42.

NORRISH, R G W. Lyon Playfair and his Work for the Great Exhibition of 1851. *Journal of the Royal Society of Arts* 99, 1951, 537-49.

OLIVER, F W. *Makers of British Botany.* Cambridge, 1913.

PARNELL, R. Fishes of the Firth of Forth [1837] *Transactions of the Royal Society of Edinburgh* 14, 1840, 146-57.

On the occurrence of the Clupea alba, or White Bait, and of the Raniceps tri-furcatus, or Tadpole-fish, in the Firth of Forth [1836] *Proceedings of the Royal Society of Edinburgh* 1, 1845, 143.

Observations on a New Species of British Gurnard, and on a Species of Sole new to Science [1837] *Proceedings of the Royal Society of Edinburgh* 1, 1845, 157-8.

An Account of a New Species of British Bream, and a Species of Skate new to Science; with a List of, and Observations on, the Fishes of the Firth of Forth and Neighbourhood [1837] *Proceedings of the Royal Society of Edinburgh* 1, 1845, 166-7.

PATRICK, J SHEDDEN. On the Fossil Vegetables of the Sandstone of Ayrshire, illustrative of a series of them, as a Donation for the Society's Museum [1844] *Proceedings of the Royal Society of Edinburgh* 1, 1845, 448-50.

PEACOCK, M A. The Geology of Iceland: The Pioneer Work of a Scottish Geol-ogist. *Transactions of the Geological Society of Glasgow* 17, 1925, 185-203.

A Contribution to the Petrography of Iceland: Being a Description of the Mackenzie Collection of 1810. *Transactions of the Geological Society of Glasgow* 17, 1925, 271-333.

PHILLIPSON, N E. Scottish Enlightenment in D Daiches *A Companion to Scottish Culture*. London, 1981, 340-4. See also Scottish Enlightenment in D. Daiches *The New Companion to Scottish Culture*. Edinburgh, 1993, 295-8.

PLAYFAIR, J. Biographical account of the late Dr James Hutton FRSEd [1803] *Transactions of the Royal Society of Edinburgh* 5, 1805, (History) 39-99.

Account of the Structure of the Table Mountain, and other parts of the Peninsula of the Cape drawn up by Professor Playfair, from Observations made by Captain Basil Hall RN FRSEd. [1813]. *Transactions of the Royal Society of Edinburgh* 7, 1815, 269-78.

POPPER, K R. *The Logic of Scientific Discovery*. Tenth impression (revised) London, 1980.

PRINSEP, H T. *A General Register of the Honourable East India Company's Civil Servants of the Bengal Establishment 1790-1842*. Calcutta, 1844.

REGAN, C TATE. Museums and research in A Dendy *Animal Life and Human Progress*, London, 1919.

REID, W. *Memoirs and Correspondence of Lyon Playfair*. London, 1899.

RICE, D TALBOT and P MCINTYRE. *The University Portraits* 1, Edinburgh, 1957.

ROBINSON, J and D MCKIE. *Partners in Science*. London, 1970.

ROBISON, J. Notice regarding a Time-Keeper in the Hall of the Royal Society of Edinburgh [1831] *Transactions of the Royal Society of Edinburgh*, 11, 1831, 345-51.

ROWATT, T. Notes on Original Models of the Eddystone Lighthouses. *Transactions of the Newcomen Society* 5, 1924-5, 15-23.

RUSKIN, J. Notice respecting some Artificial Sections illustrating the Geology of Chamouni, Communicated in a letter to Professor Forbes and read 15th February 1858. *Proceedings of the Royal Society of Edinburgh*, 4, 1862, 82-4.

[SCOTT, D] Notice respecting the Eggs of the Boa Constrictor, and of a young Brood hatched from these in Assam by a correspondent in India. *Edinburgh Journal of Science* 4, 1826, 221-2. The correspondent was David Scott writing from Gowahutty to George Swinton (Swinton 1827).

SCOTT, H W. *Lectures on Geology By John Walker*. Chicago and London, 1966.

Walker, John in C C Gillispie *Dictionary of Scientific Biography* xiv, New York 1976.

SCOTT, W. *The Journal of Sir Walter Scott*. 2 vols. Edinburgh, 1891.

SEYMOUR, J WEBB. An Account of Observations, made by Lord Webb Seymour and Professor Playfair, upon some Geological Appearances in Glen Tilt, and the adjacent Country. Drawn up by Lord Webb Seymour [1814] *Tansactions of the Royal Society of Edinburgh* 7, 1815, 303-75.

SHAPIN, S. Property, Patronage, and the Politics of Science; The Founding of the Royal Society of Edinburgh. *British Journal for the History of Science* 7, 1974, 1-41

Science in D Daiches *The New Companion to Scottish Culture*. Edinburgh, 1993, 275-8.

SHAW, J. Account of Experimental Observations on the Development and Growth of Salmon-Fry, from the exclusion of Ova to the age of two years [1839] *Transactions of the Royal Society of Edinburgh* 14, 1840, 547-66.

On the Growth and Migrations of Sea-Trout of the Solway (Salmo trutta) [1843] *Transactions of the Royal Society of Edinburgh* 15, 1844, 369-75.

Experiments on the Development and Growth of the Salmon, from the exclusion of the ovum to the age of two years [1839] *Proceedings of the Royal Society of Edinburgh* 1, 1845, 275-9.

SIBBALD, R. *Auctarium Musaei Balfouriani e Musaeo Sibbaldiano* Edinburgh, 1697.

SIMPSON, A D C. Sir Robert Sibbald – the Founder of the College in R Passmore *Proceedings of the Royal College of Physicians of Edinburgh Tercentenary Congress 1981.* Edinburgh, 1982, 59-91.

Newton's Telescope and the Cataloguing of the Royal Society's Repository. *Notes and Records of the Royal Society London*, 38, 1984 187-214.

SKINNER, B. *Scots in Italy in the 18th Century.* Edinburgh: Scottish National Portrait Gallery, 1966.

SMITH, G. Cardwell, Edward, Viscount (1813-1886) in *Dictionary of National Biography*, 9,1887, 43-5.

SMITH, J A. Notice of the discovery of remains of the Elk (*Cervus alces* Linn., *Alces malchis* Gray) in Berwickshire; with notes of its occurrence in the British Islands, more particularly in Scotland[1871] *Proceedings of the Society of Antiquaries of Scotland* 9, 1873, 297-345.

SMITH, P *Memoirs and correspondence of the late Sir James Edward Smith MD.* 2 vols. London, 1832.

SMYTH, C PIAZZI. Accompanying Note to Portions of Lead from the Roof of the Lower Storey of Nelson's Monument injured by lightning on the evening of 4th February 1863 [1863] *Proceedings of the Royal Society of Edinburgh* 5, 1866, 105-12.

Life and Work at the Great Pyramid During the months of January, February, March and April A.D.1865... 3 vols. Edinburgh, 1867.

Notice of the Completion of the New Rock Thermometers at the Royal Observatory, Edinburgh, and what they are for [1880] *Transactions of the Royal Society of Edinburgh* 29, 1880, 637-56.

SPRY, E. An Account of the Case of a Man who died of the Effects of the Fire at Eddystone Light-house. *Philosophical Transactions of the Royal Society of London* 49, 1756, 477-9.

STACE, H E, C W A PETTITT and C D WATERSTON. *Natural Science Collections in Scotland.* Eds. D Heppell and K J Davidson. Edinburgh: National Museums of Scotland, 1987.

STARK, J. Observations on Two Species of Pholas, found on the Sea-coast in the neighbourhood of Edinburgh [1826] *Transactions of the Royal Society of Edinburgh* 10, 1826, 428-39.

Notice regarding the Salamandra atra. *Edinburgh Journal of Science* NS 4, 1831, 373.

On the Food of the Herring and Salmon. *Proceedings of the Royal Society of Edinburgh* 1, 1845, 170-1.

STEVENSON, R B K. The Museum, its Beginnings and its Development in A S Bell *The Scottish Antiquarian Tradition* Edinburgh, 1981, 31-85, 142-211.

SWEET, J M. The Collection of Louis Dufresne (1752-1832). *Annals of Science* 26, 1970, 33-71.

Instructions to Collectors: John Walker (1793) and Robert Jameson (1817); with Biographical Notes on James Anderson (LLD) and James Anderson (MD). *Annals of Science* 29, 1972, 398-400.

SWEET, J M and C D WATERSTON. Robert Jameson's Approach to the Wernerian Theory of the Earth, 1796. *Annals of Science* 23, 1967, 82-4.

SWINNEY, G N. Wyville Thomson and the Edinburgh Museum of Science and Art. In preparation.

SWINTON, A C. The Swintons of that Ilk. *History of the Berwickshire Naturalists' Club*, 8, 1877, 328-52.

The Swintons of that Ilk and their Cadets. privately printed, 1883.

[SWINTON, G] Narrative of the Proceedings and Scientific Observations of the late Mission to Ava. *Edinburgh Journal of Science* 8, 1828, 10-25.

[SWINTON, G] Account of the Fossil Bones discovered on the left bank of the Irawadi in Ava. *Edinburgh Journal of Science* 8, 1828, 56-60.

SWINTON, G. Account of one of the Brood of Boa Constrictors in a letter from David Scott to George Swinton Esq, written from Gowahutty on 10th September 1827. *Edinburgh Journal of Science* 9, 1828, 153-4.

TAYLOR, G. John Walker DD FRSE 1731-1803, A Notable Scottish Naturalist. *Transactions of the Botanical Society of Edinburgh* 38, 1959, 180-203.

TAYLOR, M A. An entertainment for the enlightened; Alexander Weir's Edinburgh Museum of Natural Curiosities 1782-1802. *Archives of Natural History* 19, 1992, 153-67.

THOMPSON, D'A W. Fifty Years Ago in the Royal Society of Edinburgh [1934] *Proceedings of the Royal Society of Edinburgh* 54, 1935, 145-57.

TRAILL, T S. Remarks on a Specimen of *Clavagella Balanorum* (Scacchi) presented by Sir Thomas Brisbane, Bart. [1840] *Proceedings of the Royal Society of Edinburgh* 1, 1845, 288-9.

Remarks on African Shells collected by J O M'William Esq. Surgeon RN [1840] *Proceedings of the Royal Society of Edinburgh* 1, 1845, 296-7

On the Fossil Fishes of the Old Red Sandstone of Orkney [1840] *Proceedings of the Royal Society of Edinburgh* 1, 1845, 314.

TURNER, E. Chemical Examination of Tabasheer. *Edinburgh Journal of Science* 8, 1828, 335-8, read at the Royal Society, London, on March 3rd 1828.

TURNER, W. Address. *Transactions of the Royal Society of Edinburgh, General Index 1889-1908*, 1909, 1-23.

The Marine Mammals in the Anatomical Museum of the University of Edinburgh. London, 1912.

UMFREVILLE, E. *The present state of Hudson's Bay* ... London, 1790.

URE, D. *The History of Rutherglen and East-Kilbride...* Glasgow, 1793.

VETCH, R H. Sir John Fretcheville Dykes Donnelly (1834-1902) in *Dictionary of National Biography*, 2nd Supplement, 1, 1912, 514-5.

WALKER, J. *A sermon preached before His Majesty's High Commissioner and the General Assembly of the Church of Scotland on May 19th, 1791.* Edinburgh, 1791.

[WALKER J] A Memorandum given by Dr Walker, professor of natural history, Edinburgh, to a young gentleman going to India, with some additions. *The Bee or Literary Weekly Intelligencer* 17, 1793, 330-3.

WALKER, J. *Economic History of the Hebrides and Highlands of Scotland.* 2 vols. Edinburgh, 1808.

VII Public Lecture Anno 1788 on the Utility and Progress of Natural History, and Manner of Philosophising in *Essays on Natural History and Rural Economy* ... Edinburgh, 1808.

Notice of Mineralogical Journeys, and of a Mineralogical System. *Edinburgh Philosophical Journal* 6, 1822, 88-94.

WATERSTON, C D. Geology and the museum. *Scottish Journal of Geology* 8, 1972, 129-44.

Konservatorer, professorer og sannhet i naturvitenskapen (Curators, Professors and truth in natural science). *Museumsnytt* 1, 1977, 2-12.

The unique role of the curator in palaeontology in M G Basset. Curation of Palaeontological Collections *Special Papers in Palaeontology* 22, 1979, 7-15.

The Home of the Royal Society of Edinburgh. *Royal Society of Edinburgh Year Book 1996*, 83-110.

WELD, C R. *History of the Royal Society.* London, 1848.

White, A. *Four short letters: on the subject of an open museum in the Scottish capital.* Edinburgh, 1850.

WHITEHEAD, P J P. Zoological Specimens from Captain Cook's Voyages. *Journal of the Society for the Bibliography of Natural History* 5(3), 1969, 161-201.

WILLIAMS, G. Andrew Graham's observations on Hudson's Bay, 1767-91 with an introduction by R Glover. *Hudson's Bay Record Society* vol 27, 1969.

Graham, Andrew. *Dictionary of Canadian Biography vol V, 1801-1820.* Toronto, 1983.

WILSON, G. *What is Technology?* Edinburgh, 1855.

WILSON, G and A GEIKIE. *Memoir of Edward Forbes FRS.* London and Edinburgh, 1861.

[WILSON, J A] *Memoir of George Wilson MD FRSE.* London and Cambridge, 1866.

WILSON, R B. *A History of the Geological Survey in Scotland.* NERC, 1977.

WITHERS, C W J. A neglected Scottish agriculturalist: the georgical lectures and agricultural writings of the Rev Dr John Walker (1731-1803). *Agricultural History Review* 33(II), 1985, 132-46.

Natural knowledge as cultural property: disputes over the ownership of natural history in late eighteenth-century Edinburgh. *Archives of Natural History* 19 (3), 1992, 289-303.

WITTLIN, A S. *The Museum, Its History and its Tasks in Education.* London, 1949.

Museums: In Search of a Usable Future. Cambridge Mass, and London, 1970.

WOODWARD, B B. White, Adam (1817–1879) in *Dictionary of National Biography* 61, 1900.

YONGE, C M. The Inception and Significance of the *Challenger* Expedition. *Proceedings of the Royal Society of Edinburgh* 72, 1972, 1-13.

NAME INDEX

Dates with the prefix 'e' give the year of election to Fellowship of the Royal Society of Edinburgh.

'n' indicates a note number

Adie, Alexander James (1808-79 e1846) 47, 193

Agassiz, Jean Louis Rudolphe (1807-73 e1835) 67, 68, 176, 177

Allan, Robert (1806-63 e1832) 174, 175

Allan, Thomas (1777-1833 e1805) 46, 48, 52, 53, 58, 60, 64, 71, 77n17, 142, 157, 158, 161, 162, 164, 165, 179

Allman, George James (1812-98 e1856) 102, 112, 121, 122, 128

Anderson, John (1726-96 e1783) 84

Anderson, John Wilson 117

Anderson, Thomas (1819-74 e1845) 88, 108n27

Anderson, William (1750-78) 26, 29-30, 147-8

Anstruther, James (d1866 e1840) 184

Archer, Thomas Croxon (1817-85 e1862) 127, 128

Bald, Robert (1776-1861 e1817) 183

Bald, William (c1789-1857 e1829) 170

Balfour, Sir Andrew (1630-94) 13-14

Balfour, D 186

Balfour, Isaac Bayley (1853-1922 e1877) 120

Balfour, John Hutton (1808-84 e1835) 88, 91, 98, 112, 120, 123, 135n20

Banks, Sir Joseph (1743-1820 e1792) 19, 25, 26, 28

Barclay, John (1758-1826 e1807) 119

Bennett, John Hughes (1812-75 e1843) 121

Berry, Andrew (1764-1833 e1796) 174

Berzelius, Baron Jons Jacob (1779-1848 e1820) 115

Birkbeck, George (1776-1841) 84

Black, John Sutherland (1846-1923 e1884) 132

Black, Joseph (1728-99 e1783) 12, 22, 28, 32, 156

Blair, Colonel 97

Bligh, William (1754-1817) 35, 152

Bonar, James (1757-1821 e1798) 77n9

Boswell, James (1778-1822) 151, 153

Bowmaker, Robert (1731-97) 147

Brewster, Sir David (1781-1868 e1808) 56, 60-62, 115, 116, 117

Bright, Richard (1789-1858) 77n18

Brisbane, Sir Thomas Makdougall (1773-1860 e1811) 164, 182, 186, 194

Brodie, James (1744-1824) 77n21

Brotherton, Joseph (1783-1857) 85

Brown, Alexander Crum (1838-1922 e1863) 118

Brown, Andrew (1763-1834 e1803) 35, 156

Brown, Robert (1773-1858 e1825) 115

Brown, Thomas (1785-1862 e1818) 50, 78n23

Bruce, James 151

Bruce, William Speirs, (1867-1921 e1905) 134

Bryson, Alexander (1816-66 e1858) 114

Bryson, Robert (e1840) 185

Buccleuch, Elizabeth, Duchess of 30

Buccleuch, 3rd Duke of (1746-1812 e1783) 50, 145

Buccleuch, 5th Duke of (1806-84) 97

Buchan, Alexander (1829-1907 e1868) 135n20

Buchan, 11th Earl of (1742-1829) 16

Bullock, George (d1818) 160

Burns, Robert (1759-96) 27

Byres, James (1734-1817 e1783) 22, 156

Cadell, William Archibald (1775-1855 e1812) 50-52

Campbell, Sir A 97

Cardwell, Edward Cardwell, Viscount (1813-86) 96, 97